BREAD AND HEAVEN

A FAMILY CHRONICLE
FROM THE RHONDDA VALLEY

Bread and Heaven

A Family Chronicle
from the Rhondda Valley

S E Taylor

ALDRIDGE PRESS

First published in United Kingdom in 2015
jointly by
Aldridge Press
24 Thorney Hedge Road, Chiswick, London W4 5SD
and
G and S Taylor Publications
Muslin Cottage, 96 Buxton Old Road, Higher Disley, Cheshire SK12 2DJ

For additional copies contact your local bookseller
or email G and S Taylor Publications: setaylor9@btinternet.com

ISBN–13: 978-0-9520651-4-2

Prepared for publication by Aldridge Press
enquiries@aldridgepress.co.uk

Editorial: Charlotte Rolfe
Design: John Aldridge
Cover design: John Aldridge
Typeset in Bembo 11.5/14.7pt
Cover photos: the Jones family © S E Taylor;
background: Wattstown, © National Library of Wales
Photo section: 7,8,9 © Rhondda Cynon Taf Library Service Digital Archive; 17a Watts-
town © National Library of Wales; 17b Wattstown and National Collieries © Old Uk
photos; 33 Lloyd George: © National Portrait Gallery, London; the remaining photos
are copyright the Jones family.

Printed and bound in UK by TJ International, Padstow

HILDA DAVIES 1915-2003

This book is dedicated to my mother, Hilda Elizabeth
Gwent Davies (née Jones), who was Margaret Ann's
granddaughter. Hilda wrote down many of the
family's original stories which are the heart of this
book, so that her own grandchildren and subsequent
generations would be helped to understand their roots.

CONTENTS

Author's Note

Some time after my mother's death in February 2003, my sister, Sarah, encouraged me to develop the anthology of anecdotes written by our mother, into a broader account of Margaret Ann's family life in the Rhondda valley. As I began to draw together the events, stories, and family myths, I became fascinated by the characters of my great-grandparents and their daily lives. Their portraits took pride of place on the wall of the family home in Gorwel, Wattstown, and over a century later, now hang on my own dining-room wall. They are a constant reminder of my roots and of why this book was written.

Many people have remarked that the family of Reverend Morgan H Jones and Margaret Ann seems to reflect the social history of South Wales during the nineteenth and early twentieth century, and I am very proud to have been able to use the stories my mother wrote down to bring to life the experiences of families in the Rhondda at that time.

Throughout the process of writing this book I have benefited from the expert guidance and encouragement of many people, most notably Sarah Harris, Joyce Marlow, Joe Keaney and my editor Charlotte Rolfe. I am indebted to my brother-in-law Nick Harris for help with the family tree and many of the photographs, and to my family and friends for their support and advice. I have been as faithful to the facts as possible and any errors are mine alone.

S E Taylor
December 2015

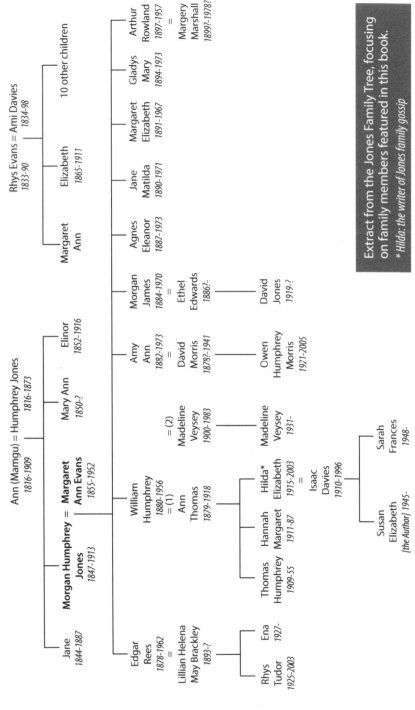

Extract from the Jones Family Tree, focusing on family members featured in this book.

Hilda: the writer of Jones family gossip

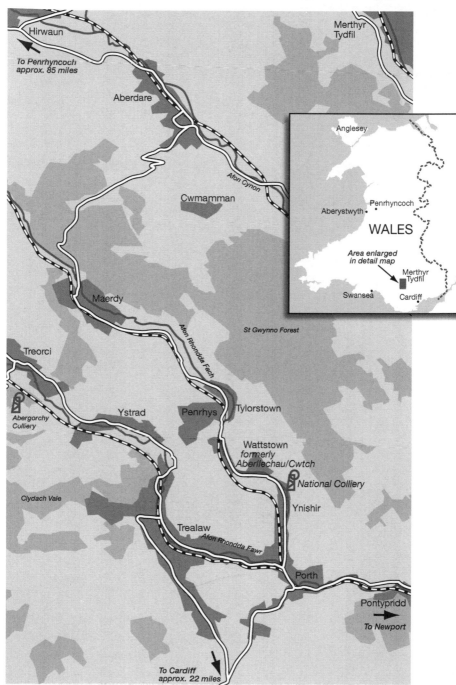

The Rhondda valley showing the main places in the Jones family chronicle.

PROLOGUE

My first clear memory of Mam Wattstown must have been in October, 1950. Half-term holidays always included a visit to Mam, as we called her. Clad in our best clothes and with immaculate white socks, we made the journey by train to Wattstown to have tea with my great-grandmother and the great aunts, in Gorwel. If my behaviour reached the necessary high standard, I would be allowed into Mam's room with its beautiful bay windows looking down the valley, to sit on the blanket chest and tell her my 'news.'

My favourite task was to give Mam the tiny triangular sandwiches she loved for her tea. On extra special days I was in time to tie the baby blue ribbons on the ends of the snowy white plaits which, in spite of her age, reached down her back. Her blue eyes still sparkled and to me she was an awesome figure, who was entitled to the greatest respect, even though she was hardly five feet tall and more than ninety years old.

She could remember a time before cars, aeroplanes, telephones, the radio and television. Margaret Ann's world as a child was unimaginably different from mine, yet the stories she told of those far away days were as vivid as though they were yesterday. Then one day the telephone rang and Aunty Glad broke the unbelievable news that Mam Wattstown was dead. She was ninety-six. It was my first experience of a family death.

The next visit a few weeks later was terrifying. The atmosphere was sombre and the great aunts, still wearing black dresses, were subdued. After tea Aunty Gladys told my sister and me to follow her upstairs to her room as she had something to show us. We did, but she didn't go into her room. She went into Mam's room. Into the room with the beautiful bay windows and the blanket chest, but there was no Mam to be seen! I stared at the chest. The cushions from the top had gone.

With a shriek I ran from the room leaving my sister behind. Inconsolable sobs finally subsided, but the great aunts decided I was too excitable for my own good and the visit was brought to an abrupt end. Eventually my mother managed to discover the reason for my 'hysteria.'

'Aunty Glad has taken Mam's room. I think she's put her away in the chest,' I sobbed. I was convinced that if Aunty Gladys had taken possession of Mam's lovely room she must have locked Mam inside the blanket box! Eventually reassured that no dastardly deed had taken place, I calmed down, but as far as I was concerned Mam had not really gone – her presence was everywhere. My sister and I loved those stories, and over the years my mother wrote many of them down so that successive generations could enjoy them too and learn something of the family's history.

After my mother's death, my sister found the stories, neatly typed up and entitled 'Jones' Family Gossip.' They form the core of this book. I have used memories from other members of the family, as well as my own imagination, to develop the story of the family's history for Margaret Ann's descendants.

Chapter 1
The Jug on the Dresser

Margaret Ann Jones dusted the dresser. A great deal of feeling was reflected in the way she worked. The array of dishes, already removed to the table, was lucky to have survived the journey down from the shelves, while the shelves themselves were nearly bent down by the force of the rubbing they were receiving.

The two small boys in the room were engrossed in their own worlds. Four-year-old Edgar was absorbed in a picture book, while two-year-old William was considering what exactly could be done with the pieces of coal he had removed from the bucket beside the kitchen range. In awe of their mother, neither wished to attract the force being directed at the dresser. Edgar, young as he was, went to great lengths to avoid his mother's displeasure, but William did not at all mind the clashes; indeed, even at two years old he seemed to relish them.

Margaret Anne knew full well the force that was possessing her. It was anger, directed mainly at the situation in which she found herself. She had learned long ago that her survival depended on her ability to work out a course of action for herself and to follow it. Though in all honesty, the decisions that had directed her life and brought her to attack the dresser here in Heol Fach, Ystrad, Rhondda in the year 1882, were hers and hers alone. Nobody, she told herself, had persuaded, guided or advised her to marry the Reverend Morgan Humphrey Jones, who was eight years her senior. She was aware her parents would have been happy enough for her to have remained at

3

home with them. Her education and good business head had been useful to them in the day to day running of their shop and post office, and her ability to manage her eleven younger brothers and sisters had often spared her mother both time and trouble.

But at the age of twenty-two, married him she had, and she could not admit that it was a mistake. She had felt a strong attraction to the quiet, studious minister, with his neatly trimmed beard and gentle brown eyes when he first arrived in the pulpit and her feelings had not really changed in the five years of her marriage. In fact, their mutual attraction had grown and the warmth of their affection, especially in the privacy of their bedroom, had become a source of wonder and joy to Margaret Ann.

The contrast between their natures was apparent to everyone, and many people wondered how such an apparently ill-matched pair would cope with each other. Margaret Ann admired Morgan's excellent English, his studious and cultured behaviour and his thoughtful manners, but the slightly subservient attitude he adopted, and his devotion to the English-speaking chapel and its congregation, frequently roused her to levels of irritation she found hard to control. She knew it was her duty to remain silent so that nothing should interfere with her husband's pastoral duties, but it became harder and harder for her to keep her own counsel.

A plate received a vigorous polish as Margaret Ann realised that it was Morgan's contentment that she found most difficult to accept. How could he be content when they lived counting every penny? Counting them did not make them go any further. How could he be content when he was at the beck and call of that chapel congregation? Margaret Ann paused to consider the congregation, many of whom she disliked heartily. How could Morgan be satisfied by writing and preaching sermons to these colliers and their wives?

Most of the congregation were incoming English or Irish, and Margaret Ann was suspicious of their alien ways and the air of superiority she felt they assumed. Morgan, who had been the prize-winning Hebrew scholar in his college was worth more than this. Did those people not realise how fortunate they were to have a minister of such intellectual standing?

Many of the Welsh-speaking chapels in the valley had to make do with ministers of significantly poorer intellect, whose preaching skills left much to be desired. Morgan had worked hard to master the English language and painstakingly wrote out every sermon so that he could correct any errors and preach in perfect English. All his life he insisted that if his children were to speak English as well as Welsh, only error-free English would do.

He was conscientious too in his pastoral duties. His visits to the sick and the bereaved were a real source of comfort to the families in his care. She had heard many complaints from customers in her parents' shop about the perfunctory visits made by other clergymen in the valley to families in need. They contrasted strongly with Morgan's devotion to his flock. Margaret Ann swore she would write his next sermon for that congregation. The text would be: 'A labourer is worthy of his hire,' and she would ensure they realised it was high time that every labourer, in a chapel or a coal mine, as a preacher or collier, was entitled to receive proper payment for work done, regularly every week.

At that point Margaret ceased abstract thinking and reached for the precious lustre jug. It had belonged to her grandmother and sat proudly on the dresser, reminding her whenever it caught her eye of the debt she owed her grandparents. The jug was waiting its turn to be dusted and her hand went into it. inside were three pieces of paper. Last time she had checked the jug there had only been two.

'I don't believe it,' she hissed, causing Edgar to look up from his book. 'So they have not paid him this week either! I swear I'll take these to the vestry and tell them there'll be no more sermons until they are paid.'

Two weeks' non-payment she knew about, but not a word had been said by Morgan about last week. There they were. In that jug were three IOUs, signed by the two chapel deacons. What use were they in a jug with the boys needing new shoes! That was bad enough but there would be another child to be clothed and fed before the end of the year. Meanwhile her husband, their father, seemed to be

5

content to work for nothing. Margaret Ann slammed the precious jug back on the dresser, and stuffed the IOUs into her apron pocket. William was grabbed from his play amongst the coal and Edgar's book pulled from his hand. The boys were stuffed into their coats like rag dolls and Margaret Ann stormed out of the house.

Images of her early childhood flashed through her mind as they hurried along. Her mother constantly pregnant and scratching round to find enough food for the ever growing family; sickly babies dying; weeks with next to no money coming in as her father struggled to keep his haulier's business going. Margaret Ann had been the oldest of those children and the memories of that childhood would remain with her until her dying day.

Down the steep hill she marched, so fast that Edgar's small legs were in danger of being dragged from under him, while William bobbed up and down in her arms. Neighbours climbing the hill paused to look at the preacher's wife in her apron and to wonder at the cause of such a flight. Margaret Ann cared nothing for looks or the gossip that might follow. She only knew that if she paused, her resolution might falter. By the time they reached the small town Edgar was beginning to whine, 'Not so quick, Mam, not so quick.'

Heedless of his protests, she marched on, past the shops selling boots, clothes and food until she found the one for which she searched. Above her head, swinging gently in the breeze, was a painted sign showing three golden balls.

The little pawnbroker looked up from his ledgers in some surprise at the jangle of the doorbell, and winced as the slam of the door brought in this unexpected customer. Monday was a quiet day in his business. Wednesdays and Thursdays saw a steady stream of women into his shop, but on Mondays there was usually enough of the Friday pay packet left to make it unnecessary to bring in the best shoes or coat for pledge. Mr Cohen looked carefully at the small fair-haired woman with the two children. Never before had he seen this one; most of his customers were regulars. They were the ones who could not manage the week's money, or those whose husbands demanded the lion's share for their drink. The pawnbroker regarded her over the top of his spectacles and waited for her to speak. Suddenly one small hand came smartly down on the counter, and the other withdrew the three IOUs from her pocket with a flourish.

'I understand you buy debts.' Her voice was calm and had more than a hint of refinement about it.

'In some circumstances,' Cohen answered as he brought his attention to the business in hand and looked more closely at the three pieces of paper.

'You'll buy these, then,' said this unusual woman. 'Read them and you will see they are signed by two God-fearing men, who will be more afraid to see you on their doorstep than they would God himself.'

Mr Cohen picked up the papers and whistled through his teeth as he read the signatures. He knew Messrs J Hopkins and Evan Morgan as two very respectable men, but who was the Reverend M H Jones to whom they promised to pay one guinea on each note? He looked again at the woman. 'Would you, madam, be Mrs Morgan Jones?'

'I most certainly am,' came the dignified and slightly haughty reply, 'and I think those two will pay you sooner than they would pay me.'

True, thought Cohen, as he slowly nodded his head. An irate minister's wife would be no threat to their treasured respectability, but for it to be known that they were doing business with a Jewish moneylender and pawnbroker would expose them to much malicious gossip and not a little ridicule.

'Now, Mrs Jones, I shall need to give this matter some thought. It's not every day I receive IOUs from the deacons. You must understand that if I take these notes I cannot pay you the full amount. I must first take out the commission.'

'Not from my money you won't.' came the swift reply. 'You know you should pay me the full amount or nothing. Take your commission from those who wrote the notes.'

Cohen moved his glasses lower down his nose in order to look once again at this pretty young woman with a sound business head on her shoulders. The commission he needed should certainly be taken from the people who issued the notes, but he had hoped to make a little, just a little, from her too.

'Come along, Mr Cohen, please, the children can't wait much longer. Do you give me the three guineas, or not?'

With a sigh, acknowledging that this woman would not be gainsaid, he took the IOU notes and placed them carefully in his money drawer. He took out three shillings, and laid them on the counter. Then he slowly reached in his pocket for a leather purse and even more slowly removed three gold sovereigns from its depths. His customer put the coins in her apron pocket.

'Thank you indeed, Mr Cohen. I am sure you will not be long without your money, as long as you make sure the deacons' neighbours see you coming when you knock on their doors. Good day!'

Holding William firmly in her arms and shepherding Edgar before her, Margaret Ann sailed out of the shop. Deportment lessons at her Cowbridge boarding school for young ladies had never been more useful than now, and she felt a surge of gratitude as she remembered the determination her mother had shown when she insisted Margaret should benefit from the good fortune which had arrived for the family so unexpectedly.

The homeward journey was more circumspect. William was put down to walk on his short legs and with a boy on each hand, their mother had time to acknowledge briefly the greetings of her neighbours. Her anger was spent, she had acted positively, rather than letting things lie, and she felt all the better for it. Her husband might mildly accept the shortcomings of his deacons, but she would not. Shortcomings were one thing, short payment was not to be accepted.

'My father would have enjoyed that little scene,' she mused. 'He always wondered whether I'd ever get a chance to put my schooling to good use.'

∽ ∽ ∽

Margaret Ann and the children entered the kitchen to find Morgan restoring the dishes which had been hastily abandoned before their flight. He replaced everything except the lustre jug precisely in its proper place on the dresser. The children ran to him and he greeted them briefly before facing his wife.

'Where on earth have you been?' He picked up the jug from the kitchen table. 'I've straightened the dresser, Margaret Ann, but the jug's empty. Where are the IOU notes from the deacons? I can't find them. Have you moved them from the lustre jug?'

'Indeed you may well ask. I'd like to know what use you think they are in a jug with the boys needing new shoes?'

Clenching his jaw in the gesture of resignation she knew so well, her husband spoke quietly. 'Now Margaret Ann, we have been over all this before. The debt for the building of the chapel must be paid off or the people will have no place to worship. Pay me, the deacons will, when they have the cash.'

'Hopkins and Evan Morgan will pay up quick enough, chapel debt or no, when they know who has those notes now.'

'Why? What have you done with them?'

Margaret Ann met his gaze steadily and produced the money from her pocket. 'I've sold them to Cohen, the pawnbroker. I suppose you could say I've sold your chapel to the Jews!' She almost allowed herself a grin.

The kitchen was suddenly very quiet. Edgar looked up from his picture book and William stopped running round the table. Husband and wife regarded each other eye to eye, there being little difference in their height, before Morgan turned and walked out of the house.

Later that day, with the boys in bed, Margaret sat at her mending, her thoughts busy with ideas about the future. Her parents had had the good fortune to inherit the old house in Merioneth from her grandparents. The sale of it had saved them from penury. It had enabled them to give up the failing hauliers' business with its worn out horse and cart and set up a now profitable grocer's shop in the next valley. But there was no chance of such a windfall from anyone to save her family. She and she alone would have to find the where-withal to feed and clothe the boys and to establish her children in prosperous and successful careers.

A rented chapel house might do for now, but Margaret Ann had every intention of living in a house which belonged to her. Her great ambitions for her two small boys, and the child as yet unborn, were buried deeply, but she was determined that they would be fulfilled. She finished patching the knee of William's little trousers and folded away her sewing neatly into the workbasket.

Morgan had still not returned as she put the kettle on for the customary cup of tea before bed. His protracted absence did not worry her. He was probably with the deacons trying to explain and excuse his wife's action. She knew she had done the right thing by her family and that was all that mattered. If her husband could not stand up for himself, she would have to stand up for him.

She cared nothing for the reaction from the chapel. Indeed she hoped fervently that the humiliation she had wrought on his employers would ensure Morgan was paid more promptly in the future. She was confident too, that when he returned, the chapel, the IOUs and the deacons would soon be forgotten in the warm and passionate reconciliation that she was sure would follow.

Morgan's key sounded in the door just as the kettle boiled. Margaret Ann looked up as he entered the kitchen. She caught sight of a small grin disappearing under her husband's beard. 'Well? Did you tell them? Am I to be cast out?'

'Mortified they were, and they'll be off to Cohen's first thing. Mind you, Hopkins couldn't help pointing out to Evan Morgan that their wives would never have done such a thing! Too weak and washy their wives are – not like mine. "Strongest woman in the valley I've got," I told them. She agreed to be my wife, and proud I am of her, too.'

Margaret Ann reached out her hand towards her husband, glad that she was no longer in his bad books. Strong minded she might be, but on Morgan's loving approval she depended completely.

Nevertheless, Morgan was about to find out just how strong minded his wife could be.

Chapter 2
The Plan

Ever since the incident of the IOUs, Margaret Ann had been allowing the germ of an idea to grow in her busy brain. Her husband's absence on a preaching engagement convinced her that she could profitably use the day to bring the idea closer to fruition. Her first and most important task was to find someone to care for the two boys, as her plan entailed a long walk, and she had no wish to arrive at her destination worn out with the effort of carrying William and coaxing Edgar along a rough mountain road.

She must at all costs look prosperous for the expedition she had in mind. chapel clothes and best bonnet it must be, but not her best boots. The mountain road would ruin them and her long skirt would hide the sturdier boots of every day. She put a lump of cheese and an apple ready for her pocket, picked up William and called Edgar to follow.

With her customary briskness she deposited William on the bedroom floor with his brick box for company and handed Edgar a book. Then she opened her wardrobe door and considered what to wear. After several moments' thought, she selected her almost new chapel-going skirt and spread two blouses out on the bed. The maroon one was definitely the more stylish, but the blue was very elegantly trimmed with lace and had an air of luxury about it. The maroon one went back in the closet, and her best cameo was lifted carefully from her small jewel case. Edgar sat watching his mother, bemused at these strange proceedings in the middle of an ordinary day. 'Is it Sunday again Mam?' he asked.

'Of course not. Quiet now,' his mother replied, adjusting her bonnet. 'I've lots of things to do today and you need to be clean and tidy too.' She picked up the face cloth draped over the side of the washbowl and dipped it in the water to clean the boys' hands and faces. Both protested vigorously at having an additional wash during the day, but Margaret Ann was in no mood to brook dissent.

'We're going down the valley, to see the family, so no nonsense now, I've no time to waste.'

Ready at last, she made her way with the children down towards the town. Her mind was busy finding the reasons it would be necessary to give her cousin Elizabeth when she asked her to look after the boys for the greater part of the day. She hoped fervently that her aunt would be fully occupied with the family's shopkeeping matters and that she could talk to Elizabeth without attracting her attention. The good Lord would have to forgive the lies which would be necessary, as the true reason certainly could not be revealed.

If it were Edgar that Elizabeth was asked to care for, there would be no problem. Her cousin delighted in playing mother to the little angel, but William was another matter. The vigilance needed to keep the youngster out of harm's way, even for an hour, was exhausting; Elizabeth would have no hope of pursuing her usual daily routine with William in her home.

Margaret Ann decided that if tell a lie she must, it had better be a good one, and that it would be better to tell it before Elizabeth could ask any questions. Entering the back door, she called out, 'Elizabeth, you will have to mind the boys for me, I have had a message from Treorci.'

Elizabeth came forward to meet her, surprised at the sight of Margaret Ann dressed to death so early in the day. 'Is Morgan's mother ill then?'

Margaret Ann hesitated. She could not make illness a reason for going to see her in-laws. Moreover, Elizabeth had already noted her best clothes and would consider it strange she should wear best clothes if she were going to tend the sick.

'No, no,' she answered quickly. 'Something to do with news from America.'

Elizabeth looked at the children. Edgar was still clutching his mother's hand but William was already under the table endeavouring to persuade the cat to come to his none too gentle embrace. 'Surely you could take William with you? I'll have Edgar with pleasure but...'

Margaret Ann interrupted. 'Oh come now, Elizabeth, it's not often I ask a favour from you. I would have to carry William most of the way which is not good in my present condition. You'd not like to think of me straining myself, would you?'

Elizabeth was startled that Margaret Ann should make such a direct reference to her pregnancy. Respectable ministers' wives did not usually refer to such intimate details. It left Elizabeth little option other than to agree to the task she felt was being imposed upon her. Will had given up trying to persuade the cat to play and was now engrossed in removing the kindling sticks one by one from the basket near the range. Margaret Ann turned towards the door and with an instruction to the boys to be good and not make trouble, she marched smartly away. Edgar stared longingly towards the door through which his mother had just disappeared and resigned himself with reluctance to a day without her.

Once escaped from the little house, Margaret Ann drew a deep breath. In spite of being heavy in the sixth month of pregnancy, she could not resist a few skipping steps as she left the town behind for the freedom of the open hillside. Her four or five mile walk was to take her out of the valley of the Rhondda Fawr into the Rhondda Fach, over the little mountain that separated the two rivers.

The talk in the chapel was of a new pit being sunk in the smaller valley, and the Colliery Estates had already built one row of terraced houses along the valley bottom. Margaret Ann had heard that the company was prepared to lease the buildings at the ends of the terrace as shop premises. She was determined that if that were true, one of them should be hers. Her parents had grasped the opportunity to escape from poverty with both hands and had prospered as shopkeepers in Cwmamman. They had lately given over another shop in Maerdy to her brother John. She knew she was much more likely to prosper as a shopkeeper than John, and with each step up the hill her determination to follow in the family business mounted.

At the top of the path she turned to look back at Ystrad. How she hated the place! Hated it because there she was the Minister's wife, a role in which she would never feel at ease. Her tongue was too quick and had already caused her husband's resignation from one chapel, and the deacons of his present one could scarce bring themselves to speak to her after the affair of the IOUs. Apart from disliking most of the congregation, she was jealous of those whose needs and problems diverted Morgan's attention from her, even though she knew Morgan would wish her to be generous and tolerant.

Margaret Ann turned to begin the descent into Rhondda Fach. Now indeed her feet were light. Below, she saw a birch wood; above, the larks were singing. When she entered the wood she stopped to draw a breath of sheer pleasure. The path down to the river was lined with bluebells, and the river bubbled and sang its way over the stones, sparkling in the May sunshine. Picking her way across the stepping stones, she headed towards the row of houses being built on the further bank. As she approached, the workmen looked up from the piles of slates they were sorting. A visitor like this small figure was an incongruous sight on a building site, but they appreciated the strand of blonde hair that had escaped from her bonnet, and her sparkling blue eyes.

After drawing a deep breath, Margaret Ann clutched at her skirt and addressed the one she judged to be the foreman. '*Bore da*,' she said firmly. 'Could you tell me, please, where the agent is to be found?'

The man counting the slates, put down his tally sheet and stared at her. 'Well, now, maybe you will find him down with the sinkers, but that is no place for a fine lady. I think it'd be better if you wait here and I'll send a man down for him.'

Margaret Ann thanked him and while she waited, began to stroll along the half-built row, taking in the details of the buildings. She produced a small notebook from her pocket and began making a quick sketch of the two end houses. After she had finished her survey, she returned to the foreman who had noted her interest in the two intended shop premises.

'Good morning, ma'am.' She turned, to see the workman who had been sent on the errand standing with an older man.

'This is the lady asking for you, sir,' said the slater.

'So I can see. Fine, fine, get back to work now.' The older man waved the foreman away.

'Good morning,' said Margaret Ann. 'You are the agent for this sinking?'

'That's right, Ma'am.'

'What is this place called?'

'It's no place yet to have a name, but the sinking is on Cwtch Farm.'

'Cwtch.' Margaret Ann repeated the word. It meant a hiding place, just the right place for me, she thought, a hiding place from those chapel deacons and their irritating congregation.

The agent stood and waited for her to explain her presence. The woman could certainly not want work, though it was not unusual for women to come seeking employment for their husbands. Her clothes were good and stylish. She had a certain air about her that did not suggest she was the wife of a sinker and her voice had a note of authority. He was certainly perplexed by his visitor but he had little time to ponder as Margaret Ann suddenly spoke.

'I'll come straight to the point. When are these buildings due to be finished? I want the lease of one of those shop premises that are being built at the end of the terraces.'

'Do you now, ma'am?' The agent was impressed with her directness.

'Yes, I do. I would be pleased if you will give me information about the rent I will have to pay and the length of lease I can expect, then I can be on my way.'

'Just a minute. Not so fast if you please, ma'am.' The agent was now very interested and not a little amused by the business-like

15

young woman standing in front of him. He wondered again who she could be and from where she had come. 'Kindly give me your name and address and I will write to the Colliery Estates and pass on your enquiry.'

Margaret Ann stared at him in disbelief. It had never occurred to her that a decision would not be reached immediately. She controlled herself with difficulty and refrained from stamping her foot with vexation. She wanted no delay.

'If there is writing to be done, I do not need anyone else to do it. I will do it myself. Give me the address of the Colliery Estates and I will get the information. How long will I have to wait for you to attend to it? Do you imagine I'm incapable of writing my own letter?'

The agent quickly realised that this was no ordinary request. Silently he reached in his pocket for his notepad, carefully wrote down the names of the administrators of the colliery and the address of the head office in Porth. He handed the page to Margaret Ann, wished her luck with her request, and turned back down the path, mulling over their brief discussion, and wondering who at head office would deal with the matter.

Hungry now, and frustrated that she did not have the desired lease already in her pocket, Margaret Ann made her way back up the mountain path. She was less aware now of the beauty of the birch wood and the little streams and more aware than ever of her hatred of Ystrad. Then she remembered the cheese and apple and sat down on the bank of the stream to plan her letter.

Back at last in the other valley, she found Elizabeth, worn out with the care of the boisterous William, but hoping to be recompensed by a good gossip about events in Treorci. But there was no time for any chat today and Elizabeth was disappointed as her cousin briefly apologised for the length of her absence, refused the offered cup of tea and hurriedly left with the children.

Once back in Heol Fach, Margaret Ann wasted no time in writing the letter. She needed it to be in the post before Morgan's return. In spite of her conviction that her plans were by far the best option, she had a nagging feeling that her husband might not view things in the same light. She wrote fast and furiously, giving her reasons for the speedy acquisition of the lease with authority and conviction. The shop would, she felt sure, be a great success, so the sooner the agents allowed her to get on with it, the better. She read through what she had written, signed her name with a flourish, and carefully folded the letter into its envelope.

'Quick now, my girl,' she told herself, 'to the post and then there'll be no going back.' Yet again she had cause to thank her parents for their insistence that the family windfall should be used to educate her. Her early childhood and her role as the eldest had been very hard. It had come late, but she was to benefit from her education for the rest of her life. So few women in the valley could have written their own letter, or interviewed the agent with such confidence.

She collected the boys from the back step where they were engrossed in making a roadway with sticks and stones and hurried them to the letterbox on the corner. As she let the envelope fall in the box, Margaret Ann drew yet another a deep breath. She was certain her life had turned a corner.

CHAPTER 3
THE LETTER FROM AMERICA

While Margaret Ann was hurrying back from her frustrating meeting with the colliery agent, Morgan Jones was in Treorci. He sat in his sister Mary Ann's kitchen behind the little bookshop, and read the regular monthly letter from his family in America. Many families had been driven to seek work in the New World as poverty and lack of work made life increasingly difficult. Another married sister, Jane, had jumped at the chance to escape the misery of the valley and had set off full of optimism, convinced that the family's life would be transformed.

Jane's husband had quickly found work as a mine manager in Nanti-coke, Pennsylvania, and the Welsh community there had welcomed the new arrivals warmly. Now Jane's health was of growing concern and she explained her great *hiraeth* for her widowed mother and two sisters. Her husband had written to beg his mother-in-law and Jane's sisters to come and join them. He assured them work was plentiful, houses were comfortable and easily come by, and that they would want for nothing if they joined Jane in America.

Morgan's mother watched him as he read the letter. He was her only son and she was proud of his learning and his status as a minister which he had only achieved after years of determined study. Years ago, when he had had no choice but to join his father in the newly opened mine, she remembered the fear in his eyes as he set off for every shift.

'I hate it down there, Mam, in the dark by myself, waiting to open the doors for the coal carts to come through,' he'd told her.

'Say your prayers Morgan, over and over, and sing every hymn we've ever sung in chapel and you'll see how quickly the time will pass.'

That was her advice, and it was there in the darkness of the mine that Morgan discovered his faith in the Almighty which never left him. He stuck it out until he finally managed to convince his family and his employers that he did indeed have a calling to the ministry. With the help of the minister of the nearby chapel, he began to study the Hebrew and Greek which he would need to go eventually to theological college. Once promoted to the status of lamp man he was able to take his beloved books to work and in between his duties as the lamp man in the colliery, he nurtured a love of study which was to remain with him all his life.

Morgan's mother loved all her children and grieved for her sick daughter so far from home, but to answer that call for help would mean leaving this very precious son. Though he was married with a growing family, she felt she still answered some need in him, and they remained very close. Her daughter-in-law resented the time and energy he devoted to his congregation, and she knew that this distressed her son even though he never spoke of it. She felt strongly that he still needed his mother's support.

Morgan folded the letter and passed it back to his sister who read it carefully, looking up now and again to glance at her mother and brother. When she had finished perusing the contents she slowly put the letter on the table and began absentmindedly smoothing out the folds.

Eventually, Mary Ann said, 'What do you think we should do, Morgan? Elinor has always wanted to follow our sister and is more than ready and willing to go to America. We could sell this bookshop with no difficulty. It's not more than a few weeks ago since the bookseller from Pontypridd came up to see if we would let him take it on, as he wants another shop further up the valley. If we did sell, it would be quick and we'd be able to put enough money by to tide us over until we were properly settled with Jane. Mam will come with us, if you will, Morgan. Then we can all be together over there.'

Mary Ann sat back in her chair, clearly confident that the matter was settled, and that she had removed all objections to the plan. Morgan looked at his sister in some surprise.

'I go with you? No, no, I can't possibly go with you. I have charge of my chapel here, and my duty is clear. This valley may be a vale of tears to many, but heaven is no nearer on the other side of the Atlantic. I must remain with my flock. I can't possibly go to America and what on earth would Margaret Ann say?'

'You listen to me, Morgan,' urged his sister. 'How long will you have a chapel to look after? Margaret Ann would soon have you away from that. You know if she says she's had enough of being a minister's wife, you'll not stand up to her.'

'Do be quiet, Mary Ann,' said her mother. 'Margaret Ann might not like the chapel, but would she like America any better? It's for Morgan to decide.'

'If he does, it will be the first decision he has made for himself since he got married.' Mary Ann glared at her brother before starting to collect the dishes to lay the table for supper. 'What about the chapel in Neyland? That's where you were pleased to go, but, oh no, hoity-toity Margaret Ann didn't like Neyland, not posh enough for her was it, so you couldn't stay there and you had to find another chapel in Ystrad. Anyway, what's going on in Ystrad, I'd like to know. There's plenty of tongues wagging over here about what that wife of yours has been up to, visiting Mr Cohen indeed!'

Morgan ignored his sister. 'Mam, what are your thoughts about all this?'

His mother was in no hurry to answer. Her mind was re-living the story the family had heard only too often. But what a story it was! The message which had come to Penrhyncoch from her husband to say he had found work in the Cwmamman valley had filled her with excitement and had fuelled her determination to set out from mid-Wales with her sister and their children for a better life in south Wales. Morgan's father had already planned to take a lease on one of the newly-built terraced cottages in the valley, as the pay for the miners was good. He could hardly wait for his wife and children to join him there. So the little group had set off to walk nearly a hundred miles, over the mountains from Cardiganshire to Cwmamman with young Morgan and the girls in tow. They joined many families from mid-Wales who were making the trek south to the 'black gold ' beyond the Brecon Beacons. The little hills to the north, dotted with sheep and abandoned farm cottages seemed to belong to the past as the little group took their last look back towards Mynydd Epynt. As they turned at the top of the mountain pass above the village of Hirwaun and looked southwards towards the rapidly growing industrial landscape, it seemed as though the blanket of smoke hanging over the valleys must surely be hiding a better future.

They began the descent into the head of the valley, exhausted from the long journey. Like most of the newly arrived women, Ann had little idea where exactly her husband had found work and nobody knew of his whereabouts. They had no choice but to search along the valley, stopping at each pithead. She and the children walked from pit to pit, standing hopefully at the colliery gates at the end of every shift. hearing the clang of the winding gear that brought the cage to the surface. Anxiously they searched the faces of the blackened miners, who were almost unrecognisable, as they streamed through the gates. Finally, one evening just as Ann was beginning to lose hope, the last shift of the day at Shepherd's Pit emerged. Morgan suddenly wrenched his hand free from her grasp and dashed through the gate shouting, 'It's Dadda! Dadda, we're here! Me and Mam and the girls!' Even now the memory of the joy on her long dead husband's sooty, work-stained face brought a smile to her lips. Going to America, she decided, could be no more challenging than that epic journey and those first desperate days in Cwmamman. With a slight shake of her head, she brought herself back to the present.

'If I cannot go home to Penrhyncoch, what difference does it make. Rhondda or America? Coal is coal, wherever it is found. It has set the boundary on my life from the very beginning so it may as well continue to be so until the end.'

With a deep sigh, she struggled to keep the resentment from her voice, and added, 'I've always done my duty by my family and it would now seem that it is to Jane I must go.'

Morgan listened with a growing sense of unease. He had always known how close was the relationship he had with his mother, and how lonely he would be without her. Why, he wondered, should he fear being lonely with a wife and children of his own? Perhaps he had need of more support and encouragement than Margaret Ann could offer. She had certainly bewitched him, with her sparkling eyes and refined ways, but perhaps it was only the people now considering going to America who had been able and willing to give him the support he craved. He was forced to admit to himself that he still needed them.

He remembered his mother's resolute words of encouragement. 'Come on, Morgan. Keep going. You've been down that pit since you were ten years old. One day, my boy, you will be out of it for good and into the pulpit.' Throughout the long years it had taken to become ordained, his mother and sisters had supported him so steadfastly. It had been so hard to make the enormous transition from the dark and airless working conditions of the mine to the rarified and enlightened atmosphere of the English-speaking Baptist theological college in Haverford West. His sisters knew how homesick he'd been. His time in Norfolk as a trainee minister where he had gone to improve his English and prepare for a chapel of his own had taxed him sorely. It was the weekly parcel of Welsh cakes and his favourite *bara brith* which had sustained him as he struggled to improve his next sermon in the tiny room in the manse belonging to his supervising minister. Separation from his mother and sisters would be difficult to bear.

Slowly, he rose from his seat, crossed the kitchen and placed his hand on his mother's shoulder. How he wished he could say, 'Stay, Mam. Don't go with the girls. Stay with me and my family.' But he knew that it could never be. His mother and his wife were highly suspicious of each other and there would never be any peace in a home they shared. The stark inevitability of the situation and the pending separation loomed in front of him. He straightened up, and squared his shoulders.

'I must be on my way. Margaret Ann will think my sermons in chapel are getting longer and longer if I don't get back soon. Make sure you take plenty of time to think about America.'

❦ ❦ ❦

Back in in Ystrad, with the children in bed, the lateness of the hour made Margaret Ann fidgety. Morgan had been at a prayer meeting in their old chapel in Cwmamman and she knew he had intended to call on his wife's family when it was over, as he often did. Even so he should be home by now, unless someone had bombarded him with some problem or other. Perhaps her father had enticed him into an argument. Rhys Evans was no chapel-goer but he delighted in using any preacher as a whetstone to sharpen his wits. His son-in-law was no exception to this rule. Just as Margaret was beginning to work herself up into a tirade against the congregation, she heard the familiar sound of her husband's boots on the flagstone path. Hastily she pulled off her apron, composed herself at the kitchen table, turned at Morgan's greeting as he came through the door and held up her face for the customary kiss.

'I'm sorry I'm late but I called in Treorci before coming on down the valley. How were the boys today? What has Will been up to? My word, hungry is what I am.'

Morgan was tired. He had walked many mountain miles that day. He had no idea yet that Margaret Ann too had walked in the opposite direction over the other mountain, but for the time being that was a secret.

'How were they all?' she asked as she brought his supper to the table. 'All in Cwmamman well, I hope? I suppose your father was busy as usual and off to some friendly society meeting. And what is going on in Treorci?'

Remembering the lie she'd told Elizabeth about going there herself, she waited anxiously for his answer. If there were startling news from Treorci Elizabeth would wonder why she had not been

23

told when Margaret had returned to collect her small sons.

'There was a letter from America,' Morgan replied sombrely. Margaret Ann felt the relief flood through her as she thought how lucky it had been that she had mentioned America to Elizabeth that very morning. 'I think Jane has gone down with consumption and my mother and the two girls may go out to be with her.'

'What, to America!' exclaimed Margaret Ann, sitting down hurriedly at the kitchen table, ignoring any mention of her sister-in-law's illness.

'Aye. If Jane needs her mother and sisters, they may well go to America.'

'Whatever will they do in America?'

'Work, no doubt, but there is still much to be settled yet. I'm not sure what decision they will make, but there seems to be plenty of work on offer and housing isn't likely to be a problem.' Morgan looked up at his wife, then back down at his plate. He paused...

'Ann asked if we would go.' He put another forkful of mutton stew into his mouth.

'Go to America?' Margaret Ann's voice rose in obvious horror at the idea.

'Well, you've found it hard to settle in Ystrad, and you are always on about the chapel and the money they give us. Perhaps American Baptists would pay more and offer me a better house there.'

'If it's to America you want to go, you will go without me and the children. You are right when you say I do not like Ystrad and that the chapel does not pay enough, but I'll find my own way out of the money problem without any need to go to America. You can please yourself. Have America with your mother and sisters if you want, but America with me, you will never have.'

With that she turned from the table towards the door. Morgan reached out as she passed his chair and pulled her back towards him. 'Margaret Ann, be quiet now. Listen. Mary Ann only asked if I would go with them and I said no.' His wife allowed herself to be drawn to his knee. Hiding his face so that she could not see his smile, Morgan added, 'I told them the chapel here needed me.'

24

'The chapel!' Margaret Ann screeched the word as she pulled away. 'Always the chapel. Who comes first in your life, that's what I'd like to know! I am going to bed.'

As she climbed the narrow stairs she thought, America indeed! But at least there is no chapel in bed. In bed she knew she reigned supreme in his thoughts and in that lay the answer to all who wondered why such an ill-assorted pair remained so close.

CHAPTER 4
THE LEASEHOLD

With increasing anxiety, Margaret Ann waited for an answer to her letter about the shop lease. Twice a day she was on tenterhooks, listening for the postman to rattle the letterbox. By Wednesday she was beginning to despair. In an effort to make the time pass more quickly, she pursued her housework with even more energy. Whenever Morgan was in the house he watched her attend to her housework with fascination. Unlike the other women he knew, his wife never dusted or polished her possessions with a tender pride, she beat them into shining submission. Carpets, curtains, cushions were vigorously beaten, not gently shaken. Floors were not softly mopped, they were scrubbed. Windows were wiped with vinegar soaked newspaper and then polished with chamois leather until they sparkled. The silverware of which she was so proud, was polished until it shimmered, the hearths and kitchen range were black-leaded within an inch of their lives, and the whole house gleamed and shone. It seemed as though the house and its contents groaned from the pressure of the constant cleaning.

Morgan, who had no further preaching engagement until Sunday, kept himself and the children out of her way. He assumed that it had been his talk of America that had called forth his wife's excessive activity and decided that nothing would be gained by interrogation. The May sunshine was tempting him outside, and the boys' constant comings and goings over the newly scrubbed back step was calling their mother's wrath down on their heads.

'I'll take the boys out, up the mountain, and they can play by the stream,' he called to his wife, who was fully occupied shaking out the rag rugs which graced the bedroom floors. 'They'll be out of your way for a bit, and I can run through my next sermon in my head while I watch them.'

William especially enjoyed the freedom to run and play beside the small streams that ran down to join the river and often had to be prevented from plunging head first into the water. Today Will spent a long time trying to make boats from twigs and leaves, and constantly called for his big brother to admire his fleet. Morgan was forced to remove his belt and attach it to William's trousers in order to prevent the Admiral of the fleet being swept down the stream. Edgar was content to stay at his father's side and listen to the stories in verse and prose that Morgan told with such skill. There was not much work done on the impending sermon as he responded to Edgar's requests. 'Just one more story, Dadda. Tell me another story from your head.'

With his customary good humour Morgan began the account of the family's journey from mid-Wales over the Brecon Beacons. As the story unfolded Edgar hung on every word. His father's description of the family falling prey to a robber as they sheltered overnight at Storey Arms never failed to grip his imagination.

Morgan was more demonstratively affectionate towards the boys than their mother, particularly with Edgar, who most needed affection. Years of carrying her frail brothers and sisters around, and trying to distract grizzling toddlers had taken their toll on Margaret Ann. She often found small children a nuisance yet at times she was jealous of the close relationship her boys had established with their father. In reality she was as possessive a mother as she was a wife. She needed to be first with Morgan but she also needed the boys, young as they were, to recognise that she was the one on whom they should depend for everything.

✍ ✍ ✍

The week dragged interminably for Margaret Ann. On Friday

27

morning Morgan decided to take the children away from the barrage of domesticity, and walk up the valley to Treorci. At this time of year the countryside looked its best. The new leaves of the birches were fully out and the fresh green gave a lightness to the valley which gladdened Morgan's heart. The hawthorn blossom was just appearing and the drifts of white on the hedges looked like lace. Along the narrow mountain road the new ferns were uncurling, buttercups were emerging and the bluebells made a patchwork of bright colour which contrasted strongly with the drabness of the valley lower down. The expansion of the pits might be good for the workers thought Morgan, but it was destroying the countryside as the mining industry continued to invade the valley. A lark rose up from nearby, disturbed by the footfall of Morgan and his sons. Up here the birdsong was the loudest sound, but once the pits were sunk, it was the harsh clang of coal trucks and the drone of the winding gear which predominated. These man-made sounds, which to Morgan were discordant and intrusive, brought back the memories of his years spent underground and he shook his head to dispel such thoughts on the bright sunny morning.

His little sons, oblivious of their father's darker mood, dashed enthusiastically along the path hopeful that the customary treats from their grandmother would be waiting for them. Morgan was anxious about the decision his mother and sisters were making and although he dreaded the possible outcome, he preferred knowledge to conjecture. His mother and sisters welcomed the walkers wholeheartedly and the boys were soon enjoying the remains of yesterday's apple tart and fresh Welsh cakes, just out of their grandmother's oven. While the inevitable cup of tea was brewing, Morgan gathered his thoughts.

'You can take those cakes out on the step if you like, boys. Then the birds can have the crumbs, instead of my floor. Just mind Will doesn't get into mischief Edgar, while I have a word with your Dadda.' Their grandmother put the impromptu picnic down on the back step and closed the kitchen door.

Decided have you?' Morgan asked.

'Aye,' replied Mary Ann who always came straight to the point. 'We've talked of little else and the men are willing. They think they will get the chance of good jobs out there and Iolo Williams from the bookshop will take this place on. It should all go through very quickly. In fact I'm looking forward to it. This valley gets on my nerves at times, with everyone poking their noses into other people's affairs. I'll relish the chance to say goodbye to that lot down by the dairy. What they don't know or can't find out, they make up, and as for that other crowd...'

She was interrupted by her mother who was well aware of the diatribe that could follow if Mary Ann got going on the subject of her neighbours. Her matter of fact tone belying her inner turmoil, she said, 'I'll be happy to see Jane and do what I can for her.'

Morgan drank his tea and looked intently at his mother.

'I'll be the poorer for your going.'

'Well, you should be coming too,' interrupted his sister. 'There are plenty of good Baptist causes to be found in America, I'm sure. Our Jane could tell them what a great preacher you are, in English as well as Welsh. The chapels would be queuing up with offers of preaching engagements and you'd have your own chapel in no time. Did you tell Margaret Ann about it?'

Morgan nodded.

'Well, what did she have to say about it?'

'Not much.' Her brother decided that unnecessary words would not help. 'I must see what the boys are doing outside. Let me know if you want any help packing up, Mam, and see that your passage is booked in good time.'

A silence fell between the brother and sister leaving, as usual, so much unsaid. The children, Welsh cakes finished, were called in from their exploration of magpie feathers in the corner of the yard. Morgan picked up his smaller son, took Edgar by the hand and walked down the narrow passage to the front door. As he stepped over the threshold his mother said, 'I hope it will not be too long before we are on our way. There's no good hanging around now our minds are made up.'

Morgan did not reply but he lifted his hand as though giving a blessing, before turning away from his mother. On their way home Edgar asked, 'Where is America, Dadda? Why were you talking about America?'

'It's across the sea, a long way off. I thought the door was shut and you and Will were busy playing. You forget all about it and don't chat about it to Mam. She's not interested in America.'

'Is Mamgu going there? Will you go to America with Mamgu?' Edgar did not give up easily.

'No, no, indeed not. It's stay here in Ystrad we will, now forget about it and run on. Will has found a dandelion clock to blow.'

'Will we stay here, for always?' Edgar held his father's hand for reassurance after the strange conversation he had half heard through the kitchen door.

'For always, now run on and catch Will.'

∽ ∽ ∽

Margaret Ann was sweeping the small yard at the back of the house when her family returned. Morgan guessed that his wife was again consumed by some passionate rage, as the broom was forced up and down the stones.

'Back, are you?' was the terse comment.

Morgan waited, in case further comment was to follow, keeping an eye on William who was looking around intent on some mischief. He realised his wife was not going to stop her sweeping and picked William up to prevent him from doing anything likely to cause his mother's rage to be transferred from the broom to him. Inside the house he lifted the box of alphabet blocks from the windowsill and left the boys with their favourite activity. Edgar was soon busy making words while Will built towers to knock to the floor with a satisfying crash. Heaving a sigh, Morgan made his way to the parlour, hoping he might at least make a start on his sermon for Sunday.

Margaret finished her sweeping and put the broom to rest on the wall before entering the house, where she picked up the letter from the corner of the dresser. It had arrived earlier and her heart had leapt at the sight of her name of the envelope. Her excitement had not lasted long. The letter's contents were the cause of her rage, as well as the reason the backyard was cleaner than most people's kitchen floors. She re-read the lines that had infuriated her:

'The mine company would be prepared to lease the premises, but only to your husband, as is their customary policy. It should be noted that women are not permitted to hold leases of colliery property in their own right.
NB. The lessee would be required to undertake the baking of bread for those employed in sinking the pit.'

Margaret Ann seethed with fury. Over and over again her mind repeated the letter'shated words. Husband indeed! It was to be her shop! What did he know about groceries, provisions, or baking! He had no idea about anything except books and sermons and deacons and his wretched congregation. A fine mess he would make of baking a loaf of bread, never mind running a shop! She would see to the bread and he could worry about heaven. Even as she marched up and down the little yard with her broom, her mind had begun to search for a solution. The more she thought about her ambition, the more she realised that her plan was in danger. She had been so sure it would work out but now she knew it could not come to fruition without Morgan's involvement. 'There's no help for it,' she decided. 'Tell him I'll have to, and the sooner the better.'

A direct approach was the only one known to Margaret Ann. Waiting only to be sure the boys remained fully occupied, she went through to the parlour. Morgan looked up as she entered and thought how pretty she looked with her blue eyes flashing, her face flushed with her exertions and her blonde hair in disarray. With each pregnancy Margaret Ann seemed to bloom. Holding out the letter she said, 'Morgan, you had better read this.'

He noticed the clasping and unclasping of her hands which meant his wife must be seriously agitated and took the letter. When he had finished reading, he said, 'What nonsense is this? I do not understand what this is all about, Margaret Ann. Why are they writing to you? Is it your father they should be writing to? Why on earth should I want to lease a shop in the Rhondda Fach, and bake bread for sinkers? I am no shopkeeper. I'm fully occupied with my ministry here.'

Morgan re-read the letter. His mind was still half on the pending departure of his mother and sisters and the mysterious letter made no sense. Then the solution came to him. It must be Rhys Evans, his father–in-law, who was thinking of leasing the shop and hoped his daughter would take charge of it.

'I think there is a mistake somewhere. They've mixed us up with your father. Your father must have decided to open another shop and so it's he would have to sign the lease.'

'My father? What has it to do with him? My father knows nothing of this. Of course you don't want a shop and you could not bake bread. I want the shop and I can bake bread, but they say that you will have to be the lessee. I want the shop, and the colliery company says it has got to be yours. Well, if that's the only way to get it, then it will have to be yours on paper and mine in fact.' Margaret Ann continued her tirade, 'And if it is getting the money they are worried about, they are a lot more likely to get it from me than you any day.'

Losing patience as her husband read the letter yet again, Margaret Ann moved closer to the table on which Morgan's books were spread out. 'Change their minds they must!' She smacked her hand down on the green chenille cloth and several books and papers toppled to the floor.

Slowly, Morgan began to understand. It was clear that Margaret Ann had been making plans about this for some considerable time. She had no doubt made all the necessary enquiries but for some reason had not mentioned them to him. He rose from his chair and began pacing up and down the little parlour. Then very quietly he said, 'Suppose you start at the beginning and tell me exactly what has been going on, because unless I know everything there will be no shop.'

Margaret told him of her journey over the mountain to the pithead. She described the conversation with the agent which had resulted in the letter he now held in his hand. Morgan did not interrupt the factual recital and when it was finished he remained silent. After a few moments he carefully folded the letter, placed it in the inside pocket of his jacket, and picked up the books and papers which had tumbled to the floor. Then he returned to his chair and sat down. 'This needs more thought, Margaret Ann. You go now and see to the children.'

Wisely Margaret Ann took her dismissal knowing that it would do no good to comment for the present. Her husband stared at his unfinished sermon and re-stacked the sheets of paper neatly on the table. As he did so, he considered his wife's astonishing behaviour. That she had gone as far as she had with the negotiations about this shop with no word to him! He knew he was only now hearing about it because of the need for his signature on the lease. He knew she was far from content with her present lot, that her boundless energy was satisfied neither by the housework nor children, and that no power he possessed could turn that energy to chapel duties. No other married woman in the valley would go to such lengths to assert her independence. Surely this was no time for her to take to shopkeeping, when three months from now there would be another child? 'She's just like her mother,' thought Morgan, 'she's on the go from morning until night and there's nothing I can do to rein her in!'

What Morgan still did not realise was that Margaret Ann was consumed with ambition. Her years in boarding school in Cowbridge had opened her eyes to a different way of life, and it was to that life she aspired. Her sons were not going down any mines and any daughters she might have, would not be dependent on any man. Her children would all go to school, and even university. It was qualifications they would earn so that they would never experience financial insecurity or loss of status in their community. Therefore she needed to be able to earn her own money in order to put the family on the upward path. She was utterly determined to live her

33

life in her own way, sublimely indifferent to the views of neighbours, family or even her husband. Somehow Morgan would need to find a way to cope with the wife he had chosen.

Morgan tidied away his books and papers, and returned to the kitchen. He knew that it had been his admiration of Margaret Ann's indomitable spirit which had been part of the reason he had been attracted to her in the first place, but he had not realised the possible consequences of her incredible drive!

There was no further discussion or argument between them until both the children were fast asleep. Then Morgan summoned his wife into the parlour. It came as no surprise to him that Margaret Ann had planned her campaign with military efficiency. Every argument he put forward in favour of his wife following a more traditional wifely path was pushed aside. Her relentless logic identified the reasons for her course of action. She needed a larger house, which the chapel could not provide, and she needed to own it. She needed more money for the children which the chapel could not pay. She needed to move away from the stultifying restrictions of being a minister's wife in a small community, and above all she needed a career of her own.

Eventually it was agreed that Morgan would own the shop on paper, but in reality it would be his wife's. In return for his putting no obstacle in her way, Margaret Ann was forced to accept one firm condition, namely that Morgan was and always would be, first and foremost a Baptist minister. She must never in the future try to make him divert from the path he had chosen, nor by word or action interfere between him and his congregation.

By the morning Morgan had agreed to sign the lease, convinced that Margaret Ann would, if prevented from pursuing a career in shopkeeping, find some other, possibly more alarming activity through which to express her independence.

CHAPTER 5
MRS JONES, THE SHOP

Margaret Ann now had plenty of outlets for her energy. In spite of her advancing pregnancy she began the plans for the move from Ystrad to Cwtch with gusto. Her parents were delighted at the turn of events and had advanced her the funds to stock the shop as well as instructing their suppliers to add the new store in Cwtch to their list of deliveries. She made several visits to the new premises and became a familiar figure to the workmen as she instructed the joiners as to the exact positioning of shelves and counter tops.

Elizabeth came up the valley to help entertain Edgar with endless stories and prevent William from falling down the cellar steps, while Margaret Ann planned and sorted and packed up the family's belongings. The future shopkeeper even refrained from complaining about the number of Morgan's books which had to be strung into bundles and stacked carefully in the narrow hall waiting for the carter. She hoped the greater distance between her new home in Cwtch and Morgan's chapel in the Rhondda Fawr might enable her to forget the chapel's very existence. She was well aware that when he stayed later after the service or insisted on making a visit to a sick member, she would have longer to cope with the children but she was confident that she had the strength to manage. Wiser now, she kept her feelings to herself, always mindful of the deal she had struck with Morgan over the move to the shop in the Rhondda Fach. Margaret Ann had never broken her word to anyone, least of all her long-suffering husband.

Eventually all the family's belongings were safely packed, Including the precious lustre jug from the dresser, and the children were despatched once again to the much put upon Elizabeth. The final boxes were loaded on to Jim Watkin's cart for the journey to Cwtch and Margaret Ann's spirits rose. She waved Jim off with repeated instructions about not allowing her best china to be shaken about and to be sure to wait for her arrival in the next valley before removing anything from the cart. Momentarily she re-entered the door of her first married home, allowing the peace of the now empty house to flow over her. Morgan was committed to a minis-ters' gathering in Porth, so she had the luxury of the rest of the day to herself. In a short while her old life would be done with and she could hardly contain her excitement. After a few undignified skips of joy around the kitchen, she proceeded sedately down the narrow hall out into the sunshine, to wait for the trap which was to convey her to her new home. Once out in the street she saw several of Morgan's congregation standing gossiping as they watched the comings and goings at the minister's home. Reluctant to speak to them, the minister's wife was relieved to see Bill Bevan's trap rattling down the road.

'Leaving us then, are you?' called Annie Jenkins, as Margaret Ann was handed up in to the little trap with the carpet bag containing the authorising letter from the agent and the all important lease, grasped firmly in her hand.

'Just as well we're keeping the Reverend Jones, though. We wouldn't want to be without him!' The other women in the group giggled nervously. Margaret Ann inclined her head graciously towards them, treated them to a ladylike wave and without looking back set her face towards the future.

It was a beautiful day and as the trap rattled and shook up the mountain road, the sun sparkled on the streams and glowed on the pony's back. Margaret Ann allowed her imagination free rein with the planning and layout of her shop. As the trap breasted the brow of the hill, she could see the valley stretching away below her. The newly erected winding gear reared upwards from the valley floor and the low roofs of the mine buildings huddled around it as though for protection. The steep sides of the valley had been cleared of many of the trees and soon she could see the new rows of terraced houses, each one exactly like its neighbour, emerging from the now bare hillside. It would not be long before every one of them would be filled with a family, all needing bread and provisions. Morgan could provide the 'Bread of Heaven' for his congregation but she would be the provider of the loaves and fishes for the bodies! The idea made her smile as she pictured herself clad in a spotless apron, dispensing essential goods to her five thousand waiting customers. She would show her parents and her brother what it was to run a successful provisions store!

In little more than an hour, the trap came to a halt behind Jim Watkins' cart. She saw the front door of the double fronted end terrace house wedged open, and Jim and his boy leaning against the cart waiting for instructions. As soon as they caught sight of Margaret Ann, Jim and his son leapt into action, busying themselves with lowering the back board of the cart and chocking the wheels firmly. Then both men began heaving the kitchen dresser down from the cart towards the door.

'Here we are then, Mrs Jones,' grinned her driver, helping her down from the trap, and handing her the carpet bag containing the precious documents. 'It's as well you've got a nice day for your move. You'll have your hands full getting this lot straight before the minister gets back. Would it help you if I gave Jim a hand? You'd be straight quicker with three of us, and perhaps then you'd have time for a sit down?'

He allowed his eyes to rest briefly on Margaret Ann's noticeably thickened waistline. Sensitive as ever to any hint that she was a help-less female, Margaret Ann was about to refuse, when she realised the scale of the task ahead of her.

'You could do with an extra bit for that wife of yours to spend, you mean! Mind you, it looks as though Jim and that lad will be here all day just trying to get the dresser into the kitchen, so it might be a good idea. I'll have enough to do sorting the shop so you can have five bob for your pains. Make sure you don't let anything scrape the walls and get the beds in first. They'll need making up for the children.'

Leaving herself no time to appreciate the elegance of her new bay window and the panelled front door, Margaret Ann disappeared round the back of the house to open up the shop to daylight. Her family's long connection with the provision business had smoothed her way with the suppliers, and some orders had already been delivered and stacked in the shop. As she stood surveying her new kingdom the door was pushed open and a small curly head appeared.

'Please Mrs Jones, mum, is it help you'll be needing? We knew you was coming and we seen the trap and me Mam thought you'd be glad of help getting tidy in the shop. I'm nearly twelve and very quick, me mam says, and I'll do exactly as I'm told.'

Margaret hid a smile as the earnest child delivered her speech. 'What's your name, girl?'

'Lizzie Jane, mum.'

'Very well, Lizzie Jane, you can start by giving the floor a good sweep. Don't miss out the corners and mind you don't raise too much dust. The joiners have left a dustpan and brush in the kitchen. Go round and look for it and be quick. Then you can wipe down the shelves.'

With a little bob the child disappeared into the house, to return triumphantly a few minutes clutching her tools. She began sweeping enthusiastically while Margaret Ann produced a neat file of orders and invoices from the brightly coloured carpet bag she had placed on the counter and began to check the sugar and flour sacks. Eventually the floor was dust free, the shelves were wiped and Lizzie Jane stood back to survey her efforts. Margaret Ann was not given to praise but she had enjoyed the company of her hard-working young assistant and was very grateful for the little girl's help.

'You can come and help again tomorrow if your mam says you can and I might find you a couple of pennies. Eight o'clock sharp and you can help me start unpacking the boxes. So you get off home now for your supper.'

As she closed the door on Lizzie she heard the trap jingling its way towards the new house and the excited shouts from William as the two little boys and Elizabeth rounded the corner. Margaret Ann put all thoughts of shopkeeping out of her mind, and went to welcome the boys into their new home. The boys were highly relieved to see their mother, as Edgar had not been at all convinced she would ever reappear. William was concerned only to get to pat the horse's nose and to reward the little pony with the remains of an apple which he had been holding fast all the way over the mountain road.

'Where are our bricks, Mam? Where's Dadda? I thought you were moving house. How did you move it?' William's questions as ever came thick and fast while Edgar clutched at his mother's skirt. Taking one look at Margaret Ann's tired face, Elizabeth produced a bag of Welsh cakes and a can of milk from her basket and left the boys on the back step with their picnic supper.

'Sit down a minute Margaret Ann, and catch your breath. I'll get the boys' beds made up and I'll get them washed and ready for bed. We'll settle them down and then I'll give you a hand down here. We don't want any more to worry about today.'

As soon as the boys had eaten, she scooped up the protesting William from the step and called Edgar to come and see his new bedroom. The excitement of the move and the thrilling ride in the trap had worn both the boys out and they were soon fast asleep. Box after box was emptied and the kitchen floor was buried under mounds of straw, as cups, saucers and plates were exhumed and neatly arrayed on the dresser.

'Mind you push those dishes well back, I don't want any break-ages, and where's my lustre jug? It was packed with the dinner service.'

Tired as she was, Margaret Ann never failed to direct operations. With a sigh, Elizabeth rummaged again round the bottom of the tea chest she had just emptied. With a flourish she produced the missing jug, and carefully installed it in its rightful place. Margaret Ann allowed herself a small smile of relief and scooped the straw back into the chest.

'No more now. The last few can be done tomorrow. We've done the most important boxes.' Another hour saw the kitchen more or less straight, with cold ham, cheese and bread ready on the table for supper. Elizabeth finally made up the matrimonial bed and put the chairs straight in the parlour.

'I'm off home now,' she announced. 'Don't overdo it now till Morgan gets back. Everything else can wait, but I must go or Mam will think I've run off with a sinker!'

'You've been a real help today Elizabeth. In fact I don't think I'd have managed without you,' answered her cousin in an unaccustomed moment of appreciation.

Gracious! The move's done her good already, Elizabeth thought to herself as she carefully closed the front door.

Margaret Ann did indeed take Elizabeth's advice and walked slowly back into the pristine shop. She pulled out one of the new chairs she had insisted on for the use of any frail or elderly customers who may present themselves, and flopped onto it. She was still sitting there when Morgan arrived. He cast an approving eye around the shop and gave his exhausted wife a kiss. 'Goodness, someone's worked hard today. Let's go and eat. We could both do with it and then we'll do a bit more in here,' he said, and he went through to the kitchen. As soon as supper was cleared away the two of them began the task of arranging the sacks of flour, currants and sugar in neat rows on the flag floor of the shop.

'Lizzie Jane can do the boxes tomorrow,' Margaret Ann eventually said. 'It's bed I need. There'll be a few days yet before I'm open for business.' With some reluctance she dragged herself away from the new project. Almost dropping with tiredness, the new shopkeeper climbed the stairs with her husband close as ever behind her.

∽ ∽ ∽

Throughout that summer more rows of houses were finished, rising up the valley sides like the tide up the sea wall. New families arrived every day, bringing a steadily growing trade into the little shop. Margaret Ann baked the bread for the sinkers as stipulated in the lease, rising every day with the sun to ensure her shelves were stacked with loaves. Even the birth of the third child, her first daughter, Amy Ann, on 15th August 1882, did not keep her away from shop and bakehouse for more than a week.

By the autumn more and more customers appeared and Morgan suggested that perhaps they should find Margaret Ann a helper for the shop. His wife quickly vetoed the idea.

'It's the children I need help with. I only needed Lizzie Jane in the shop while we were setting up. The shop is mine. I do whatever is needed there. You could get Lizzie Jane to help you to look after the children. Her mam could do with the extra money with six of them to feed. The child's finished with school this summer and she's a sensible little thing who'll do as you tell her.'

It came as no surprise to Morgan that his wife was happy to delegate the care of her children with rather more willingness than she would delegate the care of her shop. To the consternation of his congregation, and in stark contrast to other men, Morgan spent much of his time caring for the children but even he had found the new baby's needs beyond him, and the boys took more precious minutes than he had available. Never slow to criticise their minister's wife, the members of the Women's Fellowship were appalled at the way in which the Reverend M H Jones was forced to devote time to being his children's nursery maid while his wife pursued her shopkeeping activities. It became apparent eventually, even to Margaret Ann, that Morgan's sermon writing could not wait, and before long Lizzie Jane became the first of many girls to find employment as child minders and housemaids with 'Mrs Jones, the shop.' The girls stayed during the four or five years they had to fill in between leaving school and marriage, and over the years they gradually became essential parts of the family at 26, Aberllechau Road even though they were hardly ever acknowledged by name, always being referred to as 'the girl.'

The children's mother had scant time and little inclination for child-minding. It was true that she would occasionally have Edgar

41

in the shop, sitting quietly watching his mother or looking at a book, but plans were afoot for him to start attending the newly opened school down the valley. The baby, Amy Ann, nursed in the shawl Welsh fashion, presented no problem either, closely swaddled as she was on her mother's hip. William, however, was different. Everything in the shop was a new discovery full of excitement for the three-year-old, and there was no knowing what havoc he might cause.

Several times a day, as long as none of his flock had need of him, and when his bible reading was finished, Morgan would appear at the door to look for ways of helping his wife in the shop. He was drawn to her as though by a magnet. He was fascinated by her. In every way she was his complete opposite. Where Morgan was patient, tolerant and calm, his wife was fiery, aggressive and utterly driven. Morgan gave her unconditional love and he had absolute confidence in her ability. He was the rock on which Margaret Ann built her fortress.

In practical ways, however, he was more of a hindrance than a help, as a short, not very muscular man and slow in his movements. His wife would complain that he was 'under her feet', but he had a certain skill in bookkeeping and she made use of that talent. It meant she could relinquish the tedious duty of balancing the books each evening. It was much more rewarding to keep a sharp eye on the weekly takings, which began steadily to mount up.

'By Christmas, I should have enough to pay back my parents for the loan they gave me to set up the shop,' she revealed to Morgan as the evenings began to draw in. 'I was afraid it would be a year or more, but I'd not realised how fast the village would grow. I might think about buying a couple of those houses down Bailey Street when they are finished. Rent money might be useful one day and there are plenty of families who'd rather have me as landlord instead of the mine owners.'

Morgan looked up from the book he was reading. 'I never thought the day would come when I'd be a landlord.'

'It hasn't,' retorted his wife with a smirk. 'I'm the landlord, not you.'

⁓ ⁓ ⁓

The great day came when the first truck of coal emerged from the pit. To Margaret Ann it was like the sight of the promised land to the Israelites. Coal mines would need sinkers, colliers, labourers, hauliers, officials, all of whom would likely have families to be fed and she had the only provision shop in the growing village. The houses along the riverbank of which the shop was one, had been long completed. Aberllechau Road had been extended to the point where the brook reached the river and now stretched up and down the valley. Along it, travelled all those with business in the Rhondda Fach. A newly extended railway track ran parallel to the road on the opposite riverbank, and there was a constant movement of trucks, full of coal journeying down the valley to Cardiff. Once empty of the black gold, the clattering and banging they made as they were hauled back up filled the valley with discordant sound.

To Margaret Ann and Morgan it seemed as if Cwtch would grow forever. Two public houses were built, one adjacent to the colliery main entrance, the other a little way up the valley on the opposite side. These were no small wayside inns along the valley floor; they pubs were the largest buildings in the village. Three storeys high, taking the space of three houses, they dominated the streets and presented a very real threat, even to Margaret Ann, who was confident that none of her family would ever enter such a building. The more beer that was drunk meant less money to spend on food, and if the beer became more necessary to the men than the food, then Margaret Ann could foresee a fall in business. In that case she would also need to withstand the entreaties of the women for 'time to pay.'

Above the new main road named Queen Victoria Street, the hill rose steeply and more terraces of houses were cut into its side. Apart from the numbers on the front doors, the houses were identical in layout, and were only distinguished from each other by the cleanliness of doorsteps and windows, and the presence or otherwise of net curtains at the front room window. Each house had a front room

– or parlour – and a kitchen at the back. Through the back door to the rear yard was the *ty bach*, which was generally an earth closet, and a coalshed where the miners stored their allocation of free coal. The neatness of the yard, the whiteness of the net curtains, and the shine on the brass door handles were the yardsticks by which the competence of the housewives were measured. It was as though most of the women were in an endless competition.

But there were women who never entered the competition, who became overburdened with children, ill health or shiftless, hard-drinking husbands. The resulting poverty spilled out from those doorsteps, and for those families destitution was never far away. The combination of debt or homelessness which followed injury or the loss of a job haunted the families of the mining community and reinforced the precarious nature of the miners' existence. Well paid they were, as long as no disaster occurred and their bodies did not succumb to the terrible conditions in which they worked.

The end houses of the terraces, sometimes a little grander than their neighbours, often double fronted and with a bay window on the upper storey, were given to the colliery officials, overmen, safety men and hauliers. Status was recognised in these new coal villages in ways it had not been in the rural areas. The colliery agent or commercial manager lived in splendid isolation, with a large house, spacious grounds and gardeners and maids to keep all in splendid order. No numbers were necessary for these houses, as elegant names remembering the fast disappearing countryside, in Welsh and English like Waun Fawr and Glenside, distinguished them one from the other.

Next to be built were the chapels – stone buildings almost as big as the pubs, built on land leased from the colliery, and funded by their congregations. For Methodists, Congregationalists, and Baptists, the language of worship was with one exception, Welsh. The Baptist chapel, Calfaria, stood proudly on the river bank, almost at the point Margaret Ann had spoken to the agent in May 1882. It was the only chapel on the main road and the one to which she transferred her membership, and where all but her first two children were baptised. Morgan noticed that in breaking her connection with his English chapel in the other valley and worshipping once more in her own language, his wife became noticeably less anti-chapel, though she retained her suspicions of anyone whom she considered overly devout. They were those whom she felt to be rather too concerned with their salvation in the next world rather than their duties in this one and for those people she had scant respect. Margaret Ann believed passionately that hard work, duty to one's family and responsibility to one's neighbours were the only attributes valued by the Almighty and so her duty was clear.

CHAPTER 6
REVEREND JONES, THE POST

It was a blustery morning in early autumn. The clouds scudding across the sun made patchwork patterns along the steeply sloping valley sides. The brook twinkled in the occasional shafts of sunlight as it tumbled down the hill and the first of the falling leaves twirled and twisted along the cobbled road outside the provision store. The Reverend Morgan Humphrey Jones had taken down the shop shutters, swept through the shop and seen that all was in readiness for the first customers. Margaret Ann was busy in the bakehouse and 'the girl' was doing her best to dress William, no easy task for one hardly out of childhood herself. Her tears were not far away as Morgan passed through the living room on his way to the bakehouse to share his plans for the day with his wife.

'Come now,' he addressed the girl. 'Give him to me and you see to the baby.' He picked up the loudly complaining William. 'Let's get these clothes on you and Dadda will take you to Pontypridd on the train. Mamgu and the Aunties are off to America today and we can go and see them off.'

At the sight of his father and the promise of a ride on the train, young Will stopped his yells and submitted quietly enough to the completion of his dressing. When his boots were firmly tied, his father put him down and he ran away to puff round the room hooting in approved train fashion.

'Come on Edgar, come on. Hold my trousers and be the carriages.' He tried to persuade his brother to join the game, but as usual Edgar wanted none of it.

'Have you opened up?' Margaret Ann stood in the doorway, a tray of newly baked loaves in her hands.

'Yes,' Morgan replied. 'but there is nobody in yet.'

'Well, do not hang about there then. Go and get ready or you will miss that train.'

'I've just told Will I would take him with me.'

'Thank goodness for that. I have no time to be watching him and that girl can do nothing with him. Can you take Edgar, too?'

'Of course, if that is what you'd like and it might make it easier for us all. Mam will be glad to see both the boys before she leaves for America. It will leave good memories for Edgar at least, as they may not have any more.'

Morgan climbed the stairs in his characteristically slow fashion, put on his jacket and waistcoat and tied his tie. He had dreaded this day ever since the final decision had been made by his Treorci family to uproot themselves and head across the Atlantic to be with Jane. He was glad the boys were coming with him to the station. Their presence would keep him from dwelling too much on the pain this farewell would cause him. He tried hard to keep his thoughts on the task of dressing, but as he laced his boots he thought of the love and care he had received at the hands of those women who would disappear from his life in only a few hours. His sisters, he knew, were looking forward to America. They had the optimism of youth, sure that their husbands would prosper and that Jane would soon be well once they were there to nurse her. As he straightened his collar and smoothed his beard he thought of his mother. She had no eager anticipation of life in America. She was answering Jane's desperate need of her, which her daughter had expressed more than six months ago. With the realism of her generation, she had prayed that the family would not be too late to bring comfort.

Morgan sighed as he went on downstairs, calling the boys to join him. They passed through the shop where Margaret Ann was serving a customer, and she looked up to inspect them briefly. It was important to her that they looked well-dressed and cared for. Giving

47

Edgar's collar a brisk tweak, straightening Morgan's watch chain, she pronounced herself satisfied and called a cheerful goodbye. Edgar gave her a little wave and Morgan hastened his pace to pick up Will before he ran out through the open shop door. With his younger son objecting vociferously to any restraint, however brief, the trio made their way a mile and a half down the valley to the railway station at Ynyshir.

On the way down they passed the colliery yard, alive with the movement of trucks, horses, carts and the shouts of the workmen. The great winding gear clanged and groaned as yet another load of full coal trucks was brought up to the surface. The small shunting engines fussed and puffed as they manoeuvered yet more trucks into position, then clattered their way over the black bridge, under which other trucks were being pushed to meet the main railway line. With the noise from the pithead, endless questions from one son and constant activity from the other, Morgan's walk to the station was far from peaceful.

'Is Mamgu going to America for ever and ever?' asked Edgar.

Morgan refused to admit the possibility that it might indeed be that. 'Ever and ever is a long time,' he said.

Edgar's questions came thick and fast. 'How far is it to America? More miles away than Cardiff? Will the train take them all the way?'

'No, first to Cardiff, then another train to Liverpool. There's a very wide river there called the Mersey, which leads to the sea. Then they will get on a big ship to cross the Atlantic ocean. It will be a long time before they get to America.' Morgan answered as patiently as he could. 'I'll show you on the big atlas when we get home. But hush your questions now, or we'll miss our train, and then we won't be able to say goodbye to Mamgu and the Aunties.'

With the station reached at last, Morgan thankfully took his seat in the train. The short journey to Pontypridd kept even William quiet. The boys were overawed by the number of people in the carriage and the countryside whizzing past. Morgan was therefore able to gather his thoughts and compose himself. At Pontypridd they left the train and crossed the platform to search anxiously for the train coming down from the other valley. The family goodbyes would need to be brief, as the train would wait only a few minutes at the junction before continuing on its journey down the valley to Cardiff. At last it drew into the platform and Morgan hurried the children along its length, looking for his mother and sisters. He soon saw his brothers-in-law leaning out of the window. The men stepped out on to the platform and lifted the boys into the carriage to see their grandmother. Morgan drew a deep breath before entering the compartment himself. His mother was holding a small brown paper parcel.

'In her last letter Jane asked me to find a copy of this before Iolo took over the stock. It's her way of saying thank you for all you are giving up.'

Holding out his arms to his mother, he took the parcel and gave her a fervent hug. She held his hands tightly, but nothing more was said. After his sisters had given him a quick kiss, Morgan left the compartment and stepped back on to the platform.

The goodbyes were soon over. With an embrace from their grandmother, a kiss for the children from their aunts, the boys were back on the platform, too. The men formally shook hands, the transatlantic travellers re-boarded the train, the whistle sounded and the guard waved his flag, Morgan shouted a quick 'God Speed' and the train steamed out. He and the boys waved until it disappeared from sight. Momentarily, Morgan was devastated by the pain of the separation, but the need to restrain William from following the train and dealing with Edgar's questions about what was in the parcel, helped him regain some composure.

'We'll open it on the train going back up. Quick now, or we'll miss it.'

In the carriage, a few minutes later, Edgar and William opened the mystery package.

'It's a book,' claimed Edgar with delight, and he began laboriously to spell out the title. 'A P.I.L.G.R.I.M's... What's a pilgrim, Dadda?'

His father swallowed the lump in his throat. 'It's a special word for someone going on a journey. Just like Mamgu and the aunties. Give

49

me the book now, we'll soon be back home to Mam and we'll tell her all about it, if she can find the time to listen.'

At home in Cwytch Margaret Ann had had a busy morning. Without the distraction of the children or Morgan's attempts at being useful, she had been able to give her whole attention to the shop. It was not only his slowness in movement that fussed her, it was his presence in the shop which prevented her enjoying a bit of scandalous gossip among the customers. Not that she joined in directly of course, or openly betrayed her interest, but she felt Morgan sensed her enjoyment of the tittle-tattle and disapproved of it. His disapproval of her was a hair shirt to his wife.

Margaret Ann's thoughts were interrupted by the arrival of one of her regular customers who was another Mrs Jones. Her husband, an overseer at the colliery, was renowned for his excellent bass voice which had earned the nickname that differentiated him from many other Joneses in the valley. Mrs Basso shared the nickname and prided herself on her own powerful soprano voice. Unfortunately, no choir had yet invited her to join their ranks so she was reduced to practising her music in the chapel. The chapel congregation did their best to drown her out when the voice was heard soaring heavenwards, and Mrs Basso Jones frequently sat in her pew alone, but today singing was not the topic for discussion. She and Margaret Ann exchanged news in Welsh about their respective children and Margaret Ann would have been happy to prolong the conversation, but the entrance of two more customers reminded them that there was business to be done.

Mrs Basso completed her purchases of flour and bacon and then asked, 'You haven't a postage stamp, Mrs Jones have you? I know the Reverend writes many letters and keeps a few stamps by him. Mr Basso has written this letter about the choir competition and if I stamped it, the postman would take it for me on his way down the Valley this afternoon.'

Margaret had no wish to leave the shop with other customers wanting her attention, but she wished to oblige Mrs Basso who was a good customer, always ready with cash in hand.

'Can you wait a minute now? Let me serve these others and I'll go and look. The Reverend Jones has taken the boys to Pontypridd, to say goodbye to his mother and sisters so I'll have to see for myself.'

Mrs Basso was quite prepared to wait. She had time to spare before getting home, so she perched herself on the chair by the counter. Besides, it put off her next task which was filling the water buckets ready for her husband's bath when he came in from the pit. She and the other customers were very keen to discuss the departure of the Reverend Jones' family to Pennsylvania and to speculate as to the reasons for the minister's family remaining behind.

Margaret hurried through to look in Morgan's stamp book for the necessary one penny stamp. Mrs Basso was profuse in her thanks and would have lingered, seeking further information about the American emigration, but Margaret cut her short. Enough was enough, good customer or not, time was moving on and her presence would shortly be needed in the house. She could hear Amy Ann's hungry cry and the girl singing as she tried to pacify the baby. Mrs Basso made her way out of the shop almost colliding with Mrs Williams, Ty'r Hir on the way. Mrs Williams' son Steffan, another mainstay of the chapel's musical life, was the proud possessor of an expressive bass-baritone voice and tensions were not uncommon between the two men as they competed for the privilege of being selected as one of the soloists at morning service. Today, though, there was more harmony than discord and the ladies contented themselves with a courteous nod.

'If Morgan is not here soon I'll have to have Amy in here,' Margaret Ann thought irritably, 'and get the girl to see to the dinner for the rest of them.' But just as she was about to call for Lizzie Jane she heard Edgar yelling and he ran into the shop. 'Mam! Mam! Mamgu has gone to America, in the train, then on a big ship. It's called a liner! Dadda's going to show me where in his atlas.'

'Has she indeed? Where's your father? Gone to America, too?' Margaret Ann's brisk tone stayed the boy's excited chatter.

'No, Mam, no. Dadda has gone to bring Will back. He saw a dog with three legs and ran after it, away up the road.' His mother brushed him aside as she came round the counter. The shop door opened at that moment to admit Morgan with the runaway Will tucked under his arm.

'Put him down, for goodness sake,' she ordered her husband. 'And mind the shop while I go and feed Amy Ann.'

Grasping William firmly by the arm and telling Edgar to go to the kitchen, she left the shop to Morgan and for a short while returned to her role as mother. Morgan picked up the weights which had been scattered as Margaret Ann whirled out of the shop. He allowed himself a few short private moments as he prayed fervently for the safety of his family in their journey to a new and better life, but soon the shop bell jangled and three small children appeared on an errand. Morgan brought himself back to earth and attended to the children with his customary patience and a gentle smile.

Back in the kitchen Amy Ann was quiet once her hunger was assuaged. When the boys were settled with their dinner, Margaret Ann drew breath. Fleetingly she felt remorse about the way she had spoken to Morgan. Her greeting could have been kinder. No doubt he was tired after the morning with the boys, and he would have found the farewell to his family very difficult. Sitting peacefully with her baby, Margaret Ann relaxed and allowed her thoughts to travel back over the morning. She remembered that she must tell Morgan she had taken the stamp for Mrs Basso. It was a nuisance the way people asked for stamps, but with no post office nearer than Ynishir what were the women to do? Margaret's thoughts leapt ahead as they usually did.

'Of course, of course, that is what we need!' Thrusting the now sleepy baby at the girl, and chivvying the boys to sit up straight and eat properly, she ran into the shop where Morgan was weighing sugar. 'Go and have your dinner with the chldren and then come back in the shop. I've got something to tell you.'

Morgan gave his wife a resigned glance before hurriedly retreating to the parlour to put his precious gift on the bookshelf. How like them, he thought wistfully, to choose such a book – *The Pilgrim's Progress*. I wonder which of us is the pilgrim?

'Morgan, your dinner's going cold.' He recognised that tone of voice, and was brought sharply back to reality. Margaret Ann re-appeared in the parlour doorway. 'Quick, come in the kitchen. I've had an idea.' She took a deep breath and ushered her husband to the kitchen table before announcing, 'I must apply for a post office! Half the income in my parents' shop comes from the post office, and I used to spend hours in there checking the books for them. I don't know why it's taken me so long to think of it. Back and forth for stamps from you all day, and having to go down the valley for a parcel and we could have one here!'

Her husband looked at her apprehensively. Was there to be no end to her ideas? Surely they carried a heavy enough workload already. He had little time to collect his wits, as Margaret Ann launched into an explanation as to how necessary a post office was in Cwtch. She knew all about running a post office, since her parents had one in their shop in Cwmamman.

When at last Morgan was allowed to speak, he said, 'You know how you have little enough time to spare for the children even now, Margaret Ann, and if a post office is added to the shop your duties will be even more onerous.'

'I'm not going to do the post office, you are. You've got plenty of time between sermon writing and meetings. No doubt they won't let a mere woman run a post office and it will be the shop lease business all over again. You will have to be the official postmaster, but this time you shall do the work as well!'

A stunned Morgan tried to explain that firstly he had no wish to be a government servant as he was first and foremost a minister of religion and secondly he could not spare the time from his pastoral work to be in charge of a post office counter. If they were both in the shop all day he reasoned calmly, the care of the children would be entirely up to the girl, who was already struggling to manage. Margaret Ann dismissed these objections with an airy wave.

'Edgar will soon be going to school all day in Ynishir and so the girl will have no need to call for your help. You'll do it easily.' With a triumphant air she returned to the shop. Yet again Morgan

53

resigned himself to the inevitable and left the kitchen to prepare his sermon in the sanctuary of the parlour and the company of his books, which were never so demanding.

Margaret Ann had once again decided on the road the family were to take. A few months later the letter arrived informing them that Her Majesty's Post Office would indeed be willing for a post and telegraph office to be established in the village, under the charge of Reverend M H Jones. But by the time the letter of approval arrived, Morgan had had sufficient time to marshall his arguments. He stipulated several conditions if he were indeed to take on responsibility for the post office. If one of his flock needed him, he would leave the counter at once and if someone called for him to visit the sick, he would go. No objections were to be raised by Margaret Ann at the length of deacons' meetings and he was to be free to attend his ministers' meetings once a month in Pontypridd without comment. His ministry to his people was to come before any post office and Margaret Ann was to realise it.

The post office working day was luckily shorter than that of the grocer's shop and at least that would give him a few hours respite in which he could fulfil his duties as a serving minister. But for the next twenty years while he planned his sermons in his head, Margaret Ann's husband served out postage stamps and money orders, took in savings, weighed parcels, and despatched and received telegrams.

CHAPTER 7
LIFE AND DEATH MATTERS

The shop with its post office in Aberllechau Road was the scene of constant activity. Opening hours were long, from eight in the morning until eight at night, and even longer on Friday or Saturday. It was only Margaret Ann's devotion to method and her organising ability that prevented chaos. Each evening the dough was prepared and left to rise. By six o'clock each morning, she had ensured the bread was in the ovens, the house fires lit and the family's breakfast prepared, before the sleepy girl arrived to dress the children and the shop opened its doors. Edgar who was now six, rose with his mother and ran up the mountain path to collect the milk for the family from the farm at the head of the valley – a pleasant enough task on a sunny summer morning, but one he dreaded in snowy, dark January.

The children were fortunately healthy and did not succumb to the dreaded and often fatal diseases of childhood then prevalent. The angels of death-carrying measles, diphtheria, scarlet fever and tuberculosis all passed over the house and left the immediate family unscathed. The American 'adventurers' as Margaret Ann referred to Morgan's family in Pennsylvania, were less fortunate. His sister Jane had lived only a few months after her mother arrived from Treorci and his younger sister was now showing signs of tuberculosis. Margaret Ann was sure her healthy children benefited from her own good management and not because of any benefits from Morgan's communications with the Divine. Cleanliness, exercise, good plain food and *not giving in* were the necessary attributes for healthy living. To give in, either to illness or misfortune was a cardinal sin in her book. By the exercise of willpower, all things could be shaped to the desired pattern. Lesser mortals, such as her own brothers and sisters, could suffer the terrible loss of children in infancy, or even worse, husbands meeting fatal accidents underground.

On the evening of 18th February 1887, the village was shaken by an enormous explosion in the pit. The blast was so powerful the winding gear was buckled and the lustre jug shook on the dresser. As the 200 men of the evening shift had not yet gone down and many of the miners from the day shift had already come to the surface, the death toll of thirty-eight men and boys was far lower than it might have been.

Morgan Humphrey spent many hours comforting and supporting the bereaved families and was rarely to be seen behind his post office counter. Apart from offering the bereaved whatever bacon and bread could be spared from her regular customers, Margaret Ann remained immune from such disasters. She was thankfully never to know what she considered the worst misfortune of all, to be married to a husband who regularly visited public houses, spending his hard-earned wages on beer for himself, instead of food for his children.

The shop thrived as the village grew. The customers were many and varied. Some were native Welsh speakers born in the valley, who with the incoming families from the more northern and western counties of Merionydd and Caernarfon, Cardiganshire and Carmarthenshire, all used Welsh as their day-to-day language. There were also many English incomers who had left their home counties of Somerset and Gloucestershire to seek work in the developing mining villages, and of course there were the Irish. These were the men who worked mostly as navvies on building the roads and railways which were needed to open up communication with docks of Cardiff and Barry from where the coal was exported all over the world. Margaret Ann and Morgan were fluent in Welsh and English, and the two languages flowed equally through the shop.

The village had now been re-named from the old Welsh names

of Aberllechau and Cwtch to the new name of Wattstown. The new pit had been sunk by Edmund Hannay Watts of Northumberland and it was he who gave his name to the growing town clinging to the valley sides. The change of name was seen to be important as a way of helping to draw these people from many different places into a close-knit community. The men, most of whom worked in the one pit, were bound together by their daily work. The women gravitated towards the shop where family concerns could be aired, and advice, sympathy and understanding extended to all. The shop with its new post office counter was rarely empty and with the Reverend and Mrs Jones always busy attending to customers, there was usually plenty of time to chat while waiting to be served.

Margaret Ann kept a firm hold on her customers and could tell a bad manager a mile off. She wanted no customers who would be forever paying off debts, or wanting more credit. She kept a slate on the wall above the till on which she wrote the names of anyone to whom she had given credit. The relief on her customers' faces when their names were rubbed out was very evident. If she black-listed anyone, they had a long walk to the next provision shop but she was not without the milk of human kindness. In times of illness or lockouts she allowed the purchase of basic foods such as flour, cheese, and bacon on credit and many hard-pressed families with young children had reason to be grateful for her generosity. She believed that her customers ran true to type, established by their place of origin, and was astonished if any showed a variation. An Irish wife telling the tale that she would have to defer payment was natural, but an Irish wife living frugally to make ends meet was to be wondered at. Likewise a Cardiganshire wife asking for credit was as astounding as the moon becoming blue cheese.

∽ ∽ ∽

The number of Jones children increased steadily. By 1886 Edgar and William had been joined not only by Amy Ann but by another brother, Morgan James. The eldest two were now in school in Ynyshir, for as yet Wattstown had no school of its own, which meant the children trudged the one and a half miles four times a day in all weathers. Every Monday both boys set off down the valley, clutching their 'school pennies' in a knotted handkerchief, for, despite the 1870 Education Act which had introduced universal primary education, school boards still had the right to demand a 'nominal fee' from their pupils; Edgar and William were also mindful of their mother's dire threats as to what would happen if the money were to be lost. Margaret Ann was utterly convinced that her children's success depended on them acquiring the best possible education and nothing was allowed to stand in its way. Regardless of minor aches and pains, homework was the only excuse permitted in a plea to be let off chores. Morgan Humphrey, too, was diligent in supporting the children's learning. He had powerful memories of his struggles to become literate and take the route out of the pit as a result of his education. He was never too busy to respond to ever increasing requests to listen to reading practice, or to correct a composition and Margaret Ann's insistence on correctly learned multiplication tables kept all her children at the top of the class.

The regularity of childbirth established its own routine, with new babies arriving every two or three years and causing as little disruption as possible. As the family increased, the task of keeping the other children in some kind of order during the shop's opening hours fell to Lizzie Jane's replacement – the long-suffering Cassie, as 'the girl.' Edgar was growing into an obedient and conscientious child who took his responsibilities as the oldest very seriously. William who was now six, had now taken over the milk-collecting duties from Edgar as his older brother had been given the more important task of collecting the first delivery of mail from the railway station about a mile away. The mail train came up the valley at 6.30 a.m. and it was eight-year-old Edgar's job to catch the sack of letters as the guard leant out from his van to throw the mailbag. Then he ran back up the valley, and before his breakfast could be eaten, the mail was sorted accurately into piles on the post office counter ready for the post boy to deliver.

Edgar was a naturally bookish child, and, like his father, was never happier than when he could shut out the world and immerse himself in his favourite books. Even though many of the words were too difficult for him, he thought nothing of ploughing his way through his favourite *Grimm's Fairy Tales*, in contrast to his brother. William could be relied upon to provoke Edgar with endless questions and to take every advantage of his mother's absence to tease his little sister, although he was unfailingly gentle with the newest baby brother. His curiosity and boundless energy never flagged and for him, adventure and exploration were a joy. His ability to get into scrapes became known throughout the village, and Margaret Ann became accustomed to 'that William of yours!' being many customers' opening remark.

In spite of the presence of the pit and the alarming increase of accidents underground there was neither doctor nor undertaker in the new Wattstown. The bodies of the deceased were attended to in their own homes by local women. Where possible the body would rest in the family's own parlour but many of the little colliery houses had only one room downstairs apart from the kitchen and so the bereaved family needed somewhere to rest the body until the funeral rose. It was on such occasions that Margaret Ann would permit the coffin to be rested in the shop overnight, using the main counter as a bier. After the shop had closed, and the blinds drawn, the deceased was reverently laid on the counter so that the body could spend its last night on earth in peace. Morgan's dual role of minister and postmaster meant he was conveniently at hand when called on to say the appropriate words as the coffin entered the shop, or to close the lid as the departed was sent to its final resting place.

One Thursday evening William, now nearly seven, his friend Jimmy Dando and two other boys were returning from playing down at the brook. Jimmy Dando was permanently hungry.

'Will, got any bread in your pocket?' he asked.

William turned out his pockets, to find only a stone and a small piece of string. Jimmy went on, 'it's starving I am. Bet there's loads to eat in your mam's shop. D'you think we could find anything?'

William thought for a moment. Unusually the shop appeared to be closed even though it was early in the evening. 'Well, we might find something but you'll have to keep quiet while I have a look,' he ordered.

As quietly as they could, the four boys crept round the corner of the house and slipped into the back of the shop. The lights were off and the blinds drawn, but William knew exactly where the apple barrel was. He slid behind the counter and reached into the barrel. As he straightened up with his hands full of apples, he noticed a very large box with a lid on the shop counter. Wondering what was in it, he put the apples down, caught hold of the rim of the box and hauled himself up to take a closer look. In doing so, he dislodged the lid, which had not yet been fixed in place; it slipped sideways, revealing the pallid face of a recently deceased neighbour.

With a shriek, William fell backwards off the counter, hitting his head with a bang, which sent the apples rolling across the floor. Sensing imminent retribution, the two other boys bolted for the door, but Jimmy Dando was more concerned about the apples. He chased after them, stuffing the fruit into his pockets. At that moment, disturbed by the din, Margaret Ann marched into the shop. She took in the situation in a moment, grabbed Jimmy by the shoulder, opened the front door of the shop and deposited him, apples and all, on the pavement. Then she turned to her frightened son who was clutching his head with one hand and trying hard to wipe away the tears with the other.

'It's arnica you'll need on that pigeon's egg,' she said mildly, 'and send Edgar in here to pick up these apples. Next time you think to poke your nose in a box you shouldn't be looking in, remember what you saw in this one!'

The apple barrel was refilled, the coffin lid replaced, and the deceased spent the remainder of the night in peace.

∽ ∽ ∽

On the morning of 2nd May, 1887, the girl, Cassie, was busy serving breakfast to the children as their father came down from the bedroom.

'Give me Morgan James, Cassie,' he said, 'and I'll take him with me. I need to go down the street to get Lizzie Jane. She'll have to see to the shop for the morning, she knows where everything is. Oh, and her mother will have to come up and see to tomorrow's bread. Mrs Jones set it to rise last night, but she won't be seeing to tomorrow' loaves.'

Cassie nodded, and as he led the toddler from the table, Morgan added, 'You can get the other three ready for school. I'll only be a few minutes.'

His father had barely left the room when seven-year-old William made a dive for the door.

'Oh no you don't,' Cassie shouted, grasping the reluctant boy by the arm and leading him back towards the kitchen sink where she began a vigorous rubbing of his face with a damp cloth. Edgar turned from the dresser where he was carefully collecting his schoolbooks to watch his brother squirm and kick at the treatment he was receiving. 'Where's Mam?' he asked Cassie.

'Goodness, boy. In her bed, of course. Edgar, come here and help Amy Ann put her coat on or it'll be dinner time before any of you get to school.'

Edgar duly did as he was told and Amy Ann stood still as her brother pushed her chubby arms into her coat. William, still wriggling away from the dreaded face cloth, needed more information about his mother's non-appearance at the busiest time of the day.

'Why is she in bed? Nobody else is. I'll go back to bed, too.'

'You've not got the reason your mam has. You'll go to school. Now stop making my life more difficult, William, and stand by the door.'

William was on the point of disappearing again when there was a voice from the passage which led from the shop. 'Are the children ready? If they hurry they can go down on Jim Rowland's cart.'

Immediately William grabbed Amy's hand. 'Amy Ann, come on, this will be fun.' He set off at a trot down the passage. If he had to go to school it would be much better to ride than to walk.

Edgar followed his brother. Then he stopped. Turning to say

goodbye to the exhausted Cassie he asked, 'Is Mam alright?'

'Yes, yes, of course, you shall see her when you come in after school.'

All through the morning, the customers in the shop came and went and all noted Margaret Ann's absence and Lizzie Jane's presence. To every enquiry about his wife Morgan made the same reply, from behind his post office counter, 'All is going well and Mrs Thomas, Ynyshir, is with her, thank you.'

Cassie's work of minding Morgan James in the kitchen, was constantly interrupted by the midwife's requests for more hot water or to put some small garment to air. To the repeated question from Cassie, 'Is it all over yet?' the reply would come 'Not long now.'

Shortly before midday Mrs Thomas reappeared. Opening the door leading to the shop she called, 'It's a girl this time, Reverend Jones. I've made Mrs Jones tidy, so you can go on up.'

With a barely perceptible sigh of relief Morgan Humphrey went through to the kitchen and picked up his little son. 'Come on, my boy, we will go and see Mam and your new sister.'

Morgan gave his new daughter the name Agnes Eleanor after his sister in America, but he chose to use the English spelling rather than the Welsh Elinor. It was always Morgan who chose the children's names and he did so with great care. Agnes Eleanor was to be the middle child of the nine children eventually born to Margaret Ann and Morgan. Agnes more than any of the other children, was to identify closely with her father. In spite of the fact that she looked most like Margaret Ann, her relationship with her mother would always be difficult, a matter which Margaret Ann put down to her daughter's cantankerous nature and her stubborn refusal to change her ways.

On this day though, future relationships were of no consequence and the three older children forgot about the non-appearance of their mother in the excitement of the journey to school in the cart. The daily walk down the valley in all weathers did nothing to increase William's love of school so the opportunity to ride down was grasped with enthusiasm. The day was further improved when a message was brought to the boys that they could stay in school and have bread and cheese in the playground at dinnertime. Amy Ann was to stay in the 'babies' class for her dinner. Clearly there was to be no going home until the end of the day, so something was up. By 3.30 p.m. William was ready to run back up the valley to see what had brought about such a change, and for once there was no need for nine-year-old Edgar to chivvy and nag at his younger brother and sister for dilly-dallying and dawdling.

The children were home in record time. The door of the shop was wide open as they rushed in, not sure what to expect. Nothing seemed to have changed. Their father sat behind the post office counter neatly filling in the endless forms required from Her Majesty's Postmaster. Lizzie Jane was still behind the counter and several customers were waiting for the slices of bacon to be weighed and wrapped ready to feed the next shift to come up from the pit.

'Where's Mam?' was Edgar's inevitable first question.

Without looking up his father replied, 'In the back.'

All the children ran through to the kitchen where their mother was in her usual chair by the range, but to see her sitting down in the afternoon was a highly unusual event. William rushed across the kitchen and came to a halt just in time to prevent himself falling headlong into the basket near his mother's feet.

'Careful now,' admonished his mother. 'Your new sister's come.'

'Where from?' demanded Will.

'Never you mind, just watch your feet. Morgan James and Cassie'll be back from the stream in a minute. Run with Edgar and see if they're coming and then get yourselves washed for tea. Dadda will be through from the shop soon.'

With a cursory glance into the basket, both the boys ran out of the back door hoping to get to the stream before Cassie and their little brother appeared. Edgar said, 'Was that all it was? Just another baby. She's very small for a sister. Amy Ann's much bigger'

'I thought it was something really exciting,' Will replied, and there the matter rested.

63

CHAPTER 8
WILL MAKES HIS MOVE

It was Autumn 1891 and the Reverend Morgan H Jones was sitting in the small room behind the shop finishing the post office accounts for the day. The post office hours, set by the General Post Office, were shorter than those worked in the shop, but the account needed to be balanced each night as inspectors gave no advance notice of their arrival. Morgan was anxious to finish his work, to have time to plan, if not complete a sermon for Sunday. This was to be denied him. There were sounds of a scuffle in the passage and twelve-year-old William was suddenly thrust through the door by an irate Margaret Ann. William was now as tall as his mother and it was a measure of Margaret Ann's rage that she found the strength to push her son into the room.

'I will have no more complaints about this boy's behaviour. It is time he was made to realise that enough is enough. Mrs Jenkins is in tears in the shop and there's plenty in there to listen to her tale and spread this boy's mischief round the houses.'

With a look of resignation, Morgan looked up from his papers. 'What is it now?'

William studied the toes of his boots and waited for the inevitable outburst from his mother.

'He's only gone and driven the brewer's dray away from outside the Butcher's Arms and then down the road. He and those friends of his unloaded a full beer barrel from the dray and then left it outside – guess where they left it – right in front of the Jenkins' house!' His mother's voice rose almost to a shriek.

Morgan was almost tempted to smile. The family in question were strictly teetotal and Mr Jenkins was a pillar of the Methodist community. He led the local temperance movement and constantly raised his voice against the peril of the 'demon drink'. There were few people in the community unaware of the views held by the Jenkins household and their views were regularly shared with drinkers and non-drinkers alike.

'You see if you are able to put some sense into him, while I go back in the shop and try and pacify Mrs Jenkins.'

His mother turned on her heel and stomped out.

William and his father looked at each other. Will had already received a push and a sharp clout from his mother but his father had never used physical violence on any of his children.

'What have you got to say for yourself this time, boy? I can't for the life of me understand why you are always getting yourself into trouble.'

William thought for a moment, debating with himself as to the better course of action.

'Dadda, it's only because there are so many *clecau* about in this village. They run to tell Mam about things all the time. We were only having a bit of fun and the horse was getting fidgety. The drayman shouldn't have let him stand for so long. Ned had disappeared and we thought we'd just walk the horse down the road a bit. We didn't drive him. She made that up. We went past the Jenkins' house and as Mr Jenkins is always going on about how he's never touched a drop we thought we'd leave him a barrel in case he'd like to taste some.'

Morgan carefully aligned his papers in front of him and refrained with some difficulty from smiling.

'Now William, that is no way to talk. Go and find your cronies quickly and load that barrel back on the dray. Then get it back to the Butcher's Arms. With a bit of luck if Ned is the driver, I doubt he will have missed it yet. He will still be drinking in the back room.'

William turned to go, highly relieved to have no worse punishment meted out. Then his father said, 'Oh! Wait a minute, you will

65

then go back to the house and apologise to Mrs Jenkins.'

'Mrs Jenkins? Why? What for?' William asked in some astonishment.

'Because son, you have caused her distress and embarrassment in front of a lot of other people which makes her feel foolish. We do not make fools of people.'

'I'll apologise to Ned, if I've got him into trouble or made him look foolish, but I'm not apologising to Mrs Jenkins. She's always going on about how good she is and…'

'Stop now. That is enough. You will do as I say, William,' Morgan said quietly. William looked at his father and recognised the voice of authority. He set off to find his friends.

Settling himself back down to work after the unwelcome interruption, Morgan applied himself to the task in hand. The post office balance was correct so he turned to the shop account book. Trade was good, no doubt of that. The colliery was now working full time and the village continued to grow but there was yet another baby to provide for. Jane Matilda had arrived in the New Year of 1890, followed eighteen months later by Margaret Elizabeth, and with seven to feed and clothe, the income from the shop and the post office left little money over to do much more than meet the day-to-day costs of the family. Luckily his wife's decision to buy two of the terraced houses further down the valley meant that regular income from the rent was enough to pay the girl's small wage as well as adding to the savings tucked away by Margaret Ann, 'just in case.' Morgan's stipend had always been small and there was no sign of the chapel increasing it and Margaret Ann rarely included it in her financial calculations.

Edgar had already decided his love of books and his desire for knowledge would dictate his future. The village school had taught Edgar all it could so his education was catered for by private tuition from a schoolmaster in Porth. This was an added cost. William still reluctantly attended the Ynyshir school, and Amy, Morgan James and Agnes were now pupils in the newly built Aberllechau infants' school in the village. The latest arrivals, Jane and Margaret, were born little more than a year apart, but even by sharing 'hand me downs', shoes had to be bought and expenses continued to rise. All the families in the valley lived on the principle of 'make do and mend' and Margaret Ann was no exception. Waste of any sort was abhorrent and extravagance was a mortal sin but the status of the family in the community meant that there was to be no evidence of penny pinching.

One memorable Friday, Morgan James had managed to rip off the sole of his shoe from the upper leather while climbing a wall on his way to school. He was mortified to be sent by his teacher to ask the headmaster for a pair of shoes from the shoe cupboard. The contents of the shoe cupboard were donated by better off families to be given to the children of the poor, to ensure they could come to school properly shod. When he arrived home from school wearing a pair of charity shoes, his mother's rage, liberally laced with shame, had left the family reeling.

On Saturday morning, leaving the shop to the tender mercies of Morgan and Edgar, Margaret Ann and Morgan James, still wearing the charity shoes, set off to Porth to visit the shoe shop. A new pair of shoes was duly bought, with accompanying threats as to what would happen to Morgan James were he to indulge in any more wall climbing. As soon as the new shoes were safely on his feet the pair visited Mr Cohen's pawnbroker's shop. With no preamble Margaret Ann enquired as to whether Mr Cohen had any small shoes which may have been brought in for pawn and were unredeemed. After a few minutes rummaging in the nether regions of the shop Mr Cohen appeared with several small pairs of shoes.

'Those brown ones will do nicely. Wrap them please,' instructed Margaret Ann.

'How do you know they'll fit him?' asked the unsuspecting pawnbroker.

'They won't need to' snapped Margaret Ann, handing over the redemption price of three shillings, and with a withering glare at Mr Cohen she ushered Morgan from the shop. On the short journey back up the valley Margaret Ann gave Morgan his list of tasks for the rest of the day. Firstly he was to take his torn shoes down to the cobbler in the valley for them to be repaired. Then he was to polish the whole family's shoes until they shone. Next he was to write a letter explaining to the headmaster that he had no need of 'shoe cupboard shoes', and it was only his own stupidity which necessitated the temporary use of the shoes. The pawned shoes were to be a 'donation' to the shoe cupboard, just in case anyone in school thought Margaret Ann's family needed charity. Finally, he was to begin to whitewash the outhouse which was to house the pony and trap she had recently bought.

Young Morgan sighed as he listened to the list of tasks. He had been planning to go up the mountain to see whether the den he and the other boys had built in the summer was still standing. He knew it was useless to remonstrate with his mother. She had been humiliated by the episode and no-one ever did that and got away with it. By Monday all his duties were complete. All that remained was for the pawned shoes to be donated on his mother's behalf to the school shoe cupboard, and the shiny borrowed pair returned. Her honour was satisfied.

🖎 🖎 🖎

While young Morgan and his mother were battling over shoes, his father was preoccupied with his older brother. William was nearly twelve and was constantly 'on the go'. Sedentary activities were not for him, although he was a fluent reader, and well able to entertain his little brothers and sisters with stories and jokes. Perhaps, thought Morgan, he should be given the chance to join Edgar and a few other pupils tutored by the schoolmaster in Porth. Children were now entitled to stay at school until they were fourteen, but many families in the valley thought the extra two years were quite unnecessary. William might enjoy an intellectual challenge, as he certainly had the mental ability, though he was rarely seen sitting down reading a book. Morgan suspected that William considered his brother's preoccupation with books to be a strange weakness in which he had no desire to share. For him, a book was a merely a source of information, to settle a question or provide an answer to a practical problem.

His thoughts were still occupied by the problems presented by his second son, when he entered the shop. The noise of shutters being bolted into place outside told him that William had returned from rectifying the trouble he had caused Mrs Jenkins earlier in the day and was now completing his regular duties in the shop. Amy and Agnes were standing on butter boxes and wiping down the counters under their mother's supervision.

'I'll be into the house now to see to the other children,' Margaret Ann told him. 'The girls can finish this. They know exactly what they have to do, and William can finish the shutters.'

Morgan went outside to speak to his son. 'Come, Will, I'll give you a hand with that. You take one end and I'll take the other.' As usual his help was more of a hindrance to the practical William who had his own particular way of doing the job. Nevertheless the two carried out the task and eventually the last shutter was bolted into place, and father and son re-entered the shop where the two little girls had finished their appointed task.

Agnes hurried towards her father, seeking the reassurance he always gave her. 'We've finished, Dadda, look! Isn't it nice now. Do you think Mam will be pleased? I did more than Amy, even though she's older than me and her cloth was bigger.'

Morgan looked down at the earnest face of his little daughter. 'Hush now, Agnes, you've both done as your mother asked you. Leave Will to his job of sweeping the floor and go to the kitchen.'

William was enthusiastically sweeping the floor but could not restrain himself from a bit of fun, by taking the opportunity to attack Amy's legs with the broom. She knew better than to fuss or cry, but waited her chance to catch the broom handle and turn the attack towards her brother. The children pushed and struggled against each other until the apple barrel, caught in the fight upturned and sent its contents rolling across the shop. William picked one up, intending to benefit from the upset, when his mother reappeared.

Agnes clutched at her father, waiting for the storm to break. With a smirk towards her brother, Amy began to explain the full extent of his responsibility for the crash, but her mother wanted no explanations. 'Go on, out of here my girl, take Agnes with you and get yourselves washed. It's bedtime.'

Margaret Ann took the broom from Amy and the apple from Will. Armed with the broom, she resembled a warrior queen ready for battle. Fearful of the possible injury she might do her son, Morgan said, 'That's enough now, Will. Take yourself into supper and let's hear no more from you. You've been in enough trouble today.'

He and his wife were left facing each other in the empty shop. 'Come, Margaret Ann, it was only childish play.'

His wife leant against the counter and wondered how it was that he could remain so untroubled by the children's skirmishes, when they only too often moved her to wrath. 'Childish play, indeed, Morgan. William should have left such things behind him. You were working underground at his age and studying as much as Edgar in what remained of your day. You never had time to play, so why should they?'

Morgan took the now abandoned broom. As he resumed the sweeping, he thought of the long hours spent in the dark where he'd minded the doors separating the mine workings. He had never forgotten the fear he had felt in the pit of his stomach as the cage hurtled downwards carrying him and the colliers into the depths of the mine. He said, 'Let us thank God our children are spared that. No child of ours will ever have to go down the pit. They will have a better life than I had at their age.'

'It did not do you any harm, and hard work cures many ills.'

'No doubt, but do not forget that working in the pit probably causes more ills than it cures. Come now, and leave Will be. Let us have supper.'

Edgar and William, the only children who shared the evening meal with their parents, were waiting while Margaret Ann put her baby in her wooden cradle by the hearth. The meal was scarcely begun when Edgar, as always quietly spoken, announced, 'Will says he is finished with school.'

Morgan stared. 'What did you say?'

'There's no need to speak for me, Edgar,' retorted his brother, 'I'll speak for myself.'

'Speak then,' his father's voice was louder than usual. It caused Margaret Ann to put down her knife and fork and give them her full attention.

'That I will. I am twelve years old, and school is nothing but a waste of my time. I add up quicker than the master, and my writing is better than anyone else's and a lot better than yours too.' Will nodded his head in Edgar's direction.

'Education is a good deal more than adding up and writing, Will,' his father began, but Margaret Ann interrupted.

'Right then. It's not five minutes since I was saying to your father that you were getting too old to behave like a child. So if it's not school, then it's work you'll go to, my boy. You get a job and you can finish school, but you get that job first.'

Edgar stared aghast at his mother. This was not the response he had expected and William's face remained expressionless.

Morgan looked across at his wife and wondered how it could be that she, who had had the benefit of several years of an expensive boarding school education in Cowbridge, which was denied to so many, should so easily dismiss her second son's right to continue his learning. By her words she seemed to deny William the opportunity of learning, which they, as parents, were offering Edgar. He knew better than to challenge her remark with the boys present, but hoped that later in the privacy of their bedroom he could persuade her to withdraw the ultimatum and join with him in an effort to encourage William to pursue his education.

His efforts proved futile. His wife insisted that if William had decided that school was not for him, it was a waste of energy to persuade him otherwise. She recognised that William had inherited her determination to control her life and was therefore conducting himself accordingly.

✍ ✍ ✍

The next morning Amy, Agnes and Morgan set off up the hill to the new Aberllechau school. Edgar had already started his long walk down the valley to Porth, but of Will there was no sign. He had done his daily chores about the shop, bakehouse and stable but now was nowhere to be found. After the conversation the previous evening Morgan doubted that William would have gone to school. Margaret Ann, busy with bakehouse, shop and the babies, hardly gave a thought to his whereabouts. It would have been another matter if she had discovered that his various early morning duties had been neglected but as his chores were done to her satisfaction, she was content to leave him to his own devices.

Shortly before noon, a delighted William came running into the shop.

'Mam, Mam. Guess what!'

'I've no time for guessing, William, with a shop full of customers. Go through into the house.'

Seeing the expression on William's face, Morgan quietly lowered the grill on the post office counter and followed his son through into the kitchen. Will strutted round the kitchen table. 'I've done it, Dadda. I've got a job. Already! With the Taff Vale Railway Company at Tylorstown station, and I can start straight away!'

'Is that really what you want, my boy, to work with the railway company and leave school? It's more education you need, not less you know. That's what will open doors for you later on.'

William looked at his father. 'Not opened many for you, has it, Dadda?'

Morgan stared at his son. William showed a maturity well beyond his twelve years. His father shook his head slowly. His vocation to the chapel was everything to him, and he had no answer to William's remark. He knew though that it was only in study and reading that he found the escape from shop and post office. Books were as necessary to him as air to a drowning man. He only withstood Margaret Ann's constant demands that he give up his chapel, because the need to prepare a sermon meant he gained the privacy and the solace offered by his books. William looked sympathetically at his father, understanding in a moment of insight, how difficult at times he must find his circumstances, but the moment did not last long. Margaret Ann bustled into the kitchen to tell Morgan that someone was waiting at the post office counter and to check that Cassie had the midday meal prepared.

'Where have you been then?' she asked William.

'Getting a job.'

'Oh, yes?' Disbelief was evident in her voice. 'And who is going to take you on?'

'The stationmaster at Tylorstown. Be a change for me to sweep the station floor instead of the shop. And I'll be paid for it!'

'Make no mistake, my boy, you will continue to sweep the shop as well, as long as I want it done, job or no job in Tylorstown station.'

'Enough,' said Morgan firmly, not wanting a verbal battle to start just as the younger children returned from school. 'You've done well, William. It's not many get the first job they go for, and on the first day of searching too.'

Margaret and William looked hard at each other, but both recognised the quiet authority in Morgan's tone and for once allowed the battle to cease before it had really begun.

The following day, armed with a letter from Morgan, William went into school for the last time, knocked on the door of the headmaster's office, handed over the letter and ended his formal education. At twelve years old his life of work had begun.

CHAPTER 9
AMBITION

Many years had passed since Margaret Ann had found the village which had three names: Pont Rhyd y Cwtch, the fording place across the stream where, in the twelfth century, Rhys the Welsh prince had hidden as he fled from his enemies; then Aberllechau which marked the confluence of the Llechau brook and the Rhondda Fach river; and lastly Wattstown after the English mine owner.

Now, the colliery winding gear dominated the village and the spoil heaps from the mine crept ever upward from the valley floor. The tram line climbed from the pit up to the tipping area and the small trucks constantly chugged up and down. The black mounds of the tips sprawled in untidy heaps covering the previously green hillsides and dust and grime hung in the air. Colliery noises filled the valley, with the beat of the ventilating fan, the clatter of trucks and above all the hooters. The shift changes were announced by the hooter and an extra blast denoted twelve noon. Clock watching, except on Sundays, was unnecessary for the village. The day and all its various activities were marked by the hooter.

Every day twelve-year-old William walked the two miles from his home to the Taff Vale railway station in Tylorstown. There was now a passenger service from Maerdy to Cardiff, but the line's main business was coal, trucks heading full down the valley and empty back up. William had soon committed the entire train timetable to memory and could recognise the freight and passenger trains by their whistles long before they arrived in the station. The floors of the waiting room and booking office were immaculate and his ability to keep the windows of the station buildings sparkling in all weathers attracted admiration from all and sundry. His cheerful disposition made him a favourite with passengers and even the more surly firemen in the engine cab gave him a salute.

Working for the railway William might be, but his pay was still handed to his mother every Friday evening, and he still had to fit in all the tasks his mother demanded. Edgar was exempted from most duties in and around the house as his studies were considered sacrosanct. Margaret Ann may have had scant regard for William's education, but she took great pride in Edgar's attainments and followed his progress assiduously. Edgar never ceased to strive for his mother's approval and he and his mother hardly ever had an altercation. This was in striking contrast to the fiery relationship between Margaret Ann and her second son. Morgan rarely intervened between mother and sons. He was well aware of the personality traits shared by William and his mother, and similarly between himself and the quiet, bookish Edgar. Eventually, he reasoned, each of the protagonists would have to work out a way to coexist, without his interference.

When their school work was done Amy Ann and Agnes shared the domestic tasks the current girl had not managed to finish by the end of her working day. They also had to take their full share of amusing the younger children, nursing new baby Maggie or minding toddler Jane. They became expert storytellers and their knowledge of nursery rhymes in English as well as Welsh was vast. Now eight years old, Morgan James was already a master at absenting himself from household chores. His ability to disappear, particularly during the busiest times of the day was a source of constant friction with his sisters who were left to do what they considered extra duties. Morgan James also had a natural propensity, quite unknown in any other members of the family, for keeping things to himself and in Amy's eyes at least was seen to be remote and secretive, a character trait he retained all his life.

William considered life as an employee of the Taff Vale railway a great improvement on that of a schoolboy. Long hours at work never worried him. With no school or homework to do, he was often to be seen with his contemporaries around the village after work, indulging his love of fun and games, and generally enjoying life. He also had an eye for a pretty girl. With his dark brown curly hair and bright blue eyes, he was much admired by the girls in the village who took to perching like a row of sparrows along the wall leading down towards to the shop, in order to admire the object of their affections. At five feet five inches he was already taller and stronger than Edgar, which secretly pleased him greatly, and he had been taller than both his parents for some time. Known to all as Will Post, his fame grew with his prowess at Whip and Top. This ability was only outclassed by his ability with *Cwn a Chati* or 'Dog and Cat'. This village game, played with one long stick and one short one, required considerable skill. The aim was to flick the *chati*, which was sharpened at both ends, from the ground and hit it in mid-air with the longer stick or *ci*. The distance the *chati* flew before it reached the ground, decided the winner. Lengthy tournaments were arranged by the village lads in a concerted attempt to beat Will Post, but no-one ever succeeded.

∽ ∽ ∽

By the time Will had been working for the Taff Vale Railway Company for four years, there was little he did not know about the running of the station, from checking timetables and booking tickets, to keeping the waiting room fire well stoked. His favourite task in the absence of the stationmaster, was blowing the whistle and giving the green flag an imperious wave to allow the trains to leave the station. On learning that the station master was to be moved to a larger, more prestigious station down the valley, William decided that he was ready to take his place.

He wrote immediately offering his services to the head office of the railway company, but to his amazement the management were not of the same mind. He was told that aged sixteen, he was considered too young for such a responsible appointment. William read the letter of rejection with a mixture of anger and scorn. His response was not unlike his mother's reaction on receipt of the letter from the colliery agents allowing her a lease of the shop only in her husband's name. Regarding himself as a man who had no further wish to serve a company blind to his true value, he promptly sent in his resignation.

His parents, unaware of William's plan to become stationmaster, were more concerned with ways of finding the money to pay for Edgar to further his studies at the newly established University College of South Wales and Monmouthshire in Cardiff. William's wages during the last four years had been a useful contribution to the family budget, and his parents assumed they could count on his wages to continue to subsidise his brother at university. The younger children were making increasing financial demands on the family's income and the eighth baby, named Gladys, had arrived. Amy and Agnes were fast approaching the stage when decisions about their futures had to be made. Both the older girls were determined that in spite of anything their school friends might plan to do, entering service or a career in shopkeeping was not an option for them. Independence was their goal and in order to achieve that they both had ambitions to gain a college place like Edgar firmly in their sights. Margaret Ann was equally determined that her daughters should have the ability to earn their own livings and never have to be dependent on a man to feed, clothe or house them. The cost of this determination was particularly daunting as she and Morgan now had five daughters.

This particular evening they were sitting together at the kitchen table working out how to meet the current demands on the family purse. Margaret Ann sighed and got up from her chair.

'I can't think straight any more Morgan. It's trying to make an inch stretch to a foot. I'm going to the bakehouse to check the orders for tomorrow and see if I can clear my head. Get Agnes to settle the children down and then I'll be back to get the supper.'

Morgan had almost finished his supper when William appeared. He had great affection for Will who uncomplainingly handed over his pay packet every Friday to his mother, and never seemed to resent the fact that his older brother had not yet contributed a penny to the family exchequer. As they sat in companionable silence over their supper, Morgan suddenly asked, 'Had a good week have you, Will? We've not seen much of you around here.'

'I've been busy investigating alternative employment Dadda. I have finished with the railway,' his son announced.

'Finished with the railway? For good? Why on earth has that happened? Have they sacked you?'

'No, I've sacked them. The stationmaster has been promoted and I applied for his job but they think I'm not good enough to take over his position. I think I'm too good for the lowly jobs they give me and I'm capable of much more, so I'm going.'

'What will happen, then? Your mother will be none too pleased to hear the news.'

'What news is that, then?' said Margaret Ann as she bustled in with a sheaf of invoices and orders in her hand.

'I've finished with the railway,' Will repeated.

His mother stood stock still, staring at him. 'Have you then!' She slapped the invoices and orders down on the table. 'And where is the next job to be? Down the pit, I suppose?'

William stood up, pushing away his plate, and looked directly at his mother. 'If need be, but unlike Taff Vale, it will be somewhere that realises what I'm worth.'

With that, he turned and left the room.

Morgan wiped his hands methodically on his napkin before looking up at his wife. 'Be careful, Margaret Ann, if you drive that boy too far, he certainly will go down the pit and I want no pit for any of my sons.'

'Has he given any reason for leaving the railway company?' Margaret Ann's tone of voice would have curdled the milk, and Morgan repeated his son's account of his resignation in as diplomatic a way as he could.

'He seems to feel he was too good for the jobs he was being given. The stationmaster's job is vacant and Will obviously felt he was capable of running the station but they felt he was not old enough. So he wants to go somewhere where he can have more responsibility and learn new skills.'

Morgan drew a deep breath and prepared himself for the inevitable tirade about William's behaviour, but to his amazement Margaret Ann said nothing for a moment, then she smiled. Inwardly, she completely accepted William's reaction as a justifiable reason for quitting. She had never undervalued herself and was pleased that even though he was not yet seventeen, Will was aware of his own worth.

'There's no need for you to fear the pit for him, Morgan. He will not go underground if he thinks like that. Will knows what he's capable of and I wouldn't be surprised if he hasn't got something up his sleeve already.'

Chapter 10
Sunday Best

Saturday was a busy day in the village. The pit worked three shifts as usual but in every house the women worked the clock round in preparation for the day of rest on Sunday. Those families who were fortunate enough to have a plot of earth behind the house spent time pruning, weeding and digging the soil so that rhubarb, gooseberries and blackcurrants could liven up the Sunday puddings. Hen houses were cleaned out, usually by the children, and paths were swept.

A visit to Rowlands the butcher needed to be made early in the morning so that the choice of the meat for Sunday dinner was as wide as the pocket would allow. Pastry had to be made for the obligatory fruit tarts, followed by another walk to the shop for a tin of fruit or a jelly as a treat for tea the next day. Then back to the house to tackle the rest of the day's work. Welsh cakes and *bara brith* were baked to ensure a proper welcome was given to any family members visiting for Sunday tea. Children free from schoolwork had chores to complete before they were allowed time to play, and the older ones had child-minding duties which often lasted most of the day. Shoes were polished until faces could be seen in them, and then lined up in pairs – largest to smallest – by the back door, ready for chapel the next day.

Houses had to be cleaned from parlour to kitchen because no cleaning could be done on Sunday. Water had to be drawn and then heated for the weekly bath, and children would suffer the ministrations of their mother in the zinc tub before the fire. Hair, ears, neck, knees and other parts of the body which might have been skipped over in a the routine daily wash were given full attention. Cleanliness was not only next to godliness, it was an essential adjunct. In an emergency God could be called upon even if one were dirty and unkempt, but in the ordinary course of events it was better to be clean and tidy, in order to show proper respect when calling on the Lord. The sharp eyes of the of the next day's congregation would certainly notice tell-tale patches of grime on the necks and hands of any child who, through defiance or poor maternal standards, had turned up to chapel less than properly turned out.

The fever of activity was apparent in the shop too. It was the day on which even Edgar was called upon to help so that he could relieve his father from his duties at the post office counter. Ever mindful of the bargain her husband had struck all those years ago, Margaret Ann recognised his need of time in preparation for his Sunday duties. William's tasks of shuttering and sweeping the shop, were done later in the evening, as on Saturday the shop stayed open until ten o'clock. He and Margaret Ann would be the last to find their way to bed and it was during those late evenings that mother and son discovered the similarities in their natures that caused so many daytime storms, and a mutual respect slowly grew. This Saturday night Margaret watched her son almost admiringly, as he made a minor repair to one of the shutters. He had a remarkable skill with any tool from penknife to axe and on a winter evening would whittle away at a piece of wood to make a *chati* for his games, or a whistle or toy for one of his little brothers and sisters. Their tasks completed, William and his mother passed through to the house and picked up the remaining candlestick to light their way to their beds.

'You will have served your leaving notice at the station any day now,' his mother remarked as casually as she could, mindful of her husband's advice about not pushing Will too far, and trying hard to contain her naturally interfering ways. 'What are you going to do now about a job?'

'Do not worry, Mam, you won't go without my money for long. It will be there in time for Edgar to go to Cardiff. I'll have something sorted soon.'

Margaret refrained from comment, but in the bedroom, while she undressed she thought about the complexities of her William's character. Outwardly he showed little regard for his brother's need to study and considered much of it was done to avoid work around the shop and stable, yet he shared the family's pride that Edgar was the first from the valley to gain the Matriculation Certificate which would allow him to enter the university. For Margaret Ann, Edgar's success was proof that her system was working and she redoubled her efforts to ensure her family's achievements continued. William was also well aware that the cost of raising eight children was very high and that his beloved father's stipend as a minister did not contribute much to the family coffers. A ninth child was imminent and Will knew he should somehow help to bear the cost of Edgar's academic ambition.

Still thinking of the costs of educating their children as she climbed into the high double bed beside Morgan, Margaret Ann mused, 'The opening of that new Intermediate School in Porth will allow the other children to get a good few more years education after Aberllechau. We're going to have to find a pretty penny to get them all through, though, to say nothing of college after. Perhaps it's just as well Morgan James doesn't seem to have the same determination as the others and Gladys only wants to play! I wonder what this next one will do? I hope it'll be the last. I don't relish the thought of another and it's almost twenty years of child bearing I've had.'

'All brought safely into this world and none left it, thank God,' muttered a sleepy Morgan Humphrey, as he dozed off. 'There's not many families in this valley or the next who can say the same.'

His wife was not given to philosophising and she drifted off to sleep with her head full of the complicated arithmetic of putting her ambitions for all her children into effect.

❧ ❧ ❧

On Sunday morning William was up early as usual and was soon hard at work in the stable behind the bakehouse to prepare the pony and trap to take his father through Penrhys to the Tabernacle chapel in Ystrad where he would preach at the eleven o'clock morning service and again in the evening. Just as he had finished tightening the pony's girth his father appeared in the stable doorway.

'Ready are you, Dadda? Got everything you need? It's a long day for you over there, but no doubt you get a good dinner with Mrs Evans the deacon's wife!'

Morgan grinned. 'Aye, you're right, son, the pony has a fair bit more weight to pull on the way back. I'm off to Mrs Williams the choir, in the afternoon after Sunday School. She does a wonderful tea! I think there's a fair bit of competition goes on with the number of different cakes they put in front of me. They don't think your mother does much in the way of fancy baking!'

He and his son exchanged a glance of understanding as Morgan climbed into the trap. Will passed his father the capacious minister's bag containing his preaching gown and tabs, his service book and prayer book and the day's precious sermons. He opened the gate from the stable onto the road and shouted to Morgan James to be sure to close it securely behind them, then he climbed into the driving seat and gave the reins a gentle tug. He turned the pony's head down the valley and settled into a rhythmical trot. The journey down the valley and over the hill into the next one gave him time to consider whether he should let his father know what his next career move was going to be. He was reluctant to say too much in case his plan did not work out, but suddenly his father interrupted his thoughts.

'Friday was it, you stopped at the station? What are you going to do then, now you have finished with Taff Vale?'

'I'm planning to go and see Meredith in the morning.'

Morgan was startled at the name Meredith which he knew to be that of the manager of the National Colliery. Anxiously he enquired, 'Not looking to the pit for a job, are you?'

'Why not? Railway or colliery seem to be the only practical

choices in this valley unless I take up shopkeeping and I don't think Mam would put up with the competition!'

Seeing his father's anxiety he said, 'I'm joking. Don't worry. Not everybody in the colliery works underground you know, Dadda. There are plenty of jobs on top. I'll see if Meredith will put a word in for me with the office manager.'

'Well, no doubt they would be glad to have you if there is a job going, but do not be too quick to walk out if it is not the office manager's own job they offer you!'

'No, no,' chuckled Will as the pony's pace increased on the downward track to Ystrad. 'I'll get a few months experience first before I ask for that one!'

The trap drew up outside the chapel and Morgan alighted to be greeted by some of his congregation making their way into the service. Will said, 'I will be back about seven for you, Dadda.' and with a jerk of the reins and a 'Gee up', he set the pony's face to home.

∽ ∽ ∽

Sunday dinner was well under way when William arrived home. Resplendent in her best clothes, covered with a large apron, to disguise the imminent arrival of her ninth child, Margaret Ann presided over the meal. She loved pretty clothes and Sunday gave her the one opportunity in the week to wear them. Although her blonde hair had lost much of its colour and was now streaked with grey she was still proud of her thick, shiny locks and took great pride in ensuring that in spite of her hectic daily life her hair was always smartly done up in an immaculate bun. She completed her finery with the few pieces of good jewellery she had received as a girl, including the gold watch on its long chain that had been a wedding present from her father.

The Sunday meal was another matter of great pride to Margaret Ann. She was surrounded by her family all in their Sunday best. They never sat down to less than a generous roast joint, several different vegetables and two types of potatoes, followed by fruit tarts. The rest of the week the menu was fixed: cold meat on Mondays, leftovers in the shape of cottage pie or rissoles on Tuesdays, liver and bacon on Wednesdays, chops on Thursdays, fish if the fishmonger made his way far enough up the valley on Fridays and 'bits' on Saturdays. Puddings were usually milk puddings or egg custards, with seasonal stewed or baked fruit for an occasional change. Margaret had no time for what she called 'picky eaters.' Anything served on to a plate had to be eaten. All the children were aware that their mother was not beyond bringing out the cold remains of a partly eaten meal and serving it up again, at several subsequent meals if necessary, until the plate was empty.

As William sat down his mother said, 'Were there many going into the Tabernacle?'

'About usual, I think. I recognised some of them waiting for Dadda.'

It was not an idle question. Margaret Ann cared deeply that the congregation in the Tabernacle should not appear small and insignificant. Morgan would be so disheartened if his flock deserted him for another preacher in another chapel. For herself she cared not a fig about what the chapel-going congregation thought of her, but for Morgan's standing in the Baptist ministry she cared a very great deal.

'There were plenty in Calfaria this morning,' said Amy. 'And Mrs Jenkins's niece from Cardigan looked ever so nice. She is staying with her aunty to learn dressmaking. She kept turning round to look at our Edgar.'

'Better she had looked at the preacher rather than our Edgar,' replied her mother curtly and gave Amy a look that meant there was to be no more talk about Mrs Jenkins's niece. Edgar's glare alone would have quietened a more submissive character than Amy.

The dinner dishes cleared, the girls returned to Calfaria for Sunday School. Margaret Ann absented herself as Gladys was too young to attend. Besides she was heavily pregnant and welcomed the afternoon as a justifiable rest period in her busy life. Morgan James was expected to attend Sunday School with his sisters but had done his usual disappearing act. His mother, guessing his whereabouts, set off for the bakehouse to find him. He was sitting on a flour sack with his pencils, and one of his father's books, attempting to copy a complicated drawing of the pyramids of Egypt.

'You'll do better listening to the bible stories of Egypt from the deacons rather than trying to draw them, Morgan. Put those things away and get on with you. If you run you'll catch the others up!'

William watched his younger brother pass through the house with a thunderous expression on his face. He thought it unlikely that Morgan James would actually reach Sunday School. It was far more likely he would be off on one of his solitary walks, hoping Amy would not notice his absence. Agnes could be relied on to keep quiet but Amy was the *clecwr*, the carrier of tales, a position she held without rival until her younger sister Maggie developed an even more formidable talent for tale-bearing.

With the Sunday School contingent out of the way, Edgar and William sat in the kitchen. William was putting the finishing touches with his knife to a wooden doll he was making for little Gladys who watched him in keen anticipation. Edgar had a book open in front of him but he too watched his brother and at length asked, 'Have you decided what you are going to do, Will?'

'About what?' said his brother, knowing full well what Edgar meant.

'You know, about the job.'

'Or lack of it, you mean. The family will have to be on short commons until I get something sorted out.' Will was not averse to making Edgar suffer a little. There was silence for a few more minutes, until he relented slightly. 'I might go and see Meredith tomorrow because there will be no peace for me in this house until I've got something. I've been thinking there may be better prospects for me with National than Taff Vale.'

Edgar was not given to effusive thanks, but he allowed a small sigh of relief to escape and reached out his hand in what might be seen as a gesture of gratitude.

The little doll was now finished and, to Gladys' delight, Will bent down to place it carefully on top of the tower his little sister had built. Suddenly he turned back towards Edgar and said, 'Don't you want to work instead of going to school all the time?'

'College is not school, and I do work at my books.'

'Huh,' snorted William. 'You would learn more if you looked about you. Four years with the Taff Vale have taught me more about this valley of ours than you will ever learn from books. All your learning from books did not teach you to read a train timetable. You had no idea how to find the time of that train from Ynishir to get you to college! You'd still be standing on the platform if I hadn't been there to show you, and you're the one supposed to be the one with the brains. You need a minder you do!'

Feeling that he had for once got the better of his brother, William went to prepare the pony and trap for the return journey to Ystrad to collect his father.

CHAPTER II
PROMOTION

It was a little after seven o'clock on the following Monday morning and the household was busy with preparations for the day. Margaret Ann had been in the bakehouse for the last hour but had come in to check that her family was tackling their various chores. Megan, the new girl, was putting more coal on the kitchen fire which Morgan James had lit earlier. Amy Ann and Agnes were putting bowls and plates on the table for breakfast, while Jane and Maggie were busy persuading Gladys into her pinafore. Morgan Humphrey had disappeared after his early morning post office mail duties to visit a sick Church member. The noise of the shop shutters being removed told Margaret Ann that William was well ahead with his tasks. He had even managed to persuade Morgan James to lend a hand by sweeping the shop floor. Edgar was already at the post office counter, checking stamps, postal orders and telegraph forms before he set off for his lectures. Margaret Ann marched purposefully through to the shop to survey her domain, casting a practised eye over her sons, the counters and the well stocked shelves and floor. Her tour of inspection over, she returned to the kitchen. The younger children were well into their bowls of bread and milk, and their mother began to fry some bacon and bread for the older boys. William passed through the kitchen on his way to see to the pony.

Amy Ann lifted her head from her breakfast to ask, 'Why hasn't Will gone to work?'

'Mind your own business, finish your breakfast, and get yourself ready for school,' was her mother's abrupt reply.

William was at work in the stable. 'I'd better put a move on,'he said to himself, 'or Meredith will be out of his office and gone down the pit before I get a chance to see him. Let's hope the children don't hang around this morning. Amy is bound to notice if I'm not in my usual working trousers and then there'll be endless questions.'

Finishing his stable chores, he went into the now empty kitchen to start the preparations at the sink for his visit to the colliery offices. About ten minutes later, clad in his best suit, collar and tie and much polished shoes, he left through the front door to avoid the necessity of explaining his unusual attire to anyone who may still not have left for school. He made his way briskly down Bailey Street to the main offices of the National Colliery.

Knocking smartly at the glass panelled door and entering the little outer office, he surprised the young clerk who said, 'Hullo, Will, not gone up the valley today?'

'No, I thought to have a word with Mr Meredith if he has not gone underground.'

'Not yet, I think. I've not seen him go past, so he'll still be in his office.'

'Then I'll go straight in.' Leaving the clerk no time to object, Will crossed the room to knock on the door marked Manager.

'Yes! Come in.' The slightly irascible tone did not daunt William. Opening the door with a flourish, he stepped purposefully towards the desk to greet the manager with what he hoped was a confident smile.

'Good morning, Mr Meredith.'

The manager regarded his smartly dressed visitor. There was no collarless shirt or 'hand-me-down trousers' for this young man. Although William was never to be a tall man, he carried himself with a natural air of authority.

'Will Post? I thought you worked for Taff Vale, young man. What are you doing here at this time of the morning? Shouldn't you be up at the station?'

'I was working for them until last week, but now I've decided I'd like to work here.'

'Have you indeed? If you've decided that, then it's an underground job you'll be wanting, I suppose. I'm surprised that your father hasn't got something to say about you going underground.'

'Oh he has, and so I'll certainly not be going underground. My father knows you would be wasting a good head for figures and the best handwriting in the whole valley, if I have to go down the pit.'

'Not afraid to blow your own trumpet are you?' Mr Meredith was rather taken aback by such a direct approach.

'No, and I will blow it loud enough to be heard in Cardiff if people here are too deaf to hear. Head office wouldn't want to miss the chance of taking on a good clerk. You won't find a better one anywhere.'

'Tell me then, why are you depriving the Taff Vale of your valuable services. Got on the wrong side of them, did you?'

'I did not, but promotion wasn't quick enough for me. Four years I worked for them and now I would prefer to work under someone who knows more than I do, not less.'

'So you think I might know more than you do you then, is that it?' Mr Meredith gave Will an appraising glance and tried hard not to smile.

'Aye, you probably do know more, about the National Colliery at least. But I can promise you it won't be like that for long if you give me a start.'

Mr Meredith was aware that the company could do with someone used to handling money to help sort out the pay packets. The present pay clerk was often hard pressed to have them all ready when the shifts finished on Fridays, and the number of men employed in the pit was continually increasing. He knew the boy's family, as he himself was a staunch Baptist. He greatly admired the Reverend Jones, and the young man's directness and determination reminded him of the mother, for whom he also had a high regard. He thought for a few moments and scribbled a few comments on a piece of paper in front of him, then he pushed back his chair and came round the desk to face William.

'Right, go across to the pay office with this note and tell them I've sent you. You can start this afternoon as junior pay clerk and begin learning about the coal industry in the morning.'

William gave a broad grin and reached out to shake hands with the older man. 'Thank you, sir. I'll not let you down.'

The hooter was sounding as Will emerged from the office. Momentarily standing still, he absorbed the sights and sounds which were to become so familiar. Then he walked towards the low building which had National Colliery Pay Office etched into its glass door. Beyond the outer door, there was another frosted glass one, and he could dimly see a figure moving behind an imposing desk. He knocked lightly on the door and walked in. The man behind the desk did not look up. Busy entering figures in a large ledger, he barked, 'Yes, name and number!'

'I've no number yet, and I've done no work you can pay me for, but I'm William Humphrey Jones, and I'm your new junior pay clerk,' and he handed over Mr Meredith's note.

The clerk looked up and saw the cheerful young man standing before him. He took the note and ran a hand through his hair.

'Thank goodness, for that,' he said. 'I'd given up hope of the manager ever sending me another pair of hands. It's completely overwhelmed with work I am. Thirty-three new men started this week and all of them will need a pay packet come Friday. I hope you can manage figures in your head. There's no time to waste in here and a good head for figures is top of the list. Oh, and a legible hand. You can start at that desk over there.'

He pointed to another tall desk with an impressive looking inkwell on the top. 'Put your coat on that hook and enter these names into that new ledger. You can deal with the back end of the alphabet. There's more Prices, Thomases and Williams in this pit than you can believe. Bring it here when you've done, and show me.'

William hung up his jacket on the coat stand, perched himself on the high desk chair, took a new pen from the rack, dipped it carefully in the inkwell and set to work. In a short while he had entered the names in the book in his excellent handwriting and submitted it to the senior clerk. The man surveyed William's work, looked up at him and then back down at the ledger.

'Well, it looks as though Mr Meredith has done a good day's work already. Go home for your dinner, lad, and be back here prompt for half past one. We've got a lot to get through. By the way, my name's Morris, Rhys Morris.'

He stood up, offering a firm handshake and a relieved smile. Will lifted his jacket from the stand and strode up the valley towards home, wondering what his parents' reaction would be. He was proud of his morning's efforts and felt sure he would find his new role more suited to his talents. Suddenly, he realised that no mention had been made of a wage.

Oh well, he thought, whatever they pay me I won't be on it for long. I'll earn a rise soon enough.

Margaret Ann was at the counter and Morgan was busy stamping a parcel behind the post office grill, as Will came into the busy shop. Both looked up, anxious to know how their son had fared at the colliery but neither wished to be the first to ask the vital question. Margaret Ann completed the weighing of the sugar for a customer, carefully pouring it into the usual blue paper bag. Then she called for Agnes to take Gladys and tell the girl to get the dinners on the table. Gladys picked up the doll she had carefully put to bed in some empty sugar bags and toddled over to her big sister who led her into the kitchen.

Morgan came from behind the grill with his eyebrows raised. Will quietly answered his unspoken question. 'It's alright, Dadda, I've started in the pay office.' Morgan gave his son's shoulder a brief pat and looked across the shop at his wife. Margaret Ann gave an almost imperceptible sigh of relief and smiled at Will. Congratulations were in the air.

'Oh! William's finished then with the Taff has he then?' enquired Mrs Jenkins who missed nothing as she paid for the sugar.

'Yes.' The monosyllabic reply was unlikely to satisfy Mrs Jenkins but that was all she was going to get from the proud mother at the moment. 'Anything more, Mrs Jenkins?' was the signal for her to collect her purchases and be gone. Margaret Ann closed the shop door and moved with Morgan towards the kitchen. 'All Cwtch will know by the time that woman gets home.'

'Know what? What will Cwtch know?' asked Jane who had overheard her mother.

'More than they need to know. Now get on with your dinner and do not have so much to say or you'll be late back to school.' Turning towards William, she said, 'Pleased are you? Satisfied?'

'For the time being,' came the brief reply.

CHAPTER 12
BEYOND THE VALLEY

The first year of William's employment with the colliery company in 1897 saw other changes in the household. At the age of forty-two, Margaret Ann gave birth to the ninth and last of her children:,the baby boy was christened Arthur Rowland. Gladys adored the new baby, considering him far superior to any toy William whittled with his knife. More and more her mother came to depend on her youngest daughter to keep the infant occupied as well as amused and a bond was thus established between them that would last a lifetime.

Edgar had secured his university place with a scholarship of £25 a year and at first travelled daily to Cardiff where he immersed himself in his studies for a BA degree. He took great satisfaction in his scholarly activities and was never seen without a collar and tie and shiny shoes. Much to his sisters' amusement he had spent the summer cultivating a neat moustache which he felt gave himself the necessary dignity for the study of philosophy, and which partly made up for his lack of height. Morgan Humphrey had bequeathed much to his eldest son, including his lack of stature, and Edgar remained sensitive about his lack of height. He was to worry less about it when, one evening after lectures, he joined a group of fellow undergraduates at the Park Hall, where a number of Welsh MPs were speaking about the parlous state of the Liberal party. Speaker after speaker mounted the rostrum to address the hall, with little response. Then, a newly elected MP, no taller than Edgar, very slim, black-haired and dressed in a frock coat, emerged from the back of the hall and began to speak. In a few minutes, Edgar and his friends were on their feet, laughing and applauding. Soon the entire hall was cheering and roaring approval. David Lloyd George, the outspoken Welsh-speaking Liberal MP for Caernarfon Boroughs had arrived and he was to change the course of Edgar's life.

ɕ๑ ɕ๑ ɕ๑

Amy too had distinguished herself in the classroom and now attended the pupil teachers' training centre in Porth where she was soon to be joined by Agnes. Their mother had always planned a place at college for the girls and this was now becoming a reality. For three members of one family to gain access to higher education was in itself remarkable for the time, and it was the subject of many hours gossip amongst the families in Cwtch. In spite of his mother's lack of confidence in his abilities, Morgan James had moved up, with some reluctance, to become a pupil at the intermediate school in Porth. Margaret Ann said little in way of praise, but her older offsprings' achievements gave her great satisfaction. The costs of these various colleges and schools were considerable and now had to be borne solely by the shop and post office takings, subsidised by William's earnings in the colliery.

Morgan had, at last, given in to his wife's constant request to be done with the chapel, and had resigned the pastorate of the Tabernacle in Ystrad. The event was marked by the congregation's presentation of an illuminated 'Address of Thanks' to their respected minister. The scroll, for which Margaret Ann ordered an impressive oak frame, was hung in the parlour for all to admire. It followed that Morgan's meagre stipend had finally ceased and was replaced by preaching fees. Now aged fifty, he was happy to be relieved of the weekly responsibility of a congregation, but he continued to serve the Baptist cause by accepting preaching engagements in other chapels. With a wider audience for his sermons he came to be recognised as a gifted preacher and was much in demand in the pulpits of the Rhondda. As usual it was William who was called upon to drive his father in the trap to many of these engagements. As a result of their peaceful times together, their affection and respect for each other grew even stronger and they were mutually supportive when either was buffeted by Margaret Ann's tongue. She still ruled her small kingdom with an iron fist, which was not always hidden in a velvet glove.

Morgan James, who was now almost fourteen, was an enigma to parents and sisters alike. He went to school dutifully but said very little about his activities there and seemed to have little to do in the evenings in the way of schoolwork. He said even less about his out of school life. He absented himself as much as possible from house and shop and not even Amy or Maggie could find out enough about him to carry *clecs* to Margaret Ann.

It was William who first heard on the village grapevine about his brother's prowess at billiards. Morgan James had taken to playing with the workmen who frequented the hall that had recently been built in Ynyshir. The Workmen's Institute acted as a magnet to the boy, and realising the appalling consequences of these activities becoming known to his parents, Will thought it wise to warn his brother that trouble awaited him if the news reached their mother. Morgan James resented any interference in his private life and unwisely chose to disregard his older brother's advice. Inevitably it was not long before Margaret Ann did indeed become aware of what were termed 'Morgan's goings on.'

Life in the village was lived cheek by jowl and there were few opportunities for youngsters to evade detection if mischief were afoot. Margaret Ann's customers were always ready to recount the misdemeanours of her children and although Margaret Ann's parenting skills were held in the greatest respect, there were few who did not relish proving that her offspring were slightly less than perfect. William had long been the leading character in these tales, so it was with some surprise that 'Mrs Jones the Shop' learned that Morgan James had now replaced his brother in these stories. Morgan James' interest in the latest girl who had arrived to help Margaret Ann, had already set tongues wagging, and several customers had alluded to his nefarious activities during school holidays as they selected their provisions. It was with growing anger one Tuesday morning, that his mother listened with horror when she overheard Cissie Thomas telling one of her customers that Morgan James not only played billiards after school hours and during the holidays, but actually during school hours as well.

'So I've heard too,' Mrs Dando paused for effect, 'he's probably in the Workmen's Hall at this very minute. My boys say he goes mostly on Tuesdays because he doesn't like looking at the skeleton Mr Williams brings in the class for science lessons.'

Action was always better than words in Margaret Ann's book. Up to her bedroom she stormed. In no time her working clothes were flung on the bed to be replaced by her second best dress and buttoned boots. Pausing only to check her appearance in the mirror, and leaving the care of the shop to Morgan, she set off for Ynyshir and the male sanctum of the Workmen's Hall. Her entrance caused considerable consternation. The patrons in the reading room looked up from their books and newspapers when they heard a confident female voice demanding to know the location of the billiard room. The secretary of the Hall came rushing from his little office in an attempt to waylay the irate lady.

'With respect, madam, no ladies are allowed in here. I must ask you to leave at once.' His voice tailed off as, recognising her, he realised any kind of remonstration would be futile. He retreated to his office to await the inevitable.

Up the stairs and into the billiard room Margaret Ann marched, just in time to witness Morgan James about to pot a ball on the green baize table. Unaware that retribution was about to descend, Morgan carefully lined up his cue and prepared to pot the red ball. Before the shot was completed he felt the firm grip on his collar and was ignominiously marched down the stairs. In spite of the fact that her errant son was now taller than his mother, he offered no resistance. Still holding Morgan James with one hand, Margaret Ann rapped loudly on the office door. The secretary opened it a little way and peered round at his nemesis.

'What kind of establishment are you running here?' she hissed, 'Show me your signing in book!'

The secretary offered no resistance and sheepishly handed the book to Margaret Ann. There was of course no evidence of Morgan James' signature.

'Have you no idea who is in this building? This boy...' she gave Morgan a shake, 'is supposed to be in school and here he is loitering upstairs with that lot of no good boyos. He is supposed to be in his classroom. Goodness knows what he's learning up there! You will be hearing from the Reverend Jones about this matter, and he may well be forced to speak to the trustees about the way you are running your precious institute.'

With that she gave Morgan James a push and sailed out into the street. Despite the not inconsiderable difference in their height, she maintained a firm grip on her son as they walked silently down the valley to the school in Porth, ignoring the amused glances of passers-by. At the school gate mother and son stopped.

'I am mortified,' his mother spoke through gritted teeth. 'Never, ever, make me feel like this again. That Hall is full of bad influences and as ever, you seem to know exactly where to find them. Your father will have to be told and there will be consequences. Our Will is giving up his pay to keep you on in school. What am I going to say to him about all this?' and she gave her third son another sharp push.

Rapping imperiously on the headmaster's door, Margaret Ann and Morgan entered. The headmaster looked up from his registers with some surprise. 'Mrs Jones, good morning!'

Margaret Ann glared at him. 'Do you know where I have just found him? Up the Hall and where should he be?' She gave her errant son another shake. 'Tell Mr Williams what you've been up to and hurry up about it. I have a business to attend to and I can't spend time running about the roads keeping an eye on boys who should know better. Neither have I the time to be doing other people's jobs for them.' She fixed the bemused headmaster with another withering stare.

Morgan James knew he had no escape and that silence would merely prolong the interview. 'I was playing billiards, sir.'

'Alone?' queried the headmaster.

'No sir, with Dai Coch and Gwyn.'

'You know full well it's with your class you should have been. Get there at once and concentrate on your lessons until the dinner bell goes and then you'll come straight back here to me.'

Relieved to be out of his mother's clutches at least, Morgan slunk off down the corridor and Mr Williams turned wearily to Margaret Ann.

'I'll deal with him later, Mrs Jones. I'll get to the bottom of what he's been up to with that no-good pair. I don't suppose this is the first time Morgan has visited the billiard room?'

'Half my customers already know "what he's been up to", as you call it, Mr Williams, and I'd be glad to be able to tell them that you have the matter in hand. I wonder how many of your other pupils are spending their time wandering the streets visiting other establishments, unknown to you apparently, instead of getting on with their studies?'

After she had given the headmaster a summary of what she considered to be his responsibilities in the matter, Margaret Ann hastened back to Cwtch to relay the events of the morning to her husband, preferably before village gossip reached him. She was too late. The shop and post office was crowded with customers several of whom had witnessed the Morgan's ejection from the Hall. A dignified silence was necessary, and the irate mother was unable to pass on the details of the morning's incident until Morgan James' parents had the shop to themselves.

'I don't know what on earth we are going to do about that son of yours,' she began. Morgan raised an eyebrow, and waited for the rest. 'There's no point in paying good money for him to be taught if he's not willing to learn, and when he'd rather be hanging about the Workmen's Hall. There's at least two families I wouldn't want him having anything to do with who are in there, all hours of the day and night. And while I think about it you can write a strong

99

letter to those trustees, about letting schoolboys play billiards during school time. That secretary was more interested in his newspaper than in who was coming in and out, and he's supposed to get the men to sign the attendance book. We are going to have to decide what we're going to do with that boy before he gets back here tonight. I'm inclined to put him to work. That way he'll lose pay if he doesn't turn up and then we'll see how keen he is on his billiards.'

'Maybe that's what he'd prefer,' said Morgan mildly. 'But I think he should be made to finish the term and complete his Intermediate level. Then at least he'll have got a certificate to show for it.'

Morgan James' interview with his father took place in the privacy of the parlour, and resulted in an absolute ban on his attendance in the Hall while he was still at school. A further discussion with his mother later that night did nothing to reinforce Morgan James' commitment to the classroom, and his enforced attendance in school did nothing to awaken in him any desire to emulate Edgar's scholarship. By the end of term his father was obliged to allow his wife to curtail what she considered to be completely unnecessary expenditure on educating someone who clearly had no wish to be educated. Fortunately for the errant scholar, his performance in the Intermediate exam which was held at the end of the summer term resulted in a pass and the awarding of the desired certificate. After a brief meeting between his parents and Mr Meredith, the manager at the National Colliery, Morgan James joined William in employment as a junior clerk in the stores, an administrative post, which was to prove very useful to him in the future.

CHAPTER 13
AGNES AND ARTHUR

'Mam,' five-year-old Gladys greeted her mother. 'Arthur won't play with me. He says it hurts.'

'What hurts, do you know?' Margaret Ann enquired, turning from the range where she was putting the finishing touches to the family's supper.

'He says his chest hurts, Mam, you come and see.' Gladys pulled her mother towards the passage where she had been trying to interest her little brother in building a tower on the bottom stair. Young Arthur was certainly in no condition to play. He sat wan and listless on the stair and at the sight of his mother, two large tears ran down his cheeks. Margaret Ann picked him up and sent Gladys for the shawl which she wrapped round herself and the child, humming a little song to him.

'Fetch him some water now, Gladys, quick. There's a cup on the draining board, and ask Carrie to leave the ironing and mind the stove, or the supper will burn.' Gladys hastened to relay her mother's request and dragged her little stool to the sink to reach the tap. Carefully she carried the cup back to her miserable little brother. 'What's wrong with him, Mam? He doesn't look right and he's all floppy.'

'He's got a fever, that's all, he'll be fine in a bit. Clear up those blocks now before the rest of them come home or we'll have broken legs to add to everything else.'

Dutifully, Gladys picked up the blocks and put them carefully in the pine chest William had made for their toys.

Margaret Ann was accustomed to nursing hot and fractious infants. Teething she could cope with, but as no serious or prolonged illness had attacked any of her children, she presumed Arthur's fever was a passing indisposition, to be cured by a little care and the obligatory dose of gripe water. When the older brothers and sisters returned from their various activities, they all took it in turns to nurse the miserable toddler. As the evening wore on it became increasingly obvious that a dose of gripe water was not going to solve the problem. Arthur became increasingly listless and feverish and his little body was shaken with paroxysms of coughing. That night brought little rest for Margaret Ann and Morgan, who took it in turns to nurse their two-year-old through the hours of darkness.

'I think Dr Davies will be needed for this,' she said to her husband as daylight stole in. 'His breathing is dreadful and he's still feverish. Wake Will and tell him to take the trap and fetch the doctor.'

Without waiting to put on his coat, William harnessed up the trap at lightning speed and set off to the next valley, for the physician who looked after the whole community. The arrival of the Reverend Jones' trap outside Dr Davies' house at six in the morning alerted the whole village to the likelihood that something was seriously wrong at the shop in Wattstown. The doctor dressed quickly, for he too knew that a call from Mrs Jones the Shop was unlikely to be a trivial matter. Will briefly filled in the details of Arthur's sudden illness on the journey back, and hastily ushered the doctor into the house. Margaret Ann was sitting by the kitchen range rocking the now very sick child on her lap. The doctor gave Arthur a careful examination and then handed him to William to hold. He asked Margaret Ann and Morgan to follow him through into the hall.

'I don't think there's much doubt about it. I'm afraid Arthur has pneumonia.' As he pronounced the dread word pneumonia, widely regarded as a killer, Margaret Ann clutched at her husband in an uncharacteristic gesture of dependence.

'What's to be done then?' asked Morgan.

The doctor explained that very little could be done. 'There's no medicine I can give him. You'll need to keep the fire lit in the bedroom and have a steaming kettle kept on the hob alongside the fire to moisten the air. That will help ease the child's breathing. Keep him sitting up in bed with as many pillows as you can find.' He added, 'You'll have to put the little girl to sleep with her big sisters. Arthur is going to need nursing day and night until he's through the worst and the illness has run its course. Try and get him to drink if you can. He's a sturdy little lad, which should help him, but there's no knowing how long this will take. It's going to take very careful nursing as well as prayers for a happy outcome. Hopefully Arthur should pull through.'

As William escorted the doctor back to the trap, he asked, 'Is it bad then, doctor? Do you think he will pull through?'

'It's a dreadful thing, Will. I lose more patients to pneumonia than almost anything else. It carries off young and old alike and there's precious little I can do. It's all down to devoted nursing and the stamina of the invalid. Your mother is going to need a lot of support to get through this.'

Back at the house Margaret Ann had already decided to leave the praying to her husband and the nursing to her daughter Agnes, as Agnes could more easily take time away from her studies than her older sister Amy. As soon as the rest of the household was up and dressed, Margaret Ann busied herself issuing instructions to her sons to move Gladys's little bed out of Arthur's room and replace it with Agnes's larger one.

As Agnes appeared from her bedroom with her hair neatly plaited ready for school, her mother announced, 'You can get that school dress off, Agnes, and an overall on. You're going to have to nurse our Arthur. He's gone and got pneumonia.'

Agnes stared at her mother in horror. 'Mam, I don't know anything about pneumonia and I've got compositions to write.'

'There'll be no time for writing compositions, or anything else for that matter my girl, until Arthur's better. Dr Davies has been and left instructions and we have just got to get on with it. You can do the nursing and your father can do the praying. I must see to the next batch of loaves.' With that her mother hurried off to the bakehouse.

Agnes realised swiftly that there was no point in remonstrating with her mother. There was an air of panic in the house and her mother had an expression on her face Agnes had never seen before.

'I'll do it for today' she said to herself, 'and then Amy can have a turn. She's older than me, and she ought to take her turn. He'll be better by Saturday.'

The girl was instructed to get the fire lit in the little bedroom and under no circumstances to let it go out until Arthur was better. Morgan James and Will heaved and tugged Agnes's bed from her room into Arthur's, and lined it up under the window. There was no space for her little bedside table which her father had saved for her from her grandmother's house, when his mother and sisters went to America. It was her prized possession. But do without it she must until Arthur recovered. Maggie and Jane were ordered to put plenty of towels and cloths in a neat pile on the hall table which was heaved up the stairs and added to the growing jumble of furniture in the little hospital room. Edgar's bedroom chair was purloined so that Agnes would have somewhere to nurse her little brother if he couldn't 'get his breath' in the night. Maggie and Jane were told to fill the big ewer from their parents' room and keep it full of water on the washstand. Meanwhile Agnes, the ailing toddler wrapped in a shawl in her arms, paced the landing. As soon as the fire was lit and the kettle was spurting out clouds of steam she tucked the feverish child into bed where within a few moments he fell into a fitful sleep. Agnes sat down on the chair and tried to make sense of the turn the morning had taken.

With everything organised to her satisfaction, Margaret Ann took herself into the shop, leaving the girls to sort breakfast for everyone. Work, she knew, was the best way to deal with her worries and there would be plenty to be done in the weeks to come. The shop and post office were what would occupy her, leaving her to maintain a purely supervisory role in both her husband's praying and her daughter's nursing roles.

Agnes, who was then thirteen years old, spent six weeks incarcerated in the sickroom with her brother, responsible for his feeding, toileting, and blanket-bathing. She delivered the arduous nursing care required for a child desperately ill with pneumonia. Agnes was exhausted by the hourly tepid sponging prescribed as essential by the doctor to reduce Arthur's high temperature, and the constant encouragement to drink sips of water throughout day and night. She spent what seemed like endless hours leaning on the window-sill, watching the grey clouds scudding across the sky. The blustery March winds rattled the shutters on the shop front as occasional sounds drifted up from below. The arrival of delivery carts bearing flour and sugar for the shop relieved the monotony of the silent sick-room, but made her feel even more cut off from normal life. The relentless ticking of the landing clock reminded her constantly of the length of time she was forced to spend in that room. 'Once I get out of here I'm never coming in this room again as long as I live,' she vowed to herself.

She missed school, her lessons and her friends. She felt as if she were a prisoner isolated in a punishment cell, and she suffered from the deprivation of her father's presence. None of her brothers and sisters did more than stick their heads around the bedroom door to check on progress or to perform their minimal duties of filling kettles and replacing towels. Agnes saw more of the girl who tended to the fire and brought her meals than she did of the family. Arthur's mother visited twice daily, once in the morning in order to check on the patient's condition overnight and once when she had closed the shop for the day. When Agnes complained tearfully that she had no way of calling for help in an emergency, her mother merely produced a small bell and told her to ring it.

The piles of books Agnes read to her little brother as he recovered grew and grew in the corner of the bedroom. Noughts and crosses were played and endless nursery rhymes were sung to her fractious little patient. All the activities made her more and more short tempered. As Arthur slowly began to recover she found the cosseted little patient increasingly irritating. She looked forward eagerly to her father's brief visits to the sickroom but once the immediate danger to his son had passed, even these became less frequent.

Apparently praying can be done without even seeing the patient, Agnes thought bitterly to herself as she spooned more blancmange down Arthur's throat.

Eventually, after six weeks, the pale and fragile invalid emerged from the sickroom to be even more fussed over by the family and Agnes rejoined the family circle. Her contribution to Arthur's recovery was never mentioned. It was an experience she never forgot and her bitterness ran deep. Never completely at ease with her mother, Agnes's resentment at the lack of acknowledgement of the role she had played in Arthur's recovery reinforced her feelings of alienation from her mother and sisters and her increasing withdrawal from the family circle partly stemmed from these experiences. She was never again to be fully involved in the family's rumbustious goings-on and her antipathy to her mother deepened.

☙ ☙ ☙

Undisturbed by Agnes's sickroom duties, Amy continued study to hard and hoped to go on to college in Cardiff. Edgar had earned his coveted degree and had been appointed to the staff of the pupil teacher training centre in Porth. He was a popular and deeply committed teacher who was already attracting the notice of his superiors. His involvement with the chapels of the Rhondda valley also grew. The Welsh Revival was gaining momentum and he worked tirelessly to extend the cultural and educational roles of the Sunday Schools and church meetings, which were supplementing the educational opportunities which had been so lacking for the majority of the chapel going public. Ever since he had attended the Park Hall meeting at which he had heard Lloyd George speak, Edgar had a new ambition. David Lloyd George had convinced him that improving the lot of families in the South Wales valleys depended on political action, and that meant joining the Liberal Party, with a view to entering parliament.

Margaret Ann's intense pride in her family remained hidden as ever. Even before her marriage to the promising young minister she had resolved that her ambitions would be realised, and nothing would be allowed to interfere. Now, the older ones were all on the threshold of success, and the younger ones would surely follow their examples. She was completely impervious to the snide remarks of the local women, which she put down to envy. She had never enjoyed a circle of friends as the other women did, preferring instead to remain aloof from them. Her family was all the company she needed. The phrase 'keeping up with the Jones's' had a literal meaning in Aberllechau and all the family were well aware of it.

✺ ✺ ✺

Morgan Humphrey, no longer in charge of a chapel, had sought election to the Board of Guardians who were responsible for administering poor relief in the locality. He had also claimed his right to the Freedom of Llantrisant through his wife's family. John Evans, Margaret Ann's grandfather, had been admitted as Freeman of the Borough in 1818, his trade entered as cordwainer. This right, which included a parliamentary vote, had been established by John Evans's predecessors generations before and was another source of great pride in the family. One evening, before an important meeting of the Guardians, Morgan took himself for a walk up the hillside behind the village and looked down on the community beneath him. From that distance there was no sign of the struggle against poverty and ill health which many families fought on a daily basis.

'Preaching is one thing,' he said to himself, 'but those families down there need more than words. I'm not sure heaven means much to them at the moment. Words won't fill their stomachs or put shoes on their feet. We'll give out poor relief tonight, but as usual it won't be enough.'

At the next Board of Guardians' meeting, Morgan expanded his thoughts to his fellow members and was soon persuaded that to achieve the greatest good one needed to be active in the field of politics. He became an active worker for the Liberal cause, in which he was enthusiastically joined by Edgar. Margaret Ann and William, both suspicious of formal organisations, whether chapel or political, remained detached, their energies being directed to the everyday problems of people's working lives.

William, whose assumption on the first day of his employment by the National Colliery that promotion was inevitable, had achieved it in record time. Still only eighteen, he had now become the Keeper of the Stores, a position of some significant responsibility, as well as young Morgan's boss. The stores held everything from pit props to horseshoes which were needed for the efficient working of the colliery, and the store-keeper's task was to ensure an adequate stock of everything and to prevent wasteful distribution of resources. William proved himself to be highly competent in his new job, and both the company and men had every confidence in him. His employment also carried with it an allocation of free coal, for which Margaret Ann was very grateful. Long years of buying expensive coal for house and bakehouse herself had resulted in her insisting on very economical use of it.

One cold wet, evening in late November, William returned from work to find his father huddled over a small fire in the parlour, well damped down with small coal dust from which little heat escaped.

'Not very warm in here, are you?' William took up the poker to stir some life into the smouldering fire.

'Careful boy, your mother has just put that small coal on.'

'Oh aye, and left you to sit in the cold while she keeps warm rushing about in the shop.'

'You know she likes to make the coal last. She burns every bit of small coal before she'll put any lumps on,' his father explained, always defensive on his wife's behalf.

'Maybe, but as long as the coal comes from me you will have a proper fire and not sit here in the cold.' William poked vigorously at the fire. The noise alerted Margaret Ann who was on her way upstairs. She looked into the room. 'I thought I heard somebody at the fire and guessed it would be you. Leave that poker alone, there's no need to burn the fire up, there's only your father in here.'

When William continued to poke the fire, she pulled it out of his hand. Mother and son looked at each other. It was William who spoke very slowly and clearly, 'Let me tell you, Mam, my father shall not sit here in the cold because you fill the grate with small coal and damp the fire down. Not while I am living here and providing the coal.'

Margaret Ann said nothing and bent down to replace the poker, as the fire, disturbed by William's efforts, burst into life. Her son left the room, returning a few minutes later with a bucket containing gleaming lumps of good quality coal. He lifted several large lumps out of the coal bucket and piled them on the fire. Flames immediately shot up the chimney and in a few minutes a warm glow began to fill the room. 'There,' he said as he finished stoking the blaze. 'That's the sort of fire my father shall sit by in the future.'

'Taking charge here are you?'

'Of this fire, yes.'

True to his word, until he left home, William kept the fire stoked up whenever his father sat in the room, defying his mother to put on the miserable black cap of small coal.

CHAPTER 14
THE STAYS

The new century brought with it an ever-increasing demand for iron to build the railway tracks of the world, and coal to fuel the steam ships of the Empire. These international developments resulted in further expansion of the pits in the valleys of South Wales. The quiet dells in which Edgar and his brothers and sisters had played were now buried under the growing slag heaps as more and more mines were sunk. Trams, trains and omnibuses rattled their way up and down the steep sided valleys carrying the growing population to the rapidly expanding towns, and the peaceful farming communities in the lower parts of the valley had all but disappeared.

Margaret Ann had succeeded in her ambition to run an even more successful emporium than her parents in Cwmamman and she had raised nine healthy children, three of whom were now contributing to the family purse. Two more houses bought in Aberllechau Road a few years previously, had proved to be another shrewd investment and had resulted in a steady income in rent. The shop and the post office were a vital part of village life and were still the only source of the daily provisions for the local families. A butcher's shop, a greengrocer's and a small hardware store had arrived but they were no competition and Margaret Ann's business flourished.

Her eldest daughter Amy had repeated Edgar's academic success and had gained a place at college in Cardiff in the autumn. Unlike Edgar, she would not travel daily to the city but would live during term time in a newly built women's hall of residence. Margaret Ann had no wish to send her daughter out into the world with darned or patched underwear or shabby outer garments. That meant that provision would have to be made for new clothes. Other young ladies collected items for their important 'bottom drawers' prior to marriage, but Margaret Ann's daughters collected items for their lives in college.

Amy, an accomplished needlewoman, was set to work by her mother to make chemises, night dresses, bodices and knickers from the bolt of fine calico Margaret Ann had purchased from a travelling salesman who had called one day at the post office. A serviceable skirt and two blouses would be all that were required for attendance at lectures. That left the need for a proper dress for chapel going or visiting. She procured the services of a young seamstress from Ynishir to 'make over' her own best dress for her daughter. The need to be economical was paramount for Margaret Ann. The years of child bearing had taken their toll on her trim figure, and although she had never succumbed to the 'middle-aged spread' of most of her contemporaries she was well aware that her twenty inch waist was a thing of the past and so the dress would have to go. A best coat and hat for Sundays would have to be purchased. Amy's current best coat could be demoted for everyday wear but it would not do for chapel.

Elizabeth was the cousin who had so unwillingly minded Edgar and William that long ago day when Margaret Ann had thrown caution to the winds and gone in search of her shop. Elizabeth was now in business with her husband as an outfitter in Ystrad, and it was their emporium Amy and her mother decided to patronise.

Elizabeth was surprised to see her cousin and her daughter in her shop, but greeted them warmly and gave them her personal attention. She knew on the family grapevine that Amy had emulated Edgar's success and was off to college. No doubt that was going to be very expensive and she was sure Margaret Ann would want good value for the money she proposed to spend. Elizabeth knew her cousin's reputation as a shrewd businesswoman and as expected, Margaret Ann examined carefully every coat brought out for her inspection. Amy stood obediently while mother and cousin bade her try this, try that, knowing better than to voice her own opinion. Black, brown, tweed and navy blue coats were tried but to Amy's eyes none compared with a fitted maroon model with a small velvet trimmed collar which she had seen on the mannequin in the corner. She could hardly believe her luck when Elizabeth, noting Amy's repeated glances towards the model, said, 'Why don't you try on the coat on the model? I may be able to offer a small discount on that one, Margaret Ann, as it's been on display.'

Amy put it on and barely recognised herself in the Cheval mirror. Gone was the schoolgirl, instead there stood an elegant young lady.

'Try that tweed on again, Amy, it won't show the marks like the plain one,' ordered her mother. 'I think she may still need room to grow in it and that maroon one is a bit tight.'

Unnoticed by her mother, Amy cast a beseeching glance at her mother's cousin who said, 'Actually, Margaret Ann, the maroon cloth is much better value for money you know. It is a better cloth and will give years of wear.'

Amy closed her eyes and prayed. The maroon one was so pretty and she liked it so much more than the others. Then she heard her mother say, 'You are probably right, Elizabeth. In that case we'll take the maroon.' Her daughter hardly dared to breathe. 'Thank you Mam,' was all she could trust herself to say. Heaven had answered her prayer! She had the coat she wanted, a coat she could wear with pride.

The purchase of the hat took less time. Margaret Ann was prepared to let Amy have a voice in the matter, only dismissing any hat she considered flighty. A sober but fetching one with a small feather was deemed by both to fit the bill and Amy was delighted to see the little hat placed carefully in a real hat box!

There was one more purchase to be made. Amy had been told by her mother that it was time she had proper stays to replace the bodices which she normally wore. The very word 'stays' signified to Amy that her mother was finally acknowledging that she was no longer a merely a girl. The possession of stays without doubt conferred the full status of womanhood.

Elizabeth conducted them to the rear of the shop. After a few whispered words to the assistant, she left such an important and private matter to her customers. Several long, narrow boxes were taken down from shelves, the assistant explaining the difference between bone and steel.

'These, madam,' she addressed Margaret Ann, 'are reinforced with whalebone, but nowadays many young women prefer to wear the softer steel strips.'

Margaret Ann, who had worn whalebone for many years, was not impressed by the assistant's suggestion that the young lady might find the steel more comfortable. The whole point of a corset or stays, as far as she was concerned, was to keep the wearer upright, to encourage good posture. Young ladies were not to bend or slouch. Whalebone therefore it had to be, but unfortunately the size was left more to chance than accurate measurement, as Margaret Ann's patience was almost exhausted. Amy's tentative suggestion that she might prefer a set in a paler shade of pink drew forth a snort of derision from her mother and an acid comment about who was going to see them? It was not easy being Margaret Ann's first daughter. Eventually, Amy was laced into the first set of stays and stood transfixed in front of the mirror.

'That will do,' said her mother brusquely, 'you've stared at yourself long enough. We'll take those.'

Her new coat and hat were now of secondary importance to Amy. She had her first stays, the possession of which reinforced her position above Agnes and most certainly above the younger sisters. She had not felt so important since the day she had first put up her hair!

On their arrival home, the hat and coat were tried on and duly admired but the narrow box remained firmly closed. Not for the eyes of brothers and younger sisters was that most intimate of garments. With her purchases in her arms, Amy escaped upstairs, followed by Agnes who demanded, 'What's in the box, then? Kept it away from the others downstairs, didn't you? What's in it?'

'It's stays,' whispered Amy, opening the box to reveal the precious garment in all its glorious pinkness, together with its complicated hooks and laces.

'Is that what they look like? I've never seen them before. You are not going to wear them, are you?'

'Of course I am.' Amy quickly removed her blouse and skirt and proceeded to demonstrate that she knew how to lace up the two separate pieces and get them round her middle, but Agnes was needed to help hook up the steel hooks in the front.

'There! How do I look?'

'Oh, different. Completely different. Everything seems pushed up and in,' observed Agnes with awe. 'You are a different shape and you seem taller all of a sudden.'

Amy turned towards the small mirror which stood on the chest of drawers, in the hope that in some wonderful way it would show her new shape, not just her face which was all that was normally reflected.

'I can't see myself in that. I'm going to look in Mam's wardrobe mirror.'

'You'll need to be quick then, or she'll catch you if she comes up to the bedroom to put her coat away,' Agnes warned as her sister ran from the room.

Amy checked that the coast was clear before creeping into Margaret Ann's bedroom. Carefully opening the wardrobe door she gazed at herself in its mirror, admiring her new shape. 'Agnes is right,' she thought. 'I am all pushed up and I am thinner in the middle, too.'

When she returned to their room, Agnes demanded to be allowed to try the stays on.

'Please, please,' she begged. '*Pleeease*, Amy, let me have a go'

'No. You're not old enough. They won't fit you anyway. We will have to unlace the back to get the stays round you and that will take ages.'

'If they go round you, then they'll go round me. I'm thinner than you.'

'No, you are not!'

Agnes was determined to discover if her shape would change as her sister's. At last Amy gave in and reluctantly laced her sister into the garment. But the ample curves of a sixteen-year-old were difficult to confine within the stays. No sooner were the hooks fastened than Agnes complained,

'I can't breathe, I can't breathe, it's horrible. Get them off me.'

Agnes began to wriggle and twist in an attempt to get out of the stays. Between Agnes's mounting panic and Amy's nervous fingers, the hooks proved stubborn and Agnes began to sob. 'Stop it,' hissed her sister, 'they will hear you downstairs. Stand still and stop wriggling. Keep quiet or Mam will be in.'

With much puffing and heaving, Amy eventually managed to release her sister who sank gasping on to her bed, vowing between sobs that she would never, ever, wear such a terrible garment as stays – a vow which Agnes kept all her life.

CHAPTER 15
CHANGE

The family in Wattstown was now adjusting to the constant change which resulted from the various successes of Margaret Ann's children. The three oldest were all financially independent even though they still lived under their mother's roof. For Amy, two years in college had now finished and by 1902 she was the proud possessor of her Board of Education Teachers' Certificate. She was transformed, her sisters believed, into a graceful young lady with an abiding love of elegant lace collars. She had spent hours in college, when not studying for her exams, perfecting the popular art of crochet and had become very skilful. Her meagre allowance could easily be augmented by producing the pretty lace collars which would liven up a fellow student's dress, and Amy's collars became a definite fashion item. Agnes, Jane and Maggie were desperate to own such a wonderful adornment and badgered their sister constantly to make them one each. But Amy was adamant. They must learn to make their own.

So, the summer holiday before she began her first teaching job was devoted to passing on her skill to her sisters. She persuaded Edgar to fund the little factory and set off to Porth to buy the necessary hooks and cottons. One afternoon after their chores were done she lined up her sisters in a row in the parlour and began the lesson.

By the end of the holiday, all her sisters were the proud owners of a white lace collar. True, Agnes's collar was not entirely symmetrical

1 Hand-tinted photo portrait of Margaret Ann Jones, processed in Merthyr Tydfil c. 1902.

2 Hand-tinted photo portrait of Reverend Morgan Humphrey Jones, Merthyr Tydfil c.1902

3 Margaret Ann Evans on her engagement to Morgan Humphrey c.1876.

4 (below left) Reverend Morgan Humphrey Jones on his engagement to Margaret Ann c.1876.

5 (below right) Margaret Ann Jones in c.1915 possibly on her 60th birthday

6 The family post office and shop in Wattstown with postmaster Morgan and seven of his children, from William to Gladys, shown in close-up with their pet dog.

7, 8 & 9 *The Wattstown colliery and the funerals for the 129 miners killed in the 1905 disaster.*

10 & 11 Edgar's wedding to May Brackley in 1919; 12 (below) William and Edgar at the races.

13 (top) Ann and baby Tom; 14 William with Tom; (below) 15 William and Ann at their wedding 1908; 16 William and Ann with their two daughters Hilda and Margaret.

Waltstown General View.   1.7a

3341. *General View of National Collieries and Wattstown.* Ernest T. Bush 7/6

17 The Jones family outside Min-yr-Afon in Wattstown about 1905: Back row l-r Edgar, Jane, William, Maggie, Morgan; front row l-r Gladys, Amy, Morgan Humphrey, Margaret Ann, Agnes, Arthur. (insets) Two views of Wattstown, the second of which shows Gorwel, the later family home — the detached house to the right of the top terrace.

18 Jane aged about 21   19 Jane, a later photo   20 Ann Thomas' sisters Joanna & Hannah

21 Gladys & Maggie (22) at Edgar's wedding; 23 Family at Glenthorpe, Annerly c.1922
(back row) Gladys, Maggie, Agnes; (middle)William, Margaret Ann; (front) Margaret, Tom, Hilda

24 Edgar's wedding: bridesmaids Hilda & Margaret; 25 Gladys & Maggie in the 1920s

26 Aberllechau School, 1900: (far left) Amy, as pupil teacher before going up to Cardiff.

27 Amy & Gladys   *28 Thomas Thomas (y ceiliog)*   *29 Morgan James c.1918*

30 Arthur c.1915   *31 Arthur c.1916*   *32 Morgan c.1916*

33 Lloyd George helped Edgar into national politics.   *34 Funeral announcement for Morgan Jones.*

35

37

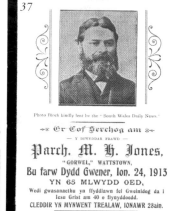

36

35 Margaret & Tom, William's children
36 Margaret & Hilda, William's children
37 Funeral announcement for Reverend Morgan H Jones in Welsh.
38 Agnes, Margaret Ann & William playing bowls.

39 Waun Fawr, Crosskeys home of William's family c.1912-1919; 40 Gorwel, Wattstown

42 Glenthorpe: William's home 1919-26

43 Mumbles: Jane's golden summer holiday

44 Amy & Agnes(?) with William outside Waun Fawr
45 William plays with his grandson Gareth c.1950

46 Hilda graduating,
UCW Aberystwyth 1936

47 Amy's wedding to David Morris, 1920 (back row) Arthur, William, Edgar; (middle) Tom, Agnes, May, unknown; (front) Mam, David, Amy, Maggie; (on ground) Gladys, Fluff, Hilda, Jane.
48 Arthur's wedding: family attending include Edgar, Will, Gladys, Maggie, Mam & Agnes.

49 Mam alone on a garden bench on her 90th birthday in 1945.

50 Mam looking cheerful on her 90th birthday in 1945 with her four sons: (back row) William, Arthur, (front) Edgar and Morgan.

Note: *The photos are taken mainly from the family scrapbooks of the nine children and grandchildren of Margaret Ann and Morgan Humphrey. They record the changes in the family's life over more than fifty years often more vividly than any words.*

and Jane's was rather uneven, but little Maggie's was a triumph and the girls never forgot the skill. In later years, every little girl they ever taught learned from Miss Jones how to crochet.

The population of the Rhondda continued to increase and there was a growing demand for school places in the rapidly expanding schools. Amy therefore looked forward to an appointment with the Rhondda Education Committee in one of the newly opened infant schools in the valley. She could barely wait to carry home her first salary and to join the ranks of her wage-earning brothers.

As the first of her daughters became independent, Margaret Ann produced a new formula by which she calculated the amount each offspring was to contribute to the family exchequer. She still controlled all money coming into the household, taking from each working member of the family exactly the same amount, irrespective of their individual earnings. As their mother was never profligate, it never occurred to any of her children to question the arrangement. She carefully considered what was necessary to cover the family's outgoings and she retained the right to increase the contribution in accordance with increased expenditure. This new method allowed the individual to retain control of whatever money was left after paying the household dues.

Margaret Ann remained queen of her empire and decided to increase the family's stock of housing by buying two more houses at the bottom of the village. 'This will make them sit up in America,' she mused, as she locked up the shop one evening. 'They are always writing about how successful they are, and how Pennsylvania is so wonderful. They should come over here and see what Morgan's family is managing to achieve.' Then an idea struck her and she marched into the parlour where Morgan was planning his next sermon.

'I think we need to go over to Merthyr, Morgan. There's a new photographer there who takes portraits. I want ours done and we can send the pictures to show them in America.'

Morgan stared at his wife in disbelief. 'What on earth are you thinking of? Photographs? Why now?'

Margaret Ann looked sheepish. She took from her pocket the cloth she used for wiping the shop counter at the end of the day and began vigorously rubbing at an imaginary mark on the window-sill. 'They are always going on about how grand they are, and I wanted to show them we can be grand, too.' She looked down at her feet and added in a small voice, 'I wanted a photograph taken before my looks go!' Morgan stared at her. Then he gave a loud guffaw. 'Margaret Ann, if we live to be a hundred you'll still be able to astound me. What ever will you think of next! As far as I'm concerned you look just as you did twenty-five years ago, but if it's what you want you'd better see if Will is free to take us over in the trap next week.'

William was free, and when he had finished chuckling to himself about his mother's vanity, he duly drove his parents, dressed in their best, to the Merthyr Photographers. The photographs were taken, tinted and mounted in large golden frames. One copy of each portrait was sent across the Atlantic and Margaret Ann hung the originals side by side in the hall.

∽ ∽ ∽

A few days after Amy's position as assistant teacher in the infants' school down the valley was confirmed, Margaret Ann was surprised to see a smartly suited young man open the door of the shop and ask her for a few moments conversation.

'What are you after, young man?'

'I'm from the Co-op,' came the reply. Margaret Ann held on to the counter and tried to prevent a feeling of panic from rising up and overwhelming her. She knew that the rapidly growing Co-operative Wholesale Society, which had its roots in the north of England, was spreading rapidly into Wales. The mighty Co-op had arrived down the valley and she was well aware of the devastating effect it was having on the small provision merchants in Pontypridd and Porth. Many of them had been taken over or forced out of business as customers deserted the corner shops for the cheaper goods and attractive dividend available to those who shopped with the

Co-op. The more enterprising among them had decided to avoid the competition and become drapers or ironmongers in order to survive.

Margaret Ann was about to speak when the young man went on, 'This is just a courtesy call to...' He got no further. A furious Margaret Ann interrupted. 'Welsh is the language I use in this shop.'

Hardly pausing, the visitor switched smoothly into Welsh and explained that the local co-operative society had decided that the growing prosperity of Aberllechau should be brought to the attention of head office. As a result, a new Co-op store would be opened lower down the village near the school. This would enable easier access to provisions for the housekeepers of the village, as well allowing them to save precious pennies. He concluded by informing Mrs Jones that a letter would shortly be sent to her containing further details of the proposed development.

Margaret Ann took a deep breath and hurled the full force of her rage and scorn on the hapless young man. She let him know exactly how much time and energy had been lavished on her shop and to have her livelihood snatched away by the dreaded Co-op was nothing short of devilish. She had no intention of giving up her shop and post office, the income from which had fed and clothed her family for twenty years, and furthermore her husband's status as postmaster had been conferred on him by the late Queen and no mere Co-op could remove it.

Not trusting herself to say more, she crossed to the door, opened it with a flourish, gave the young man a haughty '*Bore da*' and showed him out. Shaking, she sat down. Just as she was about to pull down the blinds to indicate to potential customers that the shop was closed, Mrs Basso loomed into view.

'Mrs Jones, Mrs Jones, have you heard? The Co-op is coming!'

Margaret Ann summoned all her composure and retreated behind her counter. She fixed Mrs Basso with a glassy smile, drew a deep breath and said calmly, 'Yes, yes, we all know about that. We have been considering a change for some time. As the children are now all doing so well, and we are so busy with our post office duties, the

Reverend Jones and I felt someone else could bake the bread and weigh out the sugar. Now, what can I get you?'

Mrs Basso departed leaving Margaret Ann to wonder how on earth she could retrieve the situation. She had saved face certainly which was no small matter for Margaret Ann in this village, but how was she to break the news to Morgan that the shop would go?

Thereafter Margaret Ann hated the Co-op, which she forever regarded as 'the enemy' that had deprived her of many customers, leaving her mostly with those poorer customers who hoped to be given a little credit. The thrifty colliers' wives were attracted to the Co-op by the dividends paid out on all purchases, which they saw as their own money, not necessarily to be revealed to their husbands. Out of the 'divi' came new clothes for Whitsun and chapel anniversaries, and Christmas presents for the children. The co-operative movement was wholesale as well as retail, which enabled the prices to be kept much lower than in the smaller retail shops. To Margaret Ann this was unfair business practice and she grumbled continuously about the perfidious Co-op.

Her husband and elder sons pointed out that as Amy would be making yet another contribution to the household, and the post office was still secure, she could at any time rid herself of the worry of shopkeeping. Morgan doubted that she would agree to such an action because however small the profits might now be, they stood for Margaret Ann's independence. It was the shop that had brought her out of the slough of despond, in which she had found herself on that long ago morning in Heol Fach when the boys needed shoes and the chapel's IOUs lay unpaid in the lustre jug.

It was not only the co-operative movement which had found ready support from the colliers. The growth of the trade unions meant the workmen were gaining more control over their wages and hours of work. Membership of the South Wales Miners' Federation encouraged many to become politically involved, committed to improving the economic and social wellbeing of themselves and their families. The life Margaret Ann had thought was indestructible was changing fast.

Political meetings were now held regularly in the valleys and a ticket to attend one of them was highly sought after. Edgar rushed into the shop one afternoon after work, brandishing an envelope with evident delight.

'Dadda, look, I've got a platform ticket for the meeting in the town hall in Ponty! Me on the platform and especially invited. Guess who's speaking?'

Margaret Ann looked up from slicing the bacon. 'Someone worth hearing, I hope. No doubt the hall will be packed with men while their wives are home doing all the work.'

'David Lloyd George, Mam. That's who, and the leader of the Liberal Party, Campbell Bannerman, as well as others no doubt. I can't wait. I'm sure education will be on the agenda, and then I'll be called to speak. I'll be able to tell them about my plans for a new institute and reading room, for the men.'

His mother looked unimpressed but Morgan Humphrey realised the significance of Edgar's excitement and was well aware of the honour extended to his son. Never had he expected a son of his to share a political platform with the leader of His Majesty's opposition and Edgar was only twenty-three.

The longed-for day of the meeting arrived, and even though the July evening was hot and sultry, Edgar emerged from the shop clad in his best suit, with his shoes again polished to perfection. An immaculate wing collar completed the outfit and even his sisters were impressed. On the way down the valley other men joined him, all agog to know how the meeting would go. Feelings were running high and many believed that the Liberal politicians were in for a rough ride. The hall was packed as Edgar made his way towards the dais. Many of the men in the audience knew him personally, and even though he was very young, he commanded much respect.

The meeting began, and Campbell Bannerman, then the compromise leader of the divided Liberal party, rose to his feet. He was heard with respect and polite attention, but little enthusiasm. Then the chairman called on Lloyd George to speak. There was uproar, and Edgar was appalled. A large part of the audience seemed determined to prevent him from speaking and reproaches and insults were hurled at the MP. For ten minutes his voice could not be heard but Edgar's hero was unperturbed. He calmly continued and the noise fell away. By the end of the meeting he emerged triumphant.

That evening Edgar gave his father an account of the meeting.

'I watched him Dadda. I watched him beat that crowd and make them listen and at the end he had them with him. He won them over and afterwards they carried him on their shoulders to the hotel. You wait and see what the *Aberdare Leader* says tomorrow.' Looking at Edgar's glowing face at that moment, Morgan Humphrey suspected that his eldest son would not remain a teacher for long, and that a career in politics was beckoning. But Edgar would have a lot to do to make that happen.

Edgar's determination to improve the lives of his fellow citizens of the Rhondda was growing steadily, and his latest plan in Wattstown was for an eight-man committee to be set up to investigate the possibility of engaging the services of a doctor for Wattstown who would be paid by levying a small charge on the colliery workmen. Before such an appointment could be made the committee needed to acquire a house and surgery but the colliery company owned most of the village houses. The only exceptions were a few of the terraces bought by the more thrifty through various friendly or building societies. The larger houses were those lived in by the colliery agents and managers such as Glenside and The Grove and they were unavailable. The Workmen's Committee was therefore faced with a problem.

∽ ∽ ∽

One October evening Margaret Ann had closed up the shop for the night and was supervising bedtime for seven-year-old Gladys and five-year-old Arthur. The task was usually done by Maggie, but tonight she and Jane were helping their father close the day's post office account. Jane's help was much appreciated by her father as her quick intelligence had easily grasped his method of accounting, but Maggie had persuaded herself that she was as good as her sister at maths and was now checking the stamp book. Morgan's patience was being sorely tried as he knew the book would need to be rechecked and he feared some errors could creep in as a result of Maggie's enthusiasm.

Suddenly, in spite of the drawn blind which signified the shop's closure, the shop door was pushed open and two men entered whom Morgan recognised as being members of the Workmen's Committee. He dismissed his two daughters and responded to the men's friendly greeting.

'Excuse the interruption, but we have come to discuss a matter of business, Reverend,' said the older of the two men whom Morgan knew as Jonathan Williams. He presumed they were seeking Edgar who was involved with them in the projected building of a workmens' institute and reading room in Wattstown.

'I'm not sure Edgar is about, gentlemen, but I'll see if I can find him for you.' Morgan moved towards the door.

'No, no, Mr Jones,' Mr Williams called him back. 'Mr Baker and I wish to discuss this matter with you.'

'Well, in that case, let me lock the outside door against interruption.' Morgan slid the bolts across and brought over the two chairs that Margaret Ann kept by the grocery counter. The two men seated themselves and Morgan resumed his seat behind the post office counter.

'Perhaps you know, Mr Jones,' began the younger man 'the Workmen's Committee is hoping to get a doctor to come to Wattstown. There's a difficulty though as there would appear to be no suitable house which could be offered.'

Morgan, a man of few words except in the pulpit, waited for further explanation. Jonathan Williams came to the aid of his colleague. 'It was decided that we would approach you.'

'Well now,' said Morgan, 'is it one of the houses in Min-Yr-Afon you are thinking of? We have two good tenants in there, and I wouldn't want to move them.'

It was the younger man, Mr Baker, who replied. 'Not Min-Yr-Afon, it's these premises we are interested in, Reverend Jones. You see the doctor might have to keep a pony and trap and you have a stable out the back, and the shop would make a perfect surgery.'

Morgan was glad he had the counter to lean on. 'This shop is only leased from the colliery you know, it is not for sale.'

It was Mr Williams' turn to speak. 'We've been into that, Reverend Jones. What we would like you to do is to surrender the remainder of your lease to the committee. For a consideration of course.'

Morgan was speechless. At last he managed a reply, 'You won't be expecting an answer straight away now, will you?'

It was now Mr Baker's turn to speak. 'Well, I am the secretary and Mr Williams is the committee chairman and the group has asked us to approach you on this subject as soon as possible. They are expecting us to report to the committee at our next meeting.'

'When is that?' Morgan asked faintly, and was told it was the following week. 'In that case, I will give the matter due consideration and let you know before that. *Nos da.*'

After he had escorted his callers to the door, he sat down in the empty shop to reflect on the situation. He suspected that Edgar and Will who had both been trying to persuade their mother to give up shopkeeping, might know something about this amazing request. He therefore decided to have a discussion with them before saying anything to Margaret Ann. Momentarily he was tempted to call Jane back to help him complete the post office account but he remembered the inevitable Maggie and wisely decided to carry on alone. The account balanced, he locked up all books in his methodical way and made his way to the kitchen where an unwilling Agnes was helping her mother prepare supper.

'You had a couple of late callers, Maggie tells me. Looking for stamps I suppose.'

'No, just a couple from the Workmen's Committee,' Morgan replied in a non-committal manner.

'Oh, then it was Edgar they were wanting, but they should have known he had to see Jack Kane tonight about that corner of spare land at the bottom of Victoria Street they're after for the Institute.'

Margaret Ann looked at her husband quizzically as she placed his supper on the table, but he was not yet ready to speak to her. He urgently needed a private conversation with his elder sons, but with his wife's curiosity roused, that would not be easy. If she were, for the present, to be kept in the dark, he would have to employ guile.

The next morning he made a point of being near the shop door as Edgar left for the pupil teacher centre. 'Call and see Will in the stores on your way home this afternoon, would you?' he said. Edgar was about to ask why, when he was prevented by his father's expression. 'No need for more now.'

William had already left for work but would be back at midday for his dinner, when Morgan intended to pass him the word of the proposed meeting. One difficulty remained; his own absence from the post office counter would have to be explained to Margaret Ann. The explanation would need to be of such reasonableness so as not to arouse any suspicion on her part. A downright lie was anathema to Morgan, so he decided that he would pay a visit to his cousin Mari Fach in Pontygwaeth and ask her husband to trim his hair and beard. Then he could call at the colliery stores on his way back and meet his sons.

Margaret Ann raised no objection to the proposed visit to the barber, only saying, 'I suppose it is time to get some of that hair off, but don't stay too long chatting to Mari, people do not like to be kept waiting if I'm running the two counters.'

The plan worked. Morgan and Edgar met their father at the stores where Will came out to meet them. Morgan told them briefly of last night's visit, finishing with the question, 'How much have you two had to do with this?'

His sons looked at each other. It was Edgar who spoke. 'We think, as you well know, it is time Mam gave up the shop. Takings are nothing like what they were. When Will heard about the need for a house and surgery for the doctor, we dropped a hint you might say.'

'Aye,' William went on, 'but I warned them that Mam would not be easy about it, so they had better make it worth her while.'

'It's surprised I am then, if that's the way you put it, that they bothered to come and see me at all. They should have been told to see your mother.'

'Now Dadda, come on.' Edgar was aware of his father's sensitivity about not appearing to be master in his own household. 'The thing needed to be done properly, and it is you who is the leaseholder.'

Pacified for the moment, Morgan asked Will if he had any idea of the amount of money that was to be offered for the relinquishing of the lease.

'Not the least idea but I made it clear that Mam was too good a businesswoman to be fooled. '

'So that's why they came to see me, then? They thought I was more likely to be fooled, did they?'

'We will all look fools, Dadda, unless Mam will agree to giving up the shop, not least Edgar and me who put the idea into their heads in the first place. But look, I still have work to do and can't stand here chatting all day.' He turned and disappeared into the stores.

Edgar and his father walked home together and the son did his best to reassure his father that nobody wished to challenge his position as the head of the household. He was the true leaseholder of the premises. Edgar suggested Morgan wrote to the committee to arrange a further meeting, to which they should come prepared to offer a substantial financial incentive for the remaining lease. Morgan accepted the soundness of Edgar's advice, but decided to say nothing to his wife until he knew when he would next meet the deputation.

✌ ✌ ✌

Two days later, with the vital meeting arranged for the next day, Morgan knew the time had come to tell Margaret Ann of the approach made to him. It was at bedtime, that he told her. She was stunned.

'Did you tell them it is my shop and your signature is only on that lease because the colliery would not give it to a woman? If we have no shop, we have no living. Do you intend to put us all out on the street?' Her voice rose ominously.

126

'Come now, Margaret Ann, you'll wake the whole house. The lease has not been given up yet, and there is no fear of having to live on the street with the houses in Min-yr-Afon and four other salaries coming in.'

'All of us in a house in Min-Yr-Afon! Where is your sense, man? How would we all fit in there? Three of the houses have been rented by good tenants since I bought them and I'm certainly not putting people out on the road. As for the end one with the Davieses in it, they are off to Swansea soon, and I was hoping to put up the rent when they left.'

'What is wrong with that, then? It's your house, and although you wouldn't be getting the rent we wouldn't have this lease to bother about. There's plenty of room. There's a parlour and a middle room as well as a kitchen, so we could keep the post office in the front room, and there's four bedrooms too.' Morgan hoped to sweeten the pill his wife was finding so difficult to swallow.

'When are you to see these men again? And how much has Will had to do with this?'

'No more than Edgar. Come, let us sleep on it.'

'Sleep on it you may! It's little sleep I'll get tonight.'

Yet it was Margaret Ann who slept, while Morgan tossed and turned, wondering how she could be persuaded to give up the shop and whether he was indeed bringing the family to the brink of financial ruin.

∽ ∽ ∽

In the morning the whole family knew their mother was 'on the warpath'. The girl had already received the rough edge of Margaret Ann's tongue, and had retreated in tears to scrub out the bakehouse. The children were sent off to school with such speed that they all knew it would be wise not to cross her path. Edgar rose from the breakfast table.

'You've told her then?'

'Aye,' replied his father, 'but I did not get much sense out of her. I'll try again later if I get the chance.'

William, who was about to leave for work, walked past his father and muttered, 'You'll do better, Dadda, if you let the money talk. Tell her she'll get a higher price for the lease if she settles now. The committee will be more generous if she doesn't keep them waiting too long. Good luck, anyway.'

His mother was in the shop, putting the last finishing touches to the display of dried fruit on the counter. 'Will,' she called after him. 'Is that committee going to pay enough for this place to compensate me for losing my living?'

William was shaken by the tone of the question. He had never before heard his mother sound anxious and almost vulnerable. Her indomitable spirit and absolute self belief had never wavered and although Will had frequently had cause to rebel against his mother's iron determination he could not help but admire it. He looked around the immaculate shop. 'I don't see much of a living here now Mam,' he said quietly. 'If you want a good price for the lease you'd best keep quiet about the customers you have lost to the Co-op.' With that parting shot, he went out.

Morgan sat on in the kitchen considering what further arguments he could put to his wife. Shortly afterwards she came in and put the shop account books in front of him. 'There's not much of a living here, according to Will, so what do the books say?'

Having kept the books for so many years, Morgan had no need to open them. 'You know as well as I do that Will is right and these books have been showing it for some while.'

'Best not let that committee see them, then,' his wife snapped. 'Or they'll think they will be able to get us out on the cheap. They'll have to compensate the Davies's too, unless they are prepared to move out to suit us.'

As she sat down at the table Morgan reached over and took her hand. 'Cheap or not, I will not sign away this lease until you tell me you are ready. I signed it because you wanted the shop, and I'll sign it away when you say you no longer want it. You and the shop have kept us clothed and fed for almost twenty years. I think it's time some of the rest of us do something about the next twenty.'

Margaret Ann pushed away the books and stood up.

'Move to Min-Yr-Afon then, and keep the post office it is. But make sure you get a fair deal.'

Morgan smiled at her. 'Do not forget, my girl, I'm originally from Cardiganshire and so I know the value of a shilling.'

On 18th November the Workmen's Committee agreed to pay the Reverend M H Jones £280 on giving up the lease of 25, Aberllechau Road. A further £100 was to be paid on or before 30th November the following year, and a further four equal instalments each quarter day. The Davies family were willing to leave a month early and were given £25 in compensation. Her Majesty's Postmaster General was agreeable to the Reverend Morgan Humphrey Jones continuing as postmaster in Wattstown at his new address, which he did until 1908. Margaret Ann was no longer to be a shopkeeper.

The move from Aberllechau Road took place at the beginning of December. To her children's amazement, Margaret Ann took the whole process in her stride. The home into which all except Edgar and William had been born was dismantled around them. The 'closing' notice went up in the window of the grocery emporium and the women of the village flocked to take advantage of any bargains Margaret Ann might be offering. Morgan James retrieved his painting materials from their hiding place in the stable and Agnes walked past the door of Arthur's little bedroom with relief, knowing she had kept her promise to herself. Margaret Ann went from room to room, recalling the very first time she had entered her domain, and resolutely closed the door on the bedroom in which she had given birth to seven of her children.

As the haulier arrived to transport the family's possessions down the road to Min-yr-Afon, Morgan placed the final pile of books at the door. Jim Lie pushed his cap to the back of his head and surveyed the contents of Morgan's library.

'Well, you didn't have this many when I moved you in here twenty years ago. Are all these going, Reverend? I don't know as you'll have room down the road. You should have got them all read before Mrs Jones decided to move.'

Morgan gave him a rueful glance and carefully picked up the little wooden cross from the windowsill which Will had whittled for him, and put it in his pocket.

CHAPTER 16
DISASTER

11th July 1905 was a sunny day so Edgar was in no hurry as he walked up the valley from the teachers' centre in Porth for his midday meal. Lessons had gone particularly well that morning and he was looking forward to tackling the causes of the Napoleonic Wars with his pupil teachers in the afternoon. As he crossed the Black Bridge he suddenly realised he could not hear the beat of the pit's ventilating fan. For twenty years he had lived within sight of the pit but he had never before known the fan to be silent, day or night. When he saw the whole colliery area was engulfed in an enormous cloud of steam it was if the sun had suddenly clouded over, and he had a sick feeling in the pit of his stomach.

He walked on hurriedly towards the pithead, musing over the possible cause of the silent fans, but as he reached the main gate he saw miners from the last shift milling around, still unwashed, while inside the yard, women stood silently in little groups. The calm routines of their morning had been shattered in an instant by the thunderous roar which had burst from the pit an hour ago. Some clutched shawls round them, some carried babies, some had not bothered even to remove their aprons or to tidy their hair, but they were drawn as though by a magnet to the pithead. As Edgar moved through the silent groups, the sick feeling in his stomach increased. Then he noticed Police Sergeant Williams from Ferndale and Dr Davies, the medical officer for the colliery, making their way through the crowd, and went over to ask what had happened.

The doctor said, 'All we know for certain, Mr Jones, is that an explosion shook the pit about an hour ago. It looks as if it is in the new shaft but it'll take a while for any news to come up because nobody can do anything till the standby fan gets going.'

All thoughts of dinner gone, Edgar walked towards the stores to find out if Will had any more information. He found his brother busy with his assistant, handing out the long rolls of brattice cloth. Edgar knew the brattice cloth was normally used in the mine to curtain off tunnels or as giant draught excluders. In disasters it had a more sinister use as temporary shrouds.

'Want any help?'

William shook his head. 'I'm nearly through with this box. I'm waiting for the next lot to come up from the lower store. The explosion is in the new shaft and I should think there are around a hundred and twenty men down there. They're checking the safety discs in the lamp room now. At least we'll soon know exactly which men went down this morning, but it was a big shift.'

As he spoke, the old familiar beat of a fan was heard. Relief flooded over William's drawn face. 'Thank God, they've got the standby working. That means the first rescue team can go down but it's not going to be good.'

'Is Meredith about?' Edgar asked, referring to the mine manager.

'He's underground I think, though why he needed to go down himself I have no idea. He never normally does these days. He rushed in here about eleven o'clock to ask if Bird had given Dai Beynon, the master sinker, any shot firing cable.'

'Who's Bird?'

'The explosives keeper,' his brother replied. 'I believe that chap Isaac Davies took a battery down, too. God help them if the shot was fired through the heading with the shift working. You know Meredith, though, too impatient to wait when he wants a job done.'

Edgar paced around the store, trying to work out where his skills could most constructively be used.

'Where is Jack Kane? He should be here.'

'He's bound to be somewhere. He's one of the best mine surveyors going, so let's hope he's got all his plans and drawings up to date because the rescue team is going to need to know where the side headings are, if they are to get the men out quickly. It's going to be difficult enough down there as it is.'

Will pushed his brother gently in the chest. 'Go on, out of my way now, Edgar, and let me get on. Find something useful to do. Or go home and get Dadda. I think prayers are going to be the only thing for some of those men, and their wives and mothers will have need of him.'

Barely a week went by in the South Wales coalfield without a fatality or serious injury and the human cost of extracting the 'black gold' was very high. Disasters of this magnitude shook whole communities to their very foundations as almost every family had at least one man working underground and for many women, their fathers, husbands, brothers and sons were all down the pit. The prospect of financial ruin and homelessness as well as bereavement, stared these women in the face as they stood in silent groups at the colliery entrance.

Edgar went outside where the sun was still shining brightly. He heard the sound of rushing feet and shouting from the enclosure near the winding gear, which meant the first rescue team was making ready for their descent into the mine. They knew well the grim task that would face them. Desperate to be of some practical use, he walked over to the general offices in the hope of getting more information from his other brother.

Morgan James was working in the inner office and Edgar found him white-faced, endeavouring to answer an unseen caller on the other end of the newly installed telephone.

'Edgar, why are you here? Has Dadda come yet? They've called for him, you know. They think the women will need him.' At that moment the telephone rang again.

'Seven calls I've taken in the last half hour. That's as many calls as I logged all last week. The *Western Mail* wants an interview with Meredith, and the *Merthyr Express* is on the way up. I've never spoken to the newspapers. Could you do that?'

'Tell them they can have a statement at the end of the day. Don't let them get in anyone's way and insist they wait for me.'

The phone jangled shrilly and Morgan James answered the new caller. Edgar turned and left him to his unhappy task.

The first of the rescue teams had now gone down. The winding gear was still. Edgar walked through the eerie quiet of the colliery yard towards the gate. He passed Sergeant Williams who was talking quietly with the farrier outside the blacksmith's shop.

'Grim day.' he said, as he caught Edgar's eye.

Edgar nodded, suddenly overwhelmed with feelings of helplessness. As they spoke standing in the sunshine, below them men were trapped, hurt, dying. The customary pleasantries between them were irrelevant. Inside the blacksmith's shop an apprentice lad was busy sweeping the floor and sprinkling it with water to lay the dust. The shelves and cupboards had been hastily tidied, and trestles were standing ready to receive the dead and injured. Edgar noticed Dr Davies in earnest conversation with the second rescue team, all equipped and ready to go down. The first aid men stood at the top of the shaft, hoping they would be needed by their fellow miners as they were brought to the surface. The tradition in the pit was that if it were humanly possible, no miner should have to call the mine his grave. All the victims would be brought up and then the dead would be returned to their families for burial.

The rescue teams had a dreadful task. Each rescue shift lasted at least eight hours and before the men below saw daylight again they would have to make the area in which they were working safe for the next team. Their faces were grim as they listened carefully to their instructions. Their own safety, as well as that of the other men in the shift, depended on each other, but their overriding responsibility was to their colleagues, both injured and dead.

Realising there was little he could do for the moment, Edgar turned towards home. There had to be a better way than this. The village lived for coal, it shouldn't have to die for it. Families would be ruined and there would be another exodus. Grief and anger in equal measure rose up in him and the desperate desire to improve the miners' lot.

As he walked past the ever growing groups of women, Edgar saw his father had arrived and was moving slowly from one to another with words of comfort and reassurance. He hurried over, and father and son exchanged a quiet greeting.

'I'm going up to the house now, Dadda. I think it's going to be a long day.'

'See if your mother needs you. I told her to let the girl go home. She's got a brother and father working the morning shift, so it was not right to keep her from her family. They've closed the school in case more space is needed, so I went to fetch Gladys and Arthur and then came on here. I've closed the post office for now. At times like this people need comfort more than they need stamps.'

'I don't think I can do much here at the moment, so I'll tell Mam I've seen you and the boys. I'll be back down later to help with the paperwork that will need to be done, and any other arrangements that have to be made.'

At home Edgar was greeted by an excited Gladys and Arthur with the news that there was to be no school that afternoon. His mother quietened them both, before asking her eldest son, 'You have been over the pit, have you, on your way up? Did you see your father?'

'Yes, Mam, I did, and I saw the boys, too. Morgan has the awful job of answering the telephone and Will's busy sorting stretchers and shrouds. I don't know which is worse. They'll be there for ages. You'd better keep their dinners till later, but you can give me mine and I'll go back over. The news will have reached Porth by now so they'll not expect me back. I don't think the centre will have need of my views on the causes of the Napoleonic Wars this afternoon.'

'Just eat your dinner and then go back and tell your father to come home. Will and Morgan James can do without food, but your father is different. I'm just setting more dough to rise. Food will be needed for the rescue teams. '

'I'll tell him but I doubt he will leave the yard until the first of the rescue teams come up and there is some news for those poor women.'

'Then there will be need of food for the women, too,' reasoned Margaret Ann and she called Gladys into the kitchen from the step where she was entertaining Arthur with a story.

'Off you two go and get the vestry keys from the chapel caretaker and bring them back here quick. When Gladys gets back, Edgar, you can get the urns and big teapots used for the Sunday School teas. They'll be in the cupboard at the back of the vestry. You can take them over to the pit when you've finished your dinner. The caretaker can go with you to help carry.'

Gladys and Arthur returned as fast as their plump little legs could carry them, with the keys rattling in Gladys' hand. 'Can I go with Edgar?'

'No, you and Arthur get the big basket and come into the pantry with me.'

Years of shopkeeping had resulted in Margaret Ann having a compulsion to keep large stocks of dry goods such as tea, sugar and flour in her store-room. After she and the children had filled the basket with tea and sugar, the new loaves of bread and some cheese, she told them to stay and play quietly indoors. Edgar had already left, but was slowed down by the elderly chapel caretaker. So Margaret Ann soon caught up with her son. Having no wish to walk through the waiting women at the pithead gate, she issued instructions to Edgar as to whom he should give the urns and provisions. Knowing his mother well, he made no objection to being treated like a child.

'Make sure they all get a bite to eat and a hot drink. Get one of those lads from the pithead baths to set up a refreshment station and keep the urns filled. I'll send more bread down as soon as it's done.'

As Margaret Ann turned for home, she noticed movement lower down the hill on the road leading to the pit.

Already, she wondered. Perhaps it would just be a few injuries after all. That's why they'd been so quick. Realising it was a small stretcher party leaving the yard, she quickened her pace, her one thought being to reach Min-yr-Afon before the sad little procession overtook her. She had only made the doorstep where Gladys was standing, when the stretcher borne by two men and followed by several women, came round the corner.

'That's Mrs Dando, Mam,' said Gladys. 'Mary Dando is in our Arthur's class, she's got a new baby sister. Why are they all crying?'

'Hush girl, go on in, there has been an accident down the pit.' Her mother pushed Gladys into the hall and shut the door behind her. She then turned to face the group. At least, she thought, this one can't be dead as the stretcher was covered by a workmen's coat, not the dreaded brattice cloth.

'Alive, is he?' she whispered to the men.

'Aye, God help him,' one of them answered. When she saw the uncovered face, Margaret Ann echoed the prayer for God's help. It was burned beyond all recognition. Mrs Dando lifted her tear-stained face to Margaret Ann, before breaking down in great shuddering sobs. One of the women walking with the stretcher looked up helplessly, before placing a supportive arm around the weeping woman. The little group continued its slow miserable trudge up the road.

An enormous feeling of gratitude that her family was spared such horror, welled up in Margaret Ann and with a sigh of relief she closed the front door and went through to the kitchen. Gladys and Arthur were fidgeting to go out to play. An afternoon without school was not to be wasted indoors, but their mother told them firmly there was to be no playing out that day because there had been a serious explosion in the pit, which had hurt many men. Gladys promptly wanted to know if Will had been hurt.

'No, of course not, girl. He and Morgan James do not work down the pit.' It's the men who work underground who are hurt. We all have to do our bit to help. You can help me start some more loaves to rise and then we'll need extra blankets and sheets before the day is done. You can both come with me to sort something out.'

CHAPTER 17
THE AFTERMATH

By four o'clock Jane and Maggie had arrived home from school. They brought with them the news that all the way up from Porth to the top of the valley, the streets were full of people making their way to the stricken pit. The yard was crammed with women, babies in their arms, and small children clutching at their skirts.

'Come now, girls, get on and eat your dinners. Your father is still over there, and there is no knowing when he will be back. Will and Morgan James are rushed off their feet and Edgar's gone down to help. We must re-open the counter and you two will have to give a hand with the post office. There will be telegrams to send and more to receive before long.'

Even as Margaret Ann spoke, the tap, tap of the receiving machine could be heard and as soon as their meal was finished, Jane went off into the post office to mind the telegraph machine, glad to be able to do something to help, while Maggie grabbed an apron to clear the table before taking up her place behind the counter. It was not long before Amy arrived home from her school. As she ate her meal she told her mother how the news had reached the Rhondda Fawr.

'The train came up just before dinner and the news was soon out. As soon as the afternoon shifts come up Mam, they'll be over to help. No-one will rest until everything that can be done is done. There won't be any shifts worked in the other pits until the men from the National are out.'

Margaret Ann listened with half an ear. She was anxious about

138

Morgan. In spite of her instructions to Edgar to send his father home, there was still no sign of him. She knew that he would have had nothing to eat since breakfast, so as soon as Amy finished her meal her mother dispatched her to find her father and bring him home. Like her mother, Amy hoped fervently that she would be able to slip into the yard unseen by the women holding vigil at the gate, but she was unlucky. Recognising the minister's daughter, the silent women moved back to let her through the gate where Sergeant Williams was on duty. Amy failed to locate her father, but she found Edgar leaning against the wall outside the blacksmith's shop which, as the rescue teams began to send up the dead, was fulfilling the function of a temporary mortuary.

Edgar had indeed found a useful job to do. A reliable record of the names of the victims, the position in which the bodies were found and the injuries they had sustained had to be prepared for the inquiry into the disaster. Edgar took the details from each of the rescue teams as they came up with the dead and entered them meticulously on the plan Will had given him of the underground workings.

He looked up when he saw his sister. 'What are you doing here?' Edgar asked. 'This is no place for you.'

'Nonsense,' replied Amy robustly. 'Mam sent me to get Dadda, but I can't find him.'

'He's not here. He has gone up to Glenside to tell Mrs Meredith and Annie Mary that they have found his body.'

'Oh no!' gasped Amy. 'Are you sure it's Mr Meredith? What was he doing down the mine? He doesn't have to go down there. He works in the office.'

'No mistaking him. No other man of his size in the pit. They have brought up four already. Dando was the only one alive and he is badly burned.'

'Is it very bad? The women say that everyone in No. 2 pit is still down there.'

'There is always hope, Amy. No-one is giving up yet. You go off home and give Mam the message about Mr Meredith, and tell her not to expect the boys for some time.'

Edgar turned to re-enter the blacksmith's shop. Amy called him back. 'Can I get through the back way into Bailey Street? I cannot face going back through those weeping women.'

'You will not escape the tears whichever way you go, but please yourself. Just be grateful you've got nothing to weep for.'

Feeling a little ashamed, Amy drew a deep breath and straightened her dress to run the gauntlet of the anxious women. She need not have worried. As she approached the gate one of the clerks came out of the offices with a sheet of paper which he attached to the board. Low moans could be heard, as the women pushed forward to read the list of names. While they scanned the list, oblivious to everything but the name for which they were searching, Amy slipped through and ran home as fast as she could. When she reached the house the door flew open, Margaret Ann grabbed her by the arm and hurried her through to the kitchen.

'Where's your father? What's Will doing? Is Edgar still down there? Is it No 2 pit that's had it? Do they know yet how many are down there?'

Amy had never seen her mother so agitated. Still gasping for breath she said, 'All the morning shift are down there according to Edgar, about a hundred and fifty men and the boys too. And Mam, Mr Meredith was down there too, though I don't know why.'

'That means,' said Margaret Ann, talking more to herself than her daughters, 'every family in Cwtch will be in mourning. It won't matter whether it's Glenside or a house in Bailey Street, there'll be the same sorrow behind the front doors tonight.'

Gladys looked up from her book. 'Whatever do you mean, Mam?'

'A house in mourning suffers as its neighbour, big or small. When it's struck with a disaster like this, it's the same sorrow, and it'll be very hard for Mrs Meredith.'

That night it poured with rain, the warm spell of weather over. A cold wind blew up the valley but the women remained, keeping a vigil in little groups, huddled under shawls and attempting to hide from the rain under the eaves of the colliery buildings. Unable to bear the sight of so much misery, Edgar came out from the task of identifying and recording the victims.

'Go home,' he begged the women. 'Go home, where at least you will be warm and dry. There is nothing to be gained now by waiting. You will need all your strength tomorrow to face what is to come. I will be here with your men if they are brought up during the night and I will see that you are informed as soon as possible.'

The women turned away, too numb with grief and exhaustion to disagree, and trudged back to their homes to wait for news.

For three days and nights, stopping only for brief rests, he recorded the findings as the medical teams identified and examined each of the bodies before each was taken to the blacksmith's shop to be shrouded and returned to his family.

The next three days saw a strangely quiet village trying to come to terms with the scale of the disaster. Every hour more bodies were brought to the surface and more families lost hope of a miracle. Fourteen boys less than fourteen years old had lost their lives and half of the one hundred and nineteen victims were under twenty. Even a message from the King failed to raise spirits. The telegraphed message received from the Prince and Princess of Wales gave a little more comfort as it spoke of the deep sorrow they felt when they were informed of 'the heartrending details of the terrible colliery accident.'

The family saw little of Morgan and his three sons, and Margaret Ann kept the other children busy, sending them about the village and beyond, to offer assistance. As one of the few local families not to have suffered directly, she felt compelled to give all possible help wherever she could. The sheets and blankets Margaret Ann and the children had put ready saw service among the bereaved, and many funeral teas were provided with bread and cakes baked in Min-yr-Afon. In accordance with his Christian ministry, Morgan sought to bring comfort to those who mourned. Edgar, his work on identifying and recording done, worked continuously arranging funerals and advising the many widows who feared themselves destitute. Memories of the suffering caused to the miners' families by the disaster haunted Edgar, and sowed the seeds of a determination to improve the lives of the mining communities in the future. The lack of any financial safety net for the families of the miners threw many into ruin and Edgar never forgot the wider impact of such a disaster.

Margaret Ann and Jane kept the post office working during Morgan's many absences. Telegrams of sympathy from 'the great and the good' including the prime minister and the Archbishop of Canterbury continued to pour in, and the ring of the telegraph boys' bicycle bells could be heard round the village. Telegrams from distant families in the coalfields of Pennsylvania added to the flood. Letters of condolence increased the usual volume of post, and post offices further down the valley sent their postmen to help deliver the mail as fast as they could.

A few days later Agnes returned from college in Exeter at the end of the summer term. Her mother insisted she call at Glenside to offer sympathy to her friend Annie Mary and Mrs Meredith. Agnes hated any demonstrations of emotion, and at first refused, but Margaret Ann was adamant. Her father, who was in the kitchen between his visits to the bereaved families, overheard the conversation between his daughters as Agnes tried to persuade her sister Amy to share the distressing duty of visiting her friend. He listened for a few minutes before saying to Agnes, 'Nearly a hundred families in this valley alone have cause to be more distressed than you, my girl. However difficult you might find such a visit, you have not lost your father. Meredith's family has more to bear than most and they are going to need all the help and sympathy we can offer over the next few months.'

'What's so special about them?' enquired Amy, detecting a hidden message in her father's voice. 'Will's friend Jimmy Davies has lost two brothers and his uncle.'

'Just leave that for now, Amy. We've got the start of the funerals tomorrow and that will be enough for everyone to cope with. Just get up to Glenside, the pair of you, and remember how lucky you are. You can tell Mrs Meredith that I'll be at the house for a quarter to one to take the service, before the procession leaves for the cemetery.'

The next day was cloudy and grey and Edgar was already break-
fasted when William joined him in the kitchen. Piles of papers were
spread over the table.

'Heavens above, you aren't marking essays on today of all days, are
you?' enquired William, as he pushed some of the papers aside to
make room for a plate.

'Don't be daft, Will. This is the funeral schedule I've drawn up.
We've over fifty men to bury today and tomorrow, and the next few
days will be the same. I've worked out a plan for every one. Every
one of those men is entitled to dignity and respect. Just because
there are so many doesn't mean each one isn't special. The first one
will rise at ten o'clock and then the processions will begin. The
bands are gathering now in the Workmen's Hall, and the ministers
will be collecting in the vestry at Calfaria.'

'Gracious me, what a job,' muttered William with admiration.
'Mind you don't mix up the clergy, now. Imagine the fuss if one of
the men is buried by the wrong minister! You'd never hear the end
of it.'

'Go on, William. This isn't anything to joke about. Get the pony
and trap sorted, we're going to need it for later. Mrs Davies from
Bailey Street has three coffins to bury and I've promised her they
will be kept together on the journey down. Her sons were only
little lads and their father wasn't much bigger, so it won't be too
much for the pony. She'll need to be brought back home in the trap
too, as I doubt she'll be up to much, after this morning. See if Jim
Lie will act as coachman.'

Suitably chastened, William went out to the shed to do his brother's bidding, and transform the family's trap into an impromptu
hearse.

Soon most of the family from Min-yr-Afon were gathered at
Wattstown Bridge to witness the start of the long funeral procession.
Morgan James, William and Edgar, clad in their Sunday suits and
wearing black ties and armbands, were to form part of the proces-

sion with other National Colliery officials. Morgan Humphrey was joined at the head of the cortege by the other ministers and clergy who were to perform the funeral rites at the gravesides. The colliery bands began to play and the sounds of *Cwm Rhondda* and *Dafydd y Garreg Wen* floated down the valley. More hearses and biers joined the long line of mourners and eventually the procession moved slowly off stopping only to allow yet another makeshift hearse to join the procession. Every colliery had sent its brass band to support the black-coated miners who walked four abreast in slow step. They were joined by the exhausted men from the rescue teams. All wore black armbands signifying their links to the men they had struggled to bring up from the hell below the ground. Representatives from the other mines in the neighbourhood marched with heads bowed. Further down the valley they were joined by the waggonettes and black-draped farm carts which had been pressed into service to carry the bodies of so many miners. Little coffins for the boys who had perished, were carried on the shoulders of men whose faces showed their terrible grief.

As the procession crossed the bridge it extended for over a mile, and Arthur, who could see the clock on the Workmen's Institute, calculated it had taken twenty-eight minutes to go by. As more people joined, it eventually stretched to more than four miles. Many of the widows huddled on the chapel doorsteps and more women and children stood in forlorn groups along the route, sobbing openly as the bodies of their friends and relatives passed by. The haunting sounds of the massed colliery bands playing familiar hymns and tunes added to the awesome atmosphere. Every few minutes voices would spontaneously join together singing the well-known words, as one after another, the coffins made their final journeys to the valley cemeteries. The scenes remained seared in the memories of the watchers for the rest of their lives. In the space of seven days the village had been changed forever.

Funeral followed funeral. Day after day the long march of mourners following the hearses wound down the valley to the cemeteries on the hillsides. Morgan left home early every morning to support the grief-stricken families who asked for his comforting presence as each funeral rose from the cottages around the pithead. For the miners who had come to find work from places outside the valley, funeral trains were organised to carry the bodies home. This was William's task, and he supervised the transfer of every victim from the colliery hearse into the black-draped guard's vans. Other mourners stood with him, bareheaded on the platform at Ynyshir station as yet another coffin started its journey back to the mountains of Meirionydd and Caernarvon, for the dead to rest amongst their own people.

William was deeply affected by the tragedy. Many of those who died in the fateful No. 2 pit had been his childhood companions who had followed him in many mischievous acts, and the girls he had teased were among the weeping women at the pithead. In his opinion the explosion should never have occurred and he never forgave the impatience of the manager, who had ordered the shot firing procedure when men were still underground. This had been William's view from the first morning of the disaster when news of the catastrophe emerged from underground. He was not the only person in the valley who believed that Meredith's actions had caused the tragedy. It was why his father had felt that Annie Mary's family would suffer even more than the other bereaved families. He was right. Without naming names, the verdict from the Coroner's Court, reported in the *Rhondda Leader* of 5th August 1905, came to the same conclusion:

'The explosion of gas was caused by shot firing in the barrier of coal at the cross heading between the sinking pit and the upcast pit. The jury recommended that shot firing should be absolutely prohibited except between shifts and only shotmen should be in the pit at the time.'

All through the school holidays, Edgar had listened to the widows as they shared their desperation about their circumstances. Most of the families lived in houses owned by the colliery and he was only too aware of the hardship which followed the death of the breadwinners. These families had no other home or means of support and he resolved to increase his political activity to improve the circumstances of the mining communities.

Margaret Ann marvelled at the strength of the human spirit as she watched women who had lost fathers, husbands, brothers and sons, drag themselves up from the depths of desolation to face the responsibility of caring for their remaining children. Even in the grimmest of circumstances these women stretched out a helping hand to each other. The admiration she felt for them never left her. She felt proud to be part of the community which had grown up around the colliery she had first seen from the birch wood on that visit to Cwtch all those years ago.

CHAPTER 18
GONE MISSING

On a June Sunday evening after chapel a year later, the family were sitting in the parlour. Margaret Ann and her family were complete again now that Agnes had returned from college in Exeter to teach at a school in the other valley. As usual, the main topic for discussion was who had or had not been seen in chapel.

'Cissie Thomas was there, flaunting pearl earrings, I noticed, and she had those new button boots on,' said Agnes. 'I heard her telling Annie Mary she bought them in New York. She's done something to her hair too. I wouldn't mind doing mine like that, I think it would suit me. It's amazing what a year in America has done for her, and she made such a fuss when her parents went over.'

Agnes was far more aware of current trends since she had returned from the world outside the valley. Although her vow never to wear stays held firm, as the proud possessor of a monthly salary, she was able to indulge her liking for elegant footwear and the prospect of a similar pair of boots was enticing.

'You leave your hair alone,' her mother said tartly. 'It's perfectly alright as it is and you won't want those children in that class of yours to be taking more notice of your hair than what you are saying. Anyway, those cousins of your father's have always had more money than sense, and I don't think living in America has changed them. They seem to think it's proper, living a life of luxury.'

Margaret Ann had been forced to moderate her criticisms of her sisters-in-law in deference to Morgan's feelings but now, alone with her children she could give her feelings full rein. The families in the valley were still struggling to come to terms with the loss of life, poverty and even homelessness that the previous year's pit disaster had caused, and she was sensitive to the ongoing misery. Many of them had been forced to leave Wattstown to find homes with families more fortunate than they and for some it was to America they went, borrowing their passage money to join relatives already settled there. Ill health added to their problems, and tuberculosis and measles were again rearing their ugly heads.

'Cissie's had to come over from Scranton, hasn't she?' said Jane, 'I expect she's here to help her sister pack. They've lost the house even though the National let them stay in it till now. Her brother's had to come back as well, to see to the paperwork. Florrie Thomas would find it very difficult to fill in all those forms you need to go to America.'

'Is it true they're all going?' enquired Maggie.

'Well, there's nothing for them here since the disaster and there's three nieces and the baby to be provided for.' her mother replied. 'Tom's helping deliver for Rhys the Milk, but you'll not feed a family on that money even though his mother's a good manager. The sooner they're gone the better and then there'll be more room for the rest of them in the other house.' As ever, Margaret Ann knew all the details of the family's distant relatives and their deteriorating circumstances. Hand-me-downs from Gladys and Arthur augmented many children's wardrobes in the valley, and Amy and Agnes kept shoe cupboards in their classrooms to keep their pupils shod. Boxes of provisions from their mother's well-filled store-cupboard were regularly left in the cottages down the valley and the detailed lives of the recipients of Min-yr-Afon's generosity were well known to Margaret Ann.

Maggie and her sisters continued to mull over the extended family's problems as they added another woolen square to the brightly coloured pile destined to keep another new village baby warm. Nothing went to waste in Margaret Ann's household and even scraps of wool could be knitted or crocheted into winter blankets.

Maggie carried on the roll call of the relatives. 'Minnie is looking peaky again. She was asleep in the sermon I noticed. With her chest, crossing the Atlantic will be hard for her. She's another one who's been forced to go, leaving her husband in the graveyard.'

Jane, who was more soft-hearted than her sisters, was sorry for the distant cousins. 'I hope she gets there in time. Her next baby is due in September she told me. It'll be difficult enough for her coping with the baby she's got already because that one's not much more than a year old. Neither of Minnie's children will have any memories of their father.'

'Cissie Thomas is going to have her hands full with getting the lot of them over the Atlantic, that's for certain. She'll have to be prepared for a bit of hard work when she gets them back to America. She might have to take out her pearl earrings!' Amy's rather acid remarks were ignored, but her sharp eyes missed little and her knowledge of the families in Cwtch was second only to Margaret Ann herself.

'Lisa Jenkins was not there, I noticed, Mam,' said Gladys, who was fed up with doing nothing but knitting, and deciding it was time she joined in the adult conversation.

'That is right, she was not. It's not often Lisa misses a Sunday night. I wonder what's going on?'

'She was not there this morning either.' volunteered Maggie. 'Looking after that lazy Tom no doubt. He's a full time job, that one. She didn't know that when she took him on as a husband for better or worse, but she's certainly having a fair share of worse. It's as well Dai is a good son.'

'Is Dai a fireman down at the National now, Will?' Morgan looked up from his book, to make an unaccustomed contribution to the family chatter. 'Wasn't he in school with you?'

'Aye, and a bright lad he was, too. Hoped to go on to Porth like our Edgar, but his parents didn't have the money so it was down to the pit for him. Mind you, it's as well he's around for his mother, seeing as his father spends more time in the Butchers Arms than he does at home. Though to be fair, Tom Jenkins is a good workman when he sobers up enough to go on shift. The trouble with him is, he's given Lisa more than one black eye when she's crossed him and I know Dai has had to intervene several times to keep his mother out of harm's way.'

'I'm sorry for Lisa, it's hard for her to keep her self-respect when Tom carries on like that,' said Margaret Ann. She was well aware of the shame felt by the wives of the men who couldn't keep away from the dreaded drink. 'Go up there after supper, Will, could you, to see everything is all right? It's number 28.' Margaret Ann had never allowed herself to make friends with the women of the village, always preferring to hold herself aloof from the day-to-day existence of her customers, but Lisa Jenkins was one of the few customers she had been genuinely pleased to see in her shop. If anyone remarked on her friendless state shehad always pointed quickly to the time-consuming activities of her shopkeeping duties, to say nothing of a house to run and nine children.

Later in the evening William walked up to Hillside Terrace. He stopped for a few minutes to look at the building that was going up on the corner by Glenside. It was to be the new Workmen's Institute, a project in which Edgar was heavily involved and to which he devoted much of his spare time. Edgar was convinced that adult education was vital to improve the lot of the families in the Rhondda and when it was completed, the Institute would provide a hall with a stage and balcony, a billiards room to rival that of the old Workmen's Hall, and most importantly, a reading room. The luxury of electric light would enable the miners and others to read and study when they had finished their shifts and Edgar and the other trustees hoped it would prove a rival attraction to the two large public houses in the village. He already had drawn up a list of potential speakers to provide interesting and informative lectures when the building was complete in the autumn.

William wondered whether Tom Jenkins would find it better for his wallet to go to the Hall rather than the Butchers Arms. It was much nearer his house even though it wouldn't have any beer. Edgar and his colleagues had worked hard to get the Institute up and running. He hoped Tom realised he and his drinking pals were very fortunate to have it. Will was so engrossed in his thoughts, he walked straight past number 28, and had to turn back. He knocked at the shiny front door of the terraced house. Lisa's son Dai, a friend for whom Will had a great affection, answered it. Noticing the work clothes Will said, 'Ready for work, I see.'

'Big firemen's shift always on a Sunday night, most important one of the week, you know. What can I do for you? Got a problem in the stores?'

'No, no.' Will shuffled his feet wondering how to broach the subject on his mind. After a pause to collect his thoughts, he remarked in as casual a tone as he could muster, 'The people at home noticed your mother was not in chapel. No trouble is there, Dai?'

His friend answered reluctantly. 'No more than usual. Dad was still in the Butchers' Arms when I went to work last night. I told Mam to go to bed out of his way, in case he let fly, but she hung about waiting till he came in. She was fussing about her best boots which she couldn't find, and when she asked him if he'd seen them she got another black eye for her pains.'

'I thought he was trying to dry himself out a bit. He doesn't often hit her, does he?'

'No, fair play, he does not, at least not regularly, but I think she went on and on about her boots. Then in the end he had to tell her he had taken them down to Mr Cohen's to pawn for beer money and there was no way of getting them back in time for chapel on Sunday.'

'She got hit because his conscience troubled him no doubt,' said William.

'You are right, but Mam is a lot more upset about the boots than the black eye. She would have gone to chapel with the black eye and made up some old tale, but she wouldn't go in her old boots. She'd be too ashamed.'

'There must be something wrong with chapel folk if they can make your Mam ashamed of her boots.'

'I don't think the chapel folk would hold it against Mam about her old boots. It's her own pride thinking everyone would know the new ones were in pawn. Anyway, Will, enough! I must go, or I'll be late to clock in.'

'I'll walk down with you then, if you are ready. And I'll tell them at home that Lisa did not feel up to chapel today.'

As he got ready for bed that night Will recalled the conversation with Dai. He was well aware that violence lurked not far below the surface in many homes in the valley, often brought about by the combination of poverty and drink. To see the effect so close to home hurt Will deeply. He resolved to take practical steps to help.

The next day in the noon break William walked down to Porth to visit Mr Cohen's shop. The little pawnbroker looked up as the bell rang and eyed William with some suspicion. There could be no reason he could think of for a family member of 'Mrs Jones the Post Office' to require the services of a pawnbroker, though he well remembered his father's oft repeated account of the incident with Mrs Jones and the Ystrad chapel's IOUs.

'Mrs Jenkins' new boots, please.'

Mr Cohen stared at William in amazement. 'Mrs Jenkins' boots? Why? What on earth have you got to do with Mrs Jenkins' boots?'

'Because she needs them, of course, straight away.'

The astonished pawnbroker disappeared behind the curtain at the back of the shop and reappeared a few moments later with the new boots. William held out his hand for the footwear.

'Not without the ticket, Mr Jones, if you please. I need the money for the boots and I need the ticket. I can't hand them over without the pledge ticket.'

'I've no ticket,' snapped William, irritated by the time the transaction was taking. 'You well know it wasn't I came to hand them in for pawning. What will it cost to redeem them?' Mr Cohen pointed to the price tag on the boots.

William fished in his pocket for his wallet. 'Here's your five shillings and sixpence. Now hurry up, please. Mrs Jenkins needs those boots and I need to be back to work for one o'clock.'

Mr Cohen was on the point of refusing when he caught William's expression. Still muttering about the non-existent ticket he handed over the boots with an ill grace. Pushing a chit across the counter, he said, 'Sign here.'

With a flourish William scribbled his name and marched towards the door, clutching the boots to his chest. 'Don't come in here again without a pledge ticket,' Mr Cohen shouted to William's retreating back.

'I hope never to have to come in here again, ever,' William retorted as the door swung to behind him. He set off back up the hill and smiled to himself. 'Touch and go there for a minute. I forgot all about needing the ticket. Still, she shall have her boots but we'll have to come up with a plan to stop Tom getting his hands on them again.'

After work that evening William took the boots up to Hillside. Lisa Jenkins opened the door. Will thrust the boots towards their owner. 'Here are your boots, Mrs Jenkins. If I were you I'd keep them where they can't be found in the future. Why don't you take them across to Mrs Basso and ask her to keep them for you, then you'll always have them to wear and there'll be no excuse for not going to chapel! Mrs Basso will not ask for reasons and she will keep her thoughts to herself.'

William gave her a cheery grin as Lisa hugged her boots and tried unsuccessfully to thank him, but he was gone, back to his end-of-the-day duties in his mother's house.

∽ ∽ ∽

The next morning as William walked down towards the colliery, he heard the dreaded sound of the wailing siren. Oh no, please God, he thought, not again.

Running all the way, he arrived breathless at his desk in the stores to find the rescue team already assembled and the manager taking a report from the shift foreman.

'There's been a fall along No. 2 level and we are waiting for the team to go down. One man's missing but all the rest are up. The safety team shouldn't have a difficult time, but we'll get nothing done today.'

The unreal silence, which settled over the pithead whenever an accident occurred, continued all day. Mine officials and safety teams worked methodically and eventually the body was safely brought to the surface, examined by the doctor and respectfully coffined. It was William's sad task to inform the family and to complete the arrangements to return the body for burial. He drafted a brief telegram to the unsuspecting family adding 'letter follows', and sent his young clerk off to Min-yr-Afon to dispatch it.

'Making the arrangements will take a while,' he said to his father that evening. 'His family is from Pwllheli and there's no direct train. I've written a letter, Dadda, giving them the details of the accident and telling them what a good worker he was. I'd be glad if you'd cast your eye over it.'

His father read the sad missive and handed it back to his son. 'It's well written and in a good hand, Will. The news is terrible for that poor family but you've done the best you could and at least they'll get him back. It's not every mine widow can have her husband to bury.'

William folded the letter carefully into its envelope and put it on the dresser, before turning his attention to the railway timetables borrowed from the office.

A day later, the customary procession drew up at the pithead to escort the miner's body to the station for its final journey. The hearse carried the body down the valley where the coffin was reverently lifted into the blacked out guard's van. William handed the necessary documents to the train guard. The miners who had acted as pallbearers stood with bowed heads as the train drew out from the station, and then retraced their steps to the colliery office. William went straight back to his office to notify the station master at Pwllheli that the deceased had begun the journey home and to check that the family receiving the body would be met by the undertakers at the station the next day.

He was therefore surprised to be interrupted on Wednesday morning by the junior store clerk with an urgent request to telephone Pwllheli station, as there was a bit of a problem. Never one to hesitate, William immediately gave the Pwllheli station number to the operator and was put through.

'National Colliery here,' he said to the stationmaster. 'I hope the undertakers have turned up.'

'They have,' came the reply, 'but there's nothing to collect.'

'What do you mean? The coffin was booked through from here yesterday via Cardiff to Pwllheli and due in at eleven thirty.'

'Well it's not here, and it's not as if he could have got off at the wrong station is it?' snapped the embarrassed stationmaster. 'Very mortifying it is, with the hearse drawn up outside and the undertakers here and I've nothing to give them. What am I going to tell the family?'

v cleared his throat, apologised to the irate official and promised to do everything he could to find the missing coffin. His work for the Taff Railway Company proved useful, for it meant he knew his way around the railway system. Three hours and many telephone calls later, the mystery was solved. A broken down train had temporarily blocked the line at Harlech and passengers had been asked to get off and change to another train. By the time the Harlech stationmaster realised that one passenger was unable to get off, the Pwllheli train had left the station. Horrified at the idea that the deceased miner should be shunted into a siding overnight, the deputy stationmaster at Harlech had ordered the body to be taken off the train to rest overnight in his office and resume its journey the next day. He had not thought it necessary to inform either Will or Pwllheli of the change in the travel arrangements. William spent several minutes explaining what had happened to the Pwllheli stationmaster. He promised to write personally to the bereaved family and to apologise on behalf of the National Colliery for their added distress. His next phone call was to the station at Harlech. William never revealed the details of his conversation with the deputy stationmaster but his store clerk always swore that the telephone receiver remained hot for several hours.

CHAPTER 19
NEW HORIZONS

Much to her husband's surprise, Margaret Ann soon settled into her new home and a different way of life at Min-yr-Afon. He had thought she would have found retirement from shopkeeping much more difficult. The post office continued to provide a certain income and as all village news filtered through it, she remained at the centre of village life. The new doctor was comfortably installed in the old house and the converted shop did indeed make an excellent surgery. Not that the old shop was forgotten and should anybody mention the Co-operative Society, Margaret Ann would tell them at considerable length how it had driven her out of business.

The family's new house was not the only change Margaret Ann had to face. Tramcars now ran up and down the valley's length. They were electrically driven and rattled on metal rails along the centre of the road, which meant they were extremely noisy. Their hard wooden seats did not make for passenger comfort either, but at least people no longer had to rely solely on 'shanks's pony' or the trains for transport, and the younger members of the family were happy be spared the long walk to Porth for school or the pupil teacher centre. The younger members of the family loved them as it meant that days out to Cardiff or Newport became a real possibility, but for their mother they were a dangerous and noisy invention which would certainly mean that the young would stray too far from the nest, and eventually lose the use of their legs. Morgan thought that his wife was in danger of forgetting that their children would eventually need a wider world than the four walls of Min-yr-Afon and the tightly knit village in which they had all grown up. Sooner or later he realised a break would be made in the close circle his wife had created and he feared for the impact it would have. He was convinced the first rift would come when Edgar took his first steps onto the national political stage.

Village life might change, but there was no change in the firm hand Margaret Ann still kept on all her children from Edgar, now approaching thirty years of age, to Arthur the spoiled baby, who was only nine. She continually instilled into all nine of her brood, the need to be responsible for their own lives even though she had not relinquished her hold on them! Her 'do as you would be done by' philosophy was as strong as ever, and the need for respectability in all things was paramount.

Although she allowed and certainly enjoyed gossip, it was strictly controlled, mainly because she recognised her husband's distaste for it. The family too, she insisted, must always present a united face to the world at large. Disagreements and complaints were only to be aired within the family, never outside it. There was a clear duty on each family member to be prepared to help each other and the family purse was there to benefit all. Attendance at one Sunday service at least in Calfaria was compulsory. In spite of her own reservations about the ostentatiously devout, Margaret Ann considered everyone benefited from being reminded each week of the duty they owed to the Almighty. Matters of faith she considered better left to those experts who preached about it. For herself and her family, duty was sufficient.

Outside the home her offspring continued to spread their wings and extend their influence. Edgar was rapidly making a name for himself in the Rhondda as a tireless worker in the cause of further education, and as a noted speaker for the National Union of Teachers. In those days the annual teachers' conference was attended by a thousand representatives and was a highly organised and spectacular event, well reported by local and national press. Customers in the post office bombarded Margaret Ann and Morgan with quotes from the local papers and questions about Edgar's speech at the Scarborough conference. His presentation had brought the audience to their feet and the applause continued long after he had sat down.

'There's proud you must be,' remarked Mrs Dando as she waited for her parcel to be weighed. 'He sounds just like his father in the pulpit, I've heard.'

'Marked out he was, for greatness,' added Mrs Jenkins, 'Goodness knows what we'd have done without him in the disaster.'

His mother gave a noncommittal grunt, and refused to be drawn into a discussion about her eldest son. Her pride, like the coal beneath her feet, was buried well below the surface, only to be dug out for a privileged few.

Increasingly Edgar travelled to London and other outlandish towns and cities, which his mother found deeply unsettling. She hated not knowing where he was and what he was doing, and more importantly whom he was with. She was determined her children were not yet to be entangled with strangers of whom she knew nothing. She was well aware that Morgan had married her before he was thirty, and when she was only twenty-two, but she had no intention of allowing her children to throw themselves into the arms of the first person who came along. She need not have worried about Edgar. His single-minded determination to forge a career left no time for entanglements. The first break in the family circle was not made by her eldest son.

Throughout their childhood, Amy and Agnes had remained close friends with Annie Mary Meredith, who had moved further down the valley when she married. The two sisters made regular trips at weekends to meet their friend and exchange the sort of gossip of which their mother would not approve. Using the few hours of freedom allowed on Saturdays by their mother, the girls would take the opportunity to admire the stylish dress shop windows in Pontypridd and debate the relative virtues of laced or buttoned boots. Later, over a cup of tea and a Welsh cake, they would call on Annie Mary to discuss the comings and goings of various friends. They were astonished when Annie Mary said she had heard that

William had been seen in Ynyshir talking with Ann Thomas, a dress-maker whose parents ran a small furniture business. Ann's mother also served as a trusted midwife to the Wattstown families and had indeed delivered several of Margaret Ann's babies. The two sisters were amazed at the news, as none of it had filtered through to them. The evidence of the first serious romantic involvement of one of their brothers created waves of excitement.

'How long do you think this has been going on then? Do you remember when she came to the house to make over Mam's dress for you to go to college? Do you think that was the start of it?' Agnes was full of questions as the tram rattled back up the valley.

'Now I think of it, for weeks now Will has been very keen to get his chores finished quickly and then disappear. He had no time to put up those hooks we wanted on our bedroom door, and he said he had stores to check last Saturday down the National when Mam wanted the windows cleaned. She made Morgan James do it and he was not best pleased. Perhaps Will was off to see Ann!'

'Do we dare ask him?' Agnes was amazed at her own effrontery.

'Not unless we can get him on his own. If Mam gets to hear of it there'll be ructions.'

Trying to corner William proved more difficult than the girls expected. He was more elusive than usual, and even their father commented that he seemed compelled to spend more time down at the colliery.

Normally, Margaret Ann had a sixth sense when it came to her children and their activities. She had been known to cross-question her grown-up sons in detail as to where, why and with whom they may have spent time on a Saturday evening. Luckily for William, his mother was preoccupied with helping a neighbour whose husband was dying of pneumoconiosis – the dreaded disease common amongst the miners and known as 'the dust'. This meant she was less often around in the kitchen in the evenings to pick up any signs of changes in behaviour or routine.

Unfortunately, he had reckoned without Amy, whose curiosity was aroused. Being by far the nosiest of her sisters, Amy was quite

159

incapable of keeping any news to herself. Bidden by her mother to help bring in the sheets from the washing line, Amy casually mentioned she hadn't seen William since tea. Margaret Ann merely said that he was probably busy at the National, and told Amy to be careful not to drag the sheet. Irritated by her mother's criticism, and annoyed that her mother had not taken the bait, with some glee she revealed the news of William's possible romantic attachment.

There was a stunned silence, then her mother's initial response, 'Hold on to the corner, girl and pull the sheet tight. Then get on and do the pillow cases.' Amy's glee was momentarily deflated, but she was not privy to her mother's reaction later that evening!

When Margaret Ann later related the news to Morgan, she was barely coherent. He sensed her utter disapproval and endeavoured to dampen down the conflagration before it got out of control. He strongly advised her not to tackle William directly, about what was, in his opinion, probably no more than girlish gossip and which had nothing to do with them anyway.

'Wait and see, Margaret Ann. But remember, Will has always put this family first, and now perhaps it's time he thought of himself for a bit.'

The sisters had indeed stumbled on the truth. William was utterly consumed by his feelings for Ann. Throughout his early manhood he had enjoyed the cheerful repartee and teasing with the village girls, and with five sisters he was no stranger to gossipy giggles and blushes. This time it was different. From Amy's meaningful looks and hints, he guessed she had heard of his interest in Ann Thomas, so he avoided his sister as much as possible. He had no desire to let Amy, or more significantly his mother, deduce how serious his intentions were. Until he could ask Ann to marry him, and she had accepted, he would not break the news in Min-yr-Afon.

William was a realist and knew he needed to accumulate more money before declaring his feelings. All his working life he had significantly subsidised the family exchequer and as a result had very little in the way of savings. When he heard that the Co-operative Society in the valley were advertising for a secretary/accountant on a part-time basis, he decided to apply for the position. Having no wish to ignite his mother's wrath at the words 'Co-operative Society', he said nothing to her about the application, nor to his Ann who might also consider it disloyal, seeing she knew at first hand how the small shopkeepers feared the Co-op's growing strength.

Requesting a clean shirt in the middle of the week had further raised his mother's curiosity but William's airy explanation of a visit from the Inspector of Mines had headed her off for the moment. It was more difficult to explain to his junior clerk why he would be out of the stores office on Thursday morning, and the most risky part of the enterprise would be the journey down the valley. He would surely be seen by one or other of his mother's cronies and then the fat would be in the fire. Providence however came to his aid. A messenger from the mine manager rushed in to the stores just as William was preparing to leave bearing an urgent request to sort out a disagreement over the delivery of seventeen tons of coal which had failed to arrive at the dock in Cardiff.

'Right away! I'll be off,' came the enthusiastic response, 'It might well take all day, so don't expect me back. Just get on with those invoices.' His clerk nodded, and an hour later William presented himself at the Cooperative Society's head office in Pontypridd. The interviewing panel had prepared a lengthy list of questions to challenge all the candidates, but as William walked in the chairman pushed his papers to one side.

'Good morning, Mr Jones, come in and take a seat. All well at the National today? We've heard a great deal of your excellent work there,' observed the Chairman.

'Both your parents well are they?' asked a grey haired gentleman sitting at the end of the large mahogany table.

'Related to Mr Edgar Jones of Wattstown, I assume,' enquired a stout fellow at the other end.

As he tried to get a word in, William felt slightly uneasy. Where were the searching questions about his book-keeping and accounting skills? When were they going to enquire into his ability to keep accurate minutes and record them in impeccable handwriting?

'How do you intend to fit in both this role and your full-time work for the National?' asked the only member of the panel who had not mentioned his family connections.

With a slight smile William explained that for the past fifteen years he had held down two jobs with no difficulty. The interviewer looked perplexed and referred to the application form in front of him, 'And in what post was that?'

William explained that his duties in the shop and post office had taken far more hours than any role the Co-op might require. 'I was responsible for opening and closing, putting up and taking down shutters, sweeping and maintaining the premises, delivery and collection of goods when required by my mother, care of the horse and other stable duties, ensuring my father was driven to and collected from his weekly preaching engagements and...'

He was interrupted by the chairman. 'Thank you, Mr Jones, I think that will do. We are all well aware of your capacity for hard work. I have a pile of testimonials here, and when we have given the matter some thought we will be in touch with you. I bid you good day.' The chairman stood up and reached across the shiny table to give William's hand a hearty shake which concluded the interview.

'Well,' William said to himself as he closed the door behind him. 'That was the strangest interview! They seemed more interested in who I was than in what I could do. Still there's nothing to do now but wait, but if they appoint me, then I'll do it. I'm more than ready to have a home of my own and there's no-one else I want in it but Ann. I'll ask her if she'll have me as soon as I know about the job,' and he continued down the valley to sort out the problem of the missing coal.

The day he heard his application had been successful, William walked down the valley in the evening sunlight, rehearsing his proposal to Ann. He was convinced she felt as he did, and he was sure her honesty and integrity would mean a straightforward answer. As he neared the draper's shop he saw her crossing the road a little way ahead with a large bolt of cloth under her arm. As she reached the pavement, he caught up with her.

'Miss Thomas,' he called, 'Ann, that's a great weight you're carrying. Give it to me and I'll take it into the shop for you.'

At the sound of his voice Ann stopped, hitched up the cloth which was indeed a considerable weight, and turned to face him. As William lifted the heavy load, their hands brushed together. Ann blushed and tried to move her hand, but William had never been one to let an opportunity slip by. He held the little hand in his firm grasp and looked Ann squarely in the eye. There followed a gaze of such intensity that both their hearts missed a beat. Neither spoke and to an onlooker it might have seemed as though the effort of preventing the cloth from falling was all that concerned them. As William took control of the fabric, he was forced to let go of Ann's hand. Still blushing, she looked down at her boots and waited.

'They've just made me Secretary to the Co-op. That's two jobs I've got, enough for two people to live on. So I can ask you the question I've been waiting to ask you for a long time now. Will you marry me, Ann? There's no girl in this valley means anything to me except you. I'll do all I can to take care of you and make you happy.'

His heart pounding, his mouth dry, he found it hard to control his desire to pick Ann up, cloth and all, in full view of the street but he managed to say, 'Do you think you can you say you'll have me, Ann? And please don't make me wait weeks for an answer.'

She lifted her face up to William and before she had said a word, her large brown eyes gave him the answer.

'We're out in the street, Will! But I've thought about it already, a lot. Of course I will. I'll be so glad to marry you, Will, and I'll try to make you happy, too.'

With their future settled entirely to their satisfaction, they crossed the pavement and carried the cloth into the shop. As the door closed behind them William pulled Ann towards him and held her tightly. Her slight frame nestling comfortably against him, he bent down to kiss her and he knew all would be well.

CHAPTER 20
A WEDDING

Half an hour later William emerged from the shop. He had asked Thomas Thomas for permission to marry his daughter, and he had agreed. It was a prospect that was greeted by Ann's parents with acceptance if not delight. The furniture shop in Ynyishir could do without losing such a useful pair of hands and Ann's parents knew it would be very hard to find someone to replace her. No other scamstress could turn a chair cover as she could. Ann was twenty-six and her parents had begun to hope that they would never lose her to marriage, keeping her with them to help in the shop and care for her ailing sisters.

William did not care a jot for the feelings of his prospective in-laws. For him the only thing that mattered was Ann's delight at his proposal. Walking slowly back up the hill, he mulled over the momentous events of the day, debating whether to announce his intention to marry Ann first and then tell the family about the new Co-op job, or whether job should come first, his engagement second. As soon as he entered the kitchen in Min-yr-Afon, Amy resolved the problem for him.

'Been to Ynyshir, have you?' she smirked, busily folding towels into neat piles.

'Yes.' Will waited, sure more was to follow.

'Mam knows,' Amy went on complacently, 'and she says you ought to be careful with those *ceiliogs*. If they get hold of you it will not be easy to escape.'

Everyone in the valley knew the nickname of Mr Thomas in Ynishir. Well known for his strutting walk, natty dressing and perkily worn hat, he reminded everyone of a proud cockerel, but he had also earned widespread admiration for the improved miners' safety lamp he had developed. Although some people resented his success and were only too willing to ridicule his way of walking, others were more accepting of him and all acknowledged his wife's skills as a midwife.

Taken unawares, Will put his jacket on the chair, reddened slightly and turned on his sister. '*Ceiliog* they may call Thomas Thomas, but I'm sure his daughter can't be a cockerel. Let me tell you, Amy, nobody gets hold of me, as you call it, and if Mam thinks I'm spending too much time with Ann, you can tell her that one day I intend to spend all my time with her.'

Amy stopped folding the towels to give her brother her full attention. 'What? What did you say? You are never going to marry her, are you?'

At that moment the kitchen door opened, and Amy's words were repeated by their mother. 'Marry! Will, who is to marry whom?'

'I am marrying Ann Thomas as soon as there is enough in the kitty, and before you start on about that, here is something else for you to know. I have been appointed part-time secretary to the Mid-Rhondda Co-op.'

William leant against the dresser, his arms folded across his chest, and looked his mother straight in the eye. Ignoring the first piece of information she said, 'I see, not enough that those Co-op people ruined my business, they are going to take my son as well. That's what will happen to you if you go and work for them, you mark my words.'

'No, Mam, I've not forgotten about what happened to the shop, you make sure of that. You would have us all believe the Co-op stole the bread out of our mouths. Well, I'm making sure they put a bit of that bread back into my mouth.'

'If it is married you intend to be, there'll be more than one mouth,' his mother snapped. 'If I know that family, your wife will want jam on the bread and probably cake as well.'

'And jam she shall have and I'll see it is spread thick too, which it has never been in this house.' William raised his voice to match his mother's and stormed out of the kitchen.

Amy finished folding the towels and started on the sheets, thoroughly enjoying the encounter between her mother and brother. Nothing so exciting had happened in the kitchen for a long time and she relished being the one to recount the tale to her sisters. A few moments later William returned to collect his jacket. In the hope of adding fuel to the fire, his sister decided to make a further contribution.

'Ann Thomas likes to dress posh, Will. She always has new clothes, expensive they are too, to match her taste I expect. She won't be content just to be tidy.'

Amy gave her brother a sly grin. Will picked up his jacket and moved towards his sister. The look on his face carried the message that it might be well for Amy to withdraw and let her mother and brother continue their battle in private. Picking up the folded laundry, she flounced out of the kitchen and shot upstairs to share the amazing scene she'd just witnessed with anyone she could find.

The minute Amy disappeared, Margaret Ann snapped, 'If you wanted a wife, why did you not take Annie Mary before Jack Beynon took her?'

'Because I did not want Annie Mary. I want Ann Thomas, and I've wanted Ann Thomas for a long time, and I will have her, carry on as much as you like.'

His mother decided to change tactics, speaking in a quieter tone.

'Will, they are a sickly lot of girls in that family and you are going to need a good strong wife who is healthy, not costing more than you can afford in doctor's bills. She's a pretty little thing, I grant you, but it's stamina that's more use in the long run.'

William gritted his teeth. He had seen exactly what a 'good strong wife' was like to live with and he had no wish to take one for himself. His mind had been made up for some time and the memory of Ann's hand in his was all he needed to withstand his mother. But he drew a deep breath before saying, 'Mam, first it was jam, then it was clothes and now it is doctor's bills. I'll tell you, if Ann needs any or all of those things when she is my wife, she shall have them. And once she is my wife you will hold your tongue, because if you do not you will have me to reckon with.'

'Oh, get on with you,' his mother hissed. 'I can't find a way to make you see sense. You'll go your own way, regardless, always have and always will.'

'Yes, Mam, and I wonder where I get that from?'

Margaret Ann glared at him, stomped over to the range and poked the smouldering kitchen fire with such force that the whole house seemed to rattle, and Will left the kitchen.

The battle was over for the time being. William was now free to persuade Ann to fix a date for their wedding without delay. He was sure they could manage with the money from the National and the extra income from the Co-op. The older brothers and sisters were all through college and he was confident that the rest of them could now take some responsibility for Gladys' and Arthur's college fees. He would find a little house down the valley, and no doubt Ann's mother could provide a stick or two of furniture from her shop if necessary. By bedtime William was feeling more cheerful and longed to know what further reaction Ann had received from her family in Ynishir, but he knew better than to rush back down. He contented himself with writing a note to his beloved, revealing his feelings more easily on paper than he had done on the road outside the shop.

His mother was certainly not finding it easy to regain her equilibrium. Alone in the kitchen, Margaret Ann relieved her feelings by scrubbing every surface until her arms ached. It was not only her body which ached, her heart ached too. The tight grip in which she had held her family was to be prised open. The son who was so like her in many ways was forsaking her. She longed for Morgan's return from his mid-week chapel meeting, to vent her rage at William's latest antics. Just as she was starting to scrub the pantry shelves. she heard the familiar sound of boots being scraped. She rushed into the passage drying her hands on her apron.

'Morgan, can you believe what William has gone and done this time?'

Her husband saw at once that his son's conduct had thoroughly upset his wife. Her usually calm exterior had deserted her, her face was flushed, her long hair, normally wound into a neat bun at the nape of her neck, was hanging in tangled strands down her back. She still wore her working clothes and the coarse brown work apron clung damply to her dress.

'What on earth is the matter? Calm down now, Margaret Ann, and get your breath back. Then we can sit down and you can try and tell me...'

'Tell you!' she shrieked. 'I'll tell you what he's done. He has taken the secretaryship in the Co-op without a word to me and he says he needs the money to marry Ann Thomas Ynyshir and...'

Morgan interrupted. 'Just a minute. There's nothing wrong with that is there? Seems a very responsible way to go about things. He's not thrown in the job with the National, has he? And please don't shriek again. My head is thumping enough after my meeting as it is.'

Margaret Ann moderated her tone a little, before telling him exactly what she considered to be wrong with William's course of action. Morgan listened patiently until the diatribe began to subside.

'I'll have a cup of tea if you wouldn't mind. It's very late and a sandwich wouldn't go amiss after the long meeting I've been in.'

Gently reminded of her wifely duties and somewhat shamefaced, she prepared his supper. Once he'd munched his way through the cold beef and pickle sandwiches and drunk the cup of strong tea, Morgan returned to the earlier topic. 'Come to bed, and listen to me for a change. Ann Thomas is a good, hard-working girl and if her father does strut about, he's got good reason to. That safety lamp he's been working on is a real improvement and will make many men safer underground. He is no fool, and he can't help his height. The family is respectable and they are regular attenders in chapel.

Mrs Thomas runs a first class shop and is always ready to help with a birth or laying out, as you well know. There is many a worse family Will could be marrying into.'

'No family is good enough for our Will,' hissed his wife 'or any of the others for that matter. Those *ceiliogs* will never stop crowing now.'

Morgan saw his wife bristle as she marched up the stairs in front of him.

'Now what?' he wondered. Aloud he said, 'Let it out, Margaret Ann. What on earth is really worrying you about all this?'

'Will is not marrying into any family, he belongs to this family, and married or not, that is not going to change.'

'Fine, but remember his wife must also become part of this family.'

'Never!' Margaret Ann almost spat out the word. 'To marry or not, I suppose is something the children will have to decide for themselves, but that does not mean that any Tom, Dick or Harry can just march into this family.'

With that she undressed, climbed into the big bed and turned her back on her long-suffering husband. Morgan was astounded by his wife's words. Although she had accepted his name of Jones, it was true that she had never sought to be included in his family, nor for that matter had she ever suggested that he should be part of her Evans family. Morgan lay in the big bed, trying to find a way to smooth matters over, before deciding enough had been said today and he'd have a quiet word with Will tomorrow.

As he lay there he resolved to disassociate himself from Margaret Ann's views and to accept any future daughter-in-law or son-in-law as a true father should. Before he fell asleep he decided to give William something special to mark the occasion, something significant. From his father William received two books, one an old family bible, the other a copy of Bunyan's *Pilgrim's Progress* which had been much treasured by Morgan. It had been a gift to him from his sister Jane, who had died in Pennsylvania so soon after her mother and sisters had arrived in America from the valley.

Unperturbed by his mother's anger, William went on with plans which moved forward more quickly than he had thought possible. The Thomas family became more and more enamoured of the prospect of Ann marrying William, whom they saw as a 'good catch.'

Annie Mary Beynon, among the first to know about the romance, suggested to her mother, that William should be offered the tenancy of a house in Ynyshir which she owned, and which was soon to become vacant. The couple were delighted and William set to tirelessly to transform the little house. In the few moments he had free between the National and the Co-op he painted walls and repaired woodwork. Ann's skill as a seamstress provided curtains and bedspreads and cushion covers and soon Gladys pronounced that her brother would be living in a palace. Ann was happy to think she would be able to start her married life near her own family and amongst her customers, while Will was of the opinion that a mile and a half between his mother and his wife could do nothing but good.

William's sisters at least, were full of excitement at the first wedding in the family. Margaret Ann had finally given in to the pleading for new dresses for the girls, and had sent for the dressmaker. There was a sting in the tale though. Amy alone was decked out in new finery. Each daughter was required to give up an existing dress, which was to be made over for the next sister down. Little Gladys became the proud possessor of a dress with the latest flounces fashioned from an underskirt belonging to her mother, although it was topped off with a brand new bonnet. The bridegroom's mother made do with her best chapel dress, but she wore all her good jewellery.

In the house in Ynyshir, sewing machines whirred non-stop as Ann and her sisters prepared her trousseau and put the finishing touches to a well-stocked bottom drawer. It was a matter of great pride that a bride would want for nothing in the way of bed linens, towels and tablecloths, and the Thomas family of Ynishir were determined that Ann should have all she needed.

A cold, bright day greeted William and Ann on 3rd March 1908, when they were married at Sardis Baptist Chapel in Cardiff, with Edgar as best man, and all eight of William's brothers and sisters crowded into one pew. William's boots shone as brightly as the smile on his face, as he saw his beloved Ann, attended by her younger sister, coming down the aisle towards him. She wore a delicate pale blue dress that she and her sisters had made. Her proud father looked up at William as he escorted his daughter to the step in front of the minister.

'Look after her, won't you?' he whispered.

William turned to Ann and took her hand. 'For ever,' he replied as the minister began the service.

For Margaret Ann it was one of the most difficult moments of her life. Much as she railed against her second son, she loved him dearly and was acutely aware of the contribution he had made to the family's prosperity and status. All his life he had put his family's needs before his own and now all that was to end. He had tied himself up with the Thomases and nothing would ever be the same again.

CHAPTER 21
READJUSTMENTS

Forced to accept the reality of her son's departure, Margaret Ann reacted by gathering the rest of her brood even more closely round her. William's absence was felt by all the family, and they were all forced to realise just how much he had contributed to life in Min-yr-Afon.

It also speeded up the growth of English as the language spoken in the home. Will had always used Welsh in his daily contact with his friends, the colliery workmen, and in his new job within the Co-op, as well as at home. He and Ann had always spoken Welsh together so naturally it became the language of their shared life. However, since the notorious 1847 government report on education in Wales, English was now enforced in all schools, and the ability to speak it was seen as the passport to success and prosperity. As a result families made sure their children became fluent as quickly as possible. The fear of being the child with the 'WELSH NOT' board hung round the neck at the end of the school day, and the inevitable beating which ensued, was a speedy and effective way of stifling the old language and promoting the growth of English. Now the old language was only kept alive in the family by continuing to worship in Welsh in Calfaria.

∞ ∞ ∞

Clinging to the old ways became more and more difficult for Margaret Ann. She dreaded the dispersal of her family and was fearful of the disruption which new relationships might bring. One of the ways in which she actively discouraged the formation of any close relationships outside the family was by giving the girls so many household tasks when they had finished their day's teaching, that there was little time to venture outside Min-yr-Afon.

Edgar was totally committed to his work for the Liberal party and continued his association with the Workmen's Institute, to which he had been appointed trustee on the completion of the building. Any spare time he had after his day in the pupil teacher centre was occupied for studying for his Bar exams. Until he could enter parliament, in the far distant future, it was as a lawyer that he hoped to make his living, working to improve the conditions for working men and their families in Wales. He did not know as yet that his colleagues had put his name forward as prospective parliamentary candidate for the Liberal party.

Morgan James remained perched on the periphery of the family where he had always been, increasingly following his own interests. He discharged his daily duties to his employers, but continued to take lessons in painting and spent much time in the New Art Gallery in Cardiff, copying pictures that appealed to him. Most of his finished work came to adorn the walls in Min-yr-Afon, proudly framed and displayed by his mother.

Margaret Ann might have raised few objections to William and Morgan James abandoning their formal education, but the girls were given no choice in the matter. Her daughters were to be equipped to earn their own living. Their mother had never forgotten how irksome it had been early in her marriage, to be dependent on her husband for every penny. Her daughters should be in a position to choose between marriage or a career. They were not to be forced into matrimony in the mistaken belief that becoming someone's wife would automatically give them status and independence.

In the autumn of 1908 it was Jane's turn to go to college. She was expected to follow Agnes's example and go to Exeter, but instead chose Swansea. The dark, coal-laden valley which had been her home for eighteen years had never appealed to her. She felt none of

173

the affection for it that her older brothers and sisters did. She longed for a sunnier, brighter place where she could blossom, and indulge her sense of style.

Jane had a strong will which she never hesitated to use to achieve her own ends, but she seldom made the mistake of direct confrontation with her mother, preferring more devious ways. She liked pretty clothes and spent hours perusing the fashion pages of magazines which had recently found their way up the valley from her new sister-in-law's house. As a young woman Margaret Ann had also relished new dresses, but the expenses of clothing nine children had left little in the kitty for maternal indulgence. On their rare shopping trips to Cardiff which Edgar occasionally financed, Jane would encourage her mother to purchase a stylish and colourful dress, rather than the hard-wearing, dark-coloured one that was her usual, frugal choice. In this way she led her mother to believe that she, Jane, was the daughter with the dress sense. This allowed Jane more freedom to choose her new college outfits in the latest fashion, and the contrasts between her outfits for college in Swansea by their younger sister, compared with those that had been packed into their trunks a few years earlier, were not lost on Amy and Agnes. After listening to several evenings of bickering between the girls, their mother brought matters to a head.

'You can stop yacketing on about Jane's clothes, you two. You never went out less than tidy, and I do remember a smart maroon coat, Amy Ann, that Elizabeth persuaded me to buy for you. Besides it's always paid to dress our Jane. She's always had good dress sense and there's a lot less fat on her.'

Her sisters gasped at their mother's remark. Her status reinforced by her mother's support, Jane swept out of the parlour and directed a self-satisfied smirk at her sisters. Later that evening as the lid of the trunk was closed for the last time, she felt a sharp stab on her arm from Amy's hat pin, followed by Agnes's speciality punishment of a swift and painful pinch.

'You can have those as presents to take to Swansea with your posh clothes, so there, our Jane.'

The evening before Jane's departure, her father called her to him. 'This is your letter from Calfaria to the minister and deacons of Bethesda chapel in Swansea, transferring your membership there while you are in college. I know the minister there and he will be happy to be responsible for you while you are in Swansea.'

Jane frowned as she took the letter. She disliked having decisions made for her.

'I thought I would find out what chapels the other girls were going to, before I asked Calfaria for my letter.'

'You want to be a sermon taster rather than a faithful member, is that it?' responded her father disapprovingly. 'You will take this letter and it is my wish that you join the congregation in Bethesda. Chapel isn't for popping in and out of. You have a duty to be a regular member.'

To him that was the end of the matter, but Morgan Humphrey had forgotten that Jane had her full share of her mother's silent obstinacy. She took the letter without a word but she never presented it in Bethesda. Within a few weeks of arriving in Swansea, she had joined a group of friends from college, all of whom worshipped in Capel Gomer. For the two years Jane spent in Swansea she too chose to worship in Capel Gomer, a smaller chapel than Bethesda but one where the congregation appealed more to Jane's sophisticated tastes.

Maggie, just eighteen months younger than Jane, missed her sorely. Agnes had once remarked, they were as 'thick as thieves'. As small children caught up in the middle of a large family, they were often overlooked and left to their own devices. Family interest frequently centred on the activities and careers of the older children, while the arrival of two more new babies diverted their mother's attention for much of the time. As the difference in age between the pair and the new babies was so small, they were not required for childminding duties and became experts at keeping out of the way and making their own amusements. Maggie admired Jane enormously. Although Maggie was the taller of the two being all of five feet four, Jane had an air about her. Her knack with clothes could make ordinary everyday wear look elegant, and she had as many different ways of arranging her long hair as there were days of the week.

Jane's natural ability with maths was a constant source of admiration too. It made Maggie's efforts look worse than they actually were. but Jane's influence over her younger sister was too strong to allow envy. At a loose end without her sister, Maggie was sitting miserably in the kitchen one dark evening in November when Morgan James came into the room. Uncharacteristically it was he who came to her rescue.

'What are you doing in here, Maggie? Don't let Mam catch you doing nothing! You know she'll find you something to do, and you'll end up hooking one of those awful rag rugs she's always on about. I think her favourite quotation is that one about the devil finding work for idle hands! I don't think she realises that by quoting it all the time she casts herself in the devil's role!'

The thought of her mother complete with horns and a long tail made even the miserable Maggie smile. 'I really miss our Jane, Morgan. She was always up to something and I just joined in with her. I'm no good at anything on my own.' A large self-pitying tear dripped down her nose.

'Don't be daft, Maggie. You're bound to be good at something! What about those lovely collars you are always making? You did a lovely cloth for Mam's tray for her birthday, didn't you? You might even be better than our Jane at something, even if it's never going to be maths!' Morgan James couldn't resist a dig at Maggie's well-known difficulty with numbers. 'Why don't you come with me to art class down the Institute on Friday evening. Mam can't raise any objection if I take you. I'll even pay your subscription as long as you stop moping around!'

It was Morgan James's timely intervention that led to Maggie's lifelong interest in art. During the two years of Jane's absence, she joined her brother in the painting class. Soon her pictures were to be seen joining Morgan James's on the parlour wall at Min-yr-Afon and were even given as wedding presents to her friends.

One evening in the early spring of 1909 Morgan Humphrey

was alone in the post office humming the last week's hymns to himself while he balanced the daily account. The heavy snowfall had deterred customers and the muffling effect of the snow had turned the little post office into a silent haven. Morgan enjoyed the silence but he was aware of his profound dislike for the task his wife had pushed him into taking on. He missed Jane's help but studiously avoided accepting Maggie's, as her slender grasp of mathematics and what her mother described as her slapdash ways could have been disastrous. He would have liked to have given up the post office when they left the shop in Aberllechau Road, but he had known that if he were to relinquish running the post office he might lose Margaret Ann's agreement to the move to Min-yr-Afon. Locking the ledgers away, he suddenly decided that it was time that he gave up the role of postmaster.

Later that night as he and his wife enjoyed a few minutes of privacy in the kitchen before bed, he voiced his thoughts. Her response was predictable.

'Whatever has put that idea into your head? I suppose you think that we can do without the post office and the money it brings in, do you? Well let me remind you, we have not got Will's money now, and Jane has not finished college and there's Maggie ready to go, and what about Gladys and Arthur? Edgar keeps all his money to finance some new scheme he is after, and all Morgan James' spare money, goes on his painting stuff. We've lost the rent from this house and there are no more instalments to come from the compensation of the shop lease.'

Morgan sighed. 'It's always the money with you, Margaret Ann, isn't it? Can you ever forget that time you were penniless? You were a small child! You had plenty of money once your father inherited that house and dried himself out a bit. You went off to boarding school! How many girls had that chance, eh? When he and your mother got rid of the haulier's business and started up the shop and the post office in Cwmamman you wanted for nothing. There are four wages coming into this house, soon to be five when Jane starts teaching, and if I give up the post office I could find time for more preaching engagements on Sundays.'

'And an extra sermon is supposed to make up the difference in the money, is it? Heaven is more important to you than bread, I suppose!' Her jaw set as firmly as usual, Margaret Ann rose from the chair and gave the cushions a vigorous shaking to show her determination not to give an inch.

This time, however, Morgan was resolved that he would not continue as postmaster. In whatever time he had left on God's earth he would follow his own vocation as a preacher of the gospel. For twenty-seven years he had struggled to satisfy Margaret Ann's desire to improve their financial situation but he knew she had no need to worry about money. There was plenty. He took several days to mull over his decision. He knew his wife conformed to chapel-going as part of her social standing in the community, and that she paid lip service to those who ministered to the congregation, but within herself she had a contempt for those prepared to accept a minimum in the service of God, especially if there were a maximum to be earned in the service of Mammon.

Having reached his decision, Morgan announced it one morning after breakfast.

'I will be writing to head office in Cardiff tomorrow to inform them of my intention to retire from the postal service.' With that he rose from he table, pushed in his chair, and left the room.

Much as she would have liked to have forbidden him to do so, Margaret Ann had to admit defeat. No further discussion took place and the letter of resignation was sent on its way.

Edgar told William of their father's decision to relinquish the post office the following evening as he walked back up the valley through the snow from Porth. It was pleasant to call in at Ynishir to visit Will and Ann, and their obvious delight in each other's company made Edgar very happy for his younger brother. William's skill with tools and Ann's skill with fabrics had transformed the once drab little house into a welcoming home and Edgar was glad of an excuse to sit in the warm comfortable kitchen while Ann made the inevitable cup of tea and produced a Welsh cake from her cake tin. Edgar recounted the breakfast-time announcement with a rueful grin.

'The atmosphere is a bit sticky at the moment, Will. They've obviously discussed it, but Mam as usual is making her feelings known.'

William decided he had better make his way to Min-yr-Afon as soon as possible to give his father the necessary support. He guessed his mother would not let the matter drop and would use every opportunity to make her husband feel the weight of her disapproval. He set out up the valley relishing the prospect of a confrontation with his mother. He walked into the kitchen, stamping the snow from his boots, to find her attacking the table with the familiar scrubbing brush. He greeted her in his usual cheery manner.

'Making the table suffer are you?' He removed the brush from her hand. 'Leave it be, Mam, you can scrub all you like, but you will not change things. Dadda has gone along with you all these years. You know he has never liked the post office work. No wonder he thinks enough is enough.'

'Liked? What has that got to do with it? If we had to like everything we did or else give it up, the world would soon come to a stop.' Grabbing the scrubbing brush from Will's hand, she said, 'Get out of my way, boy. Go and see your father, and leave me to get on.'

Morgan was collecting up the few parcels ready for the postman's next collection.

'Hullo, my boy. How is Ann?' He never failed to enquire after his daughter-in-law for whom he had a great respect and he would have welcomed more opportunity to know her better.

'Well enough, though I wish she would not spend so much time helping her mother. Joanna's cough is getting worse and worse and I don't think there's much more the doctors can do. She's had a bad winter and I know Ann is worried about her.'

'I heard there was illness in the Thomas's and sorry I am, but it's only right she should help her mother look after her sister at such a time.'

'You are right, but enough about that.' William paused as the postman came in to collect the parcels. and waited while his father signed the relevant chits. 'When are you to finish with all this?'

'Edgar told you, did he?'

William nodded.

'I'll finish in another month. Head office in Cardiff need the time to organise another post office in Wattstown, and a postmaster to run it. Your mother is not overly pleased about it.'

William grinned. 'Give her time, Dad. When she finds that none of you is starving because of your reckless decision she will cool down.'

His father joined him with a conspiratorial smile. 'No doubt that's right. The trouble is how long will it take for the cooling down? We will all suffer in the meantime.'

'With luck the furniture will take the brunt of it. The kitchen table was having a proper scrub as I came through. It'll be several inches thinner by the time she's finished! Anyway, Dadda, do not forget. Just keep your head down, and remember you are always welcome in Ynishir, if it's a bit of peace you need.' He turned towards the door. 'By the way, if you and Mam are a bit short, Ann and I could spare something if it's needed to see Jane finish in Swansea.'

'Thank you, Will, but there is no need for that. You have done your bit and more for this family and those you helped earlier can do a bit more now if necessary, for the younger ones. You see to your own wife.'

William was correct when he told his father that his mother would cool down given time. She put the time to good use as usual, and at the end of the month she began returning the now redundant post office back to its original use as a parlour. Amy, Agnes and Maggie were unwilling conscripts in their mother's campaign, but a visit to Cardiff to choose the furniture for the new room, helped them to overcome their reluctance, particularly as Amy had promised to treat the girls to tea in a newly opened teashop in the Arcade.

The latest embossed wallpaper was chosen and William persuaded two of his friends to become 'paper hangers' for a week to ensure his father need have nothing to do with the redecoration. Ann willingly put aside time to make the new curtains for her mother-in-law, and was rewarded by Margaret Ann with unexpected thanks for her talents. Even Arthur and Gladys were required to make a contribution by stuffing the new cushions with feathers saved from the butcher's poultry store. Then every other corner of the house had to gleam with polish to vie with the new parlour, and the polish had to be applied with the maximum amount of elbow grease.

By the time the improvements were complete, Margaret Ann and her daughters were exhausted, but the goal of having the most stylish parlour in the Rhondda had been achieved. Peace eventually returned, Margaret Ann's resentment died away, and she thoroughly enjoyed inviting privileged visitors to take a cup of tea with her in order to admire the new parlour.

CHAPTER 22
NEW CHALLENGES

Throughout the late winter and spring of 1909 the upheavals within the Liberal party only occasionally impinged on life in Min-yr-Afon. Edgar and his father were constantly at meetings but that was not very different from their usual way of life. Margaret Ann continued to exercise strict control over her older daughters' comings and goings but Jane was much harder to control than the others. Her latest purchase of a pair of high heeled boots had produced caustic remarks from her mother, and it was only by hiding them in her sister-in-law's wardrobe that she managed to save them from the rag and bone man's cart.

The younger children had their own activities to attend to, as exams were looming for fifteen-year-old Gladys. Arthur, who was twelve, had the run of the roads, as he had none of the duties his three older brothers had been required to fulfill at the same age. He was busy discovering the delights of belonging to a gang of boys in the village.

One Thursday morning the sleet was swirling down the valley and the grey clouds sat so low that even the tops of the colliery chimneys and the winding gear were hidden. The latest girl was rattling the coals in the range in an attempt to warm up the kitchen, when in a change to his usual procedure the postman arrived at the back door rather than the front, with a pile of letters.

'Too fat for the letter box one of these is, Minnie,' he explained as she opened the door. 'Thought I'd bring them round rather than rattling the knocker. Mind you, it's freezing out here. Is Mrs Jones about?'

'Gone to see Mrs Basso, whose chest is playing up again, and the Reverend is writing his sermon for next Sunday. Get those boots off and don't drip on my floor. You can have a cup of tea if you are quick. She won't be back for half an hour.'

The shivering postman needed no encouragement to enter the warm kitchen and thaw out. He dumped the pile of letters on the kitchen table as Minnie put the teapot to warm.

'The regular one from America, I noticed, as well as this fat one. All the way from London and franked by the Liberal party, too. My word, important family this is.'

'Get your nose out of the family's business Dai, and drink your tea,' admonished Minnie, 'or Mrs Jones will be back and we'll both be in trouble.' The cup of tea and a slice of *bara brith* soon revived him, and he heaved up the sack of post and hurried off to complete his round.

That morning's delivery was to bring about several significant changes for the family in Min-yr-Afon. As usual, the girl put the letters on the designated tray on the dresser ready for Morgan to collect when he emerged from the parlour. In spite of his wife's domination of the household, checking the post remained Morgan's privilege and until he had checked each letter, no-one would dream of removing one from the pile, regardless of the recipient's name on the envelope. Minnie, however, could not resist a surreptitious glance at the pile which included a much more interesting letter than a London one. It had a Swansea postmark addressed to Miss J M Jones.

'Well, Miss Jane,' she thought to herself, 'that's a man's writing I'm sure. You'd better pick it up before your mother sees it. I hope the Reverend doesn't put it on the top when he's checked through.'

She need not have worried. The contents of the one addressed to Edgar were to eclipse all the rest of the news in the morning's post. Each member of the family arrived home for the mid-day break and Jane managed to slip her letter into her skirt pocket without attracting anyone's notice. Edgar as usual was last in. By that time Maggie and Gladys were beside themselves with curiosity about the fat envelope. Edgar carefully and methodically opened it and slowly read the contents.

'Well, well?' The family at the table were agog. Edgar lifted his head and announced solemnly that he had been selected as the official Liberal candidate to stand as MP for the boroughs of Merthyr and Aberdare, following the resignation of the sitting Liberal MP, Mr D A Thomas. Edgar had enormous respect for Mr Thomas and was highly honoured to follow in his footsteps. The constituency was a joint one which returned two members of parliament. It was no safe seat he was being offered, as one of the sitting members was the leading socialist and popular politician, Keir Hardie. Morgan was delighted that his son's years of dedicated hard work had at last been recognised by the Liberal party, and that he now he would have the opportunity to become an MP. Edgar's father felt confident there was still room for a Liberal in the area.

'Well done, son. Just as well you've finished your law studies too. There'll not be much time for study now.' He congratulated his son with a deep sense of pride and patted his shoulder in an unaccustomed gesture of affection. Edgar looked up at his mother.

'Get on now with that food, or you'll be late back. Punctual is what you need to be, whatever you're doing,' and she closed the oven door with a bang. Her life was about to change yet again and she knew it.

After the excitement had died down and the family had returned to their afternoon activities, Morgan quietly re-read his own letter from America. Over the years since his sisters and his mother had settled in the Welsh mining community in Pennsylvania, their correspondence and the exchange of family photographs had been regular. Morgan had taken great pains to ensure his own family was aware of their American relations, but only Edgar, as the oldest child, retained any real memory of them. Since the pit disaster, several more distant members of the family had emigrated from the Rhondda to the USA, so for his other children, the American branch existed on paper only, and through the stamps which Arthur collected with pride to show off to the other children in school.

This particular letter told Morgan that his mother was now becoming increasingly frail, but remained in good spirits. News from his sisters Ann and Elinor told him that they had settled well and were living close by in Nanticoke. Although his sister Jane had died several years ago, Elinor had made a full recovery from tuberculosis and Morgan was suddenly overcome by a strong desire to see the rest of his family again; the mother and sisters who had given him such loving support throughout his struggle to leave the colliery and fulfill his vocation for the church. He sat looking out at the miserable weather and wondered idly if the sun were shining in Pennsylvania. Putting the letter in his pocket, he resolved to walk down to Ynyshir later in the day, to see Will, and give him the rest of the family's news.

Since his retirement from the post office, Margaret Ann had not found it easy to accept her husband's ability to live a life she considered to be one of comparative idleness. She dreaded the evils likely to befall those with time on their hands and found endless tasks for Morgan to do. She was therefore relieved when he announced that he would walk down to Ynishir to share the good news of Edgar's selection as a candidate in the next general election with Will.

'What else was in the post?' she enquired absentmindedly as she folded the now dry washing in neat piles on the kitchen table. 'Did I see an American stamp? Don't forget to save it for Arthur.'

'There was indeed one. I am relieved to see it as I've heard nothing from them since I gave them the news about relinquishing the post office.'

Margaret Ann gave her usual non committal grunt. 'What news do you have from America then?' she asked without ceasing her laundry tasks.

'They are all well. Ann's daughter is looking forward to her marriage and Elinor's family are fine. It's strange to think how many years have passed. Edgar and Will were hardly more than babies when they came with me to say goodbye to their Mamgu. Wait till

185

she and my sisters hear the news about Edgar!'

Brusquely his wife said, 'Time passes the same for all of us, whether it's in Pennsylvania or Rhondda! No doubt they think they have done better for themselves than if they had stayed in the valley. By the way, if you are planning to go down to Ynyshir, you can tidy up around the yard for me first.'

Physical effort, as hard as possible, was the medicine Margaret Ann doled out to anybody in danger of indulging in what she considered an excess of emotion. Unwilling to feel sentimental herself, she accepted that others might be afflicted from time to time, but that was no reason to allow Morgan to dwell on the day his family went to America or his feelings for his mother and sisters.

An hour later, with the yard at Min-yr-Afon swept and tidied to his wife's high standards, Morgan set off in the miserable drizzle, on the familiar walk down the valley for a comforting visit to his second son. William arrived home from work to find his father still sitting companionably with Ann and chatting over a cup of tea about the news that Edgar had been accepted as a Liberal candidate.

William gave his young wife his customary kiss, sat down, pulled off his boots and reached for the cup of tea Ann handed him, 'It's cold out there. I hope you wrapped yourself up before you came out, Dadda. I don't think I've seen the snow lie on the tops so long for several winters. I'll be glad when the spring comes. Now what about Edgar's news! He told me himself not half an hour since as he called in at the stores on his way home. He deserves it with all the work he's put in at the Institute as well as all the help and advice he gives. He's been working from dawn till dusk and it's time he was recognised. What has Mam got to say about it?'

'You know your mother, boy, proud as Punch but pretending that it is nothing to shout about. She will wait for the day he is returned.'

'And you, Dadda? What do you think?'

'It is what Edgar has been aiming at for a while now and I truly believe he wants to do something for our people here. They are well aware of what he's done already, so I don't think he's wasting his time by standing as a candidate.'

'I'm sure he won't be doing that. I've never seen Edgar waste a minute. He could always stick his nose in a book! Anyway, you will stay for supper, will you? Then we can start to think what we'll need to do for Edgar. We had better have a plan in mind in case an election comes.'

'Yes, I will do that. The longer I am out the better, at the moment. Your mother will be pleased. She finds it hard to have me about the place all day.'

'Give me a couple of minutes to tidy up, then we can put the world to rights while Ann gets the meal ready.'

Morgan made himself comfortable in the cosy kitchen and listened to Ann's friendly conversation. When William reappeared he said, 'I heard from America this morning but hardly had time to read it with everything else going on.' He handed his son the envelope with the distinctive US stamp. William read it and returned it to his father with the comment, 'Well, they all seem to be doing well out there. How many years now is it since they went?'

'More than a quarter of a century; they are Americans now, no doubt.' A wistful note crept into his father's voice. 'I don't suppose they'd recognise me if I walked through the door,' and he stroked his beard which had rather more white hairs than ginger now.

'Come on, Dadda, they'd know you the minute they saw you. Now pull up your chair and let's enjoy the ham Ann's done for us.'

Ann brought the supper to the table and Morgan noted with pleasure a rounded figure that promised a future grandchild, but made no reference to it other than to ask her how she was. Suddenly turning to William, and hardly able to believe his own voice he suddenly blurted out, 'Do you know, Will, I would like to see my mother and sisters again.'

For years he had dreamed that one day, in some way, he would journey to America to see his mother and sisters once more. He had borne his grief over his sister Jane's death in private, well aware that sympathy was a scant commodity in his wife's emotional repertoire. Yet a day had rarely passed without a recollection of some long-held memory, and his nightly prayers always included his family on the other side of the ocean. A surprised William paused in the act of carving the ham. He had never heard his father express such a wish before. It was Ann who broke the silence that followed her father-in-law's statement.

'America is a long way to go.'

'That it is,' sighed Morgan. 'And it's a pity that wishing to go doesn't bring it any nearer.'

William put down the carving knife and sat back in his chair. 'Wishing certainly will not get you there, so what about some action? That might make it happen. You have just said Mam finds it difficult to have you about the house, so leave her alone for a while and maybe she will be glad to have you around again. You will only need passage money. The family over there will look after you.'

'Steady on, boy, I am not sure that if a wish is fulfilled it might not bring more troubles with it.'

'Come on, Dadda, there is only one way to find out about that, isn't there? Have your wish granted and see what happens. You eat your supper and we can talk about it after. I will walk up to Min-yr-Afon with you. Ann and I have a bit of news for Mam and I want to tell her myself before our Amy or Maggie gets wind of it.'

Supper finished, the two men walked up the hill in the biting wind which whistled down the valley. Morgan took the opportunity to refer indirectly to Ann's pregnancy. 'I couldn't help noticing that you will soon have another entry to put in the bible I gave you. The child will be lucky to have you for a father. A good brother you have always been, a good son too, and that adds up to a good father when the time comes.'

It was a day full of surprises, William thought. Praise and appreciation were seldom voiced in the family, never by his mother, and only occasionally by his father!

Margaret Ann's greeting rang out as William and his father entered the yard. 'About time you were back.'

'What's time got to do with it, Mam?' William enquired. 'Dadda's entitled to his own time these days, surely?'

'What are you doing here, Will? You've not walked up for the exercise.'

'Quite right, Mam, I've come to see Edgar and to give you a bit of news.'

'Let's have the news first, and then you can go through and see Edgar. I suppose you have heard his news?'

'I have, Mam, and very pleased Ann and I were to hear it, but I'll be a father before he is a Member of Parliament!'

'So that's it, is it, and when will it be?'

'In June, Ann tells me.'

'Tell her to take care then. Too much sitting around sewing will do neither her nor the child any good, and mind you keep her away from that family of hers. From what I hear, another of them has gone down with TB.'

'Now Mam, just for once leave them out of this, and trust me to look after Ann.'

After the usual brisk encounter with his mother, Will found Edgar busy amongst his papers. 'Seen the letter from America, have you?' enquired Edgar, 'There was nothing to worry about in it, was there?'

'No, but it made Dadda aware of his longing to see his mother and sisters again.'

'Only natural, I suppose, after all these years.'

'Natural it may be, but this *hiraeth* of his should be satisfied. I am here to find out how it can be managed. He has spent years doing Mam's bidding, and helping the rest of us to satisfy our aspirations, so you can get busy and find out how much he will need to get to Pennsylvania and back. You and I are now in a position to contribute something towards the passage, and we can get a bit more off Amy and Agnes.'

Edgar regarded his brother quizzically. 'What about Mam? Is she to go as well?'

'Mam will decide that for herself, but I am determined that my father shall go to America and Mam is not to prevent it. So you go and find out about the cost of the passage. Oh, and by the way, Ann and I are delighted with your news. It won't be long before we see MP after your name.'

189

With that Will called goodnight to any who might hear, and left the house. Edgar tidied away his papers and smiled to himself. No doubt, Will would consider he had agreed to his plan, even though he had not been asked for his opinion. As was Will's way, Edgar had just been told in no uncertain terms, to find out the cost. Edgar had no objection to doing that, but he did wonder about his mother's reaction to the proposed visit. Would she veto the idea and if she did, would his father go to America in spite of her disapproval?

'I'll just wait and see,' he reasoned, 'but I might as well drop a line to the shipping company to see what the cost might be.'

Within a few days Edgar had discovered that his father could travel on a ship of the Cunard Line for £16 return in a second class cabin, which would entitle him to four meals a day. 'He'll get more food on board than he does at home,' Edgar chuckled to himself, 'and I don't suppose the rail fare will be much.'

When told by his sons the following week that the second class passage money and the train fare could be found from his five children who were now earning, Morgan called a halt to any further progress. He was very touched by his children's generosity but until their mother was told of the proposed plan, nothing further was to be done. He would discuss the idea with her on their own. Edgar was almost certain that his mother would object to her husband's long absence and doubted his father would agree if he considered his going would cause her any distress. William, on the other hand, was prepared to fight his mother to the finish, to ensure his father saw America and his family before it was too late.

To William's amazement, no fighting was needed, as the battle never commenced. Margaret Ann was astounded that her husband should harbour such a far-fetched idea as going to America. She decided that if he were so irrational as to entertain such a wild idea, no rational arguments could prevail. She came to the conclusion that her husband had become possessed. First he had abandoned the post office, now it was she and the children who were to be left. One thing she made perfectly clear when Edgar tentatively suggested she might like to accompany her husband, was that nothing on earth would tempt her to undertake such a voyage. Margaret Ann had seldom wanted to visit her sisters-in-law when they lived in the next valley, so she certainly was not going to America to see them.

Her tacit agreement to the proposed visit made no difference to her belief that Morgan would, indeed must, come to his senses. She was convinced that the idea of seeing his sisters would retreat into his imagination which, in her opinion, it should never have left.

It was not until Morgan was about to depart that Margaret Ann finally grasped the fact that the idea had not gone away. Once she realised the inevitable, it was William who had to face the full force of her anger. He was accused of encouraging his father to forsake his wife, of involving his brothers and sisters in in his devious plan and was told it was high time he minded his own business and stopped interfering with hers. William's ability to turn a deaf ear only increased his mother's ire. He waited until the ranting finally stopped, said goodnight to his mother and left for the peace and quiet of his own home, knowing full well that she feared for her husband and dreaded his absence. Her raging was just a front for her anxiety.

In spite of his reluctance to become involved, Edgar found time to acquire the necessary tickets and travel documents for his father. His cabin was booked, his passport arrived and Margaret Ann herself supervised his packing. She folded each garment with great care, issuing dire threats about the dangers of dampness, and failing to wear a muffler on deck.

Within six weeks of receiving the letter which had so troubled Morgan, he was on his way. The spring sunshine was streaming into the steep-sided valley the morning William arrived early to collect his father at the start of the journey. His parents had said their good-byes the night before in the privacy of their bedroom and now there was no sign of his mother and all the curtains were still drawn. He picked up the new suitcase Margaret Ann had insisted upon, leaving his father to carry the venerable carpet bag he always used. With no other goodbyes to be said, the two set off for the station. Clumps of wood anemones made bright patches along the bank below Min-yr-Afon as Morgan and his son hurried along the still quiet streets. William enjoyed the peaceful journey down to Cardiff to see his father safely on the train for Liverpool at the start of the eight day voyage.

'Give my love to Mamgu, and don't forget to tell her the next generation's on the way. Everything will be fine here. With a bit of luck, Mam will have calmed down by the time you get back! Just enjoy yourself and send us one of those new fangled postcards to tell us how you are doing.'

William waved his father off and watched while the train disappeared round the curve, then he crossed the platform to take the train back up the valley to start work for the day.

Agnes sorely missed her father but in her accustomed way kept her feelings to herself. To have expressed them would have met with little sympathy. She blamed her mother for her father's absence, quite convinced it was her mother's sharp tongue that had driven him away. In fact, Morgan was missed by them all, not least by Margaret Ann who found the old double bed she had shared with him for over thirty years particularly cold and empty. She dosed herself and the rest of the family with her usual physic of hard work, it being the surest defence against any lowering of the spirits, yet everyone noticed how those spirits rose when the frequent postcards arrived with news of the traveller.

William called regularly in at Min-yr-Afon as he felt mainly responsible for his father's departure to America. Edgar was still living at home as was Morgan James, but neither could be relied upon to be of practical assistance to their mother. One evening he was busy fixing a new lock on the coalhouse door when Margaret Ann came out. Brusquely she said, 'Is there anything you need, now Ann is nearing her time?'

'Everything is ready, Mam, but I will be glad when it is over.'

'Mrs Thomas will be the midwife I suppose, but make sure you call the doctor in good time, and keep those *ceiliog* girls away from the baby.'

'Mam, when will you stop bothering about Ann's family?'

'Never!' his mother's reply was sharp. 'Joanna and Hannah Jane are riddled with TB, if I know anything about it. Having Ann around them might be good for them but it is not good for her or the baby.'

On 25th June 1909 Margaret Ann's first grandchild was born and six weeks later William brought Ann and his new son to receive her blessing. This was freely given to Thomas Humphrey who carried the names of both his grandfathers, but in spite of having presented the family with the first of a new generation, there was no blessing for Ann. William was forced to accept what his father had always known – that Margaret Ann would never allow into her family any that were not her own.

CHAPTER 23
AMBITIONS

Morgan spent twelve weeks in America in 1909 and his return from Pennsylvania was eagerly anticipated by the family. Edgar journeyed to Liverpool to be the first of the welcoming party. As Morgan came down the gangway, his son realised with a shock how much he had aged, but he also sensed seeing his father's bowed head, that something was wrong. After a warm greeting, quietly he asked, 'All well with Mamgu and the aunties?'

'The girls are fine, but I was too late for Mamgu. The day before we docked in New York, the captain received a telegram for me on board. It was from my brother-in-law to say Mam had gone. How I wished I hadn't delayed so long. If only I'd gone sooner.'

Edgar put a sympathetic hand on his father's arm. 'Why didn't you write?'

'I couldn't put that news on a picture postcard. It wouldn't seem right, and there was nothing any of you could do,' replied his father. 'One day was all I needed and I could have been there at the end, and we could have said our goodbyes. It was hard, but at least I was there for the funeral and I could help their minister with the service. It meant a lot to my sisters too, and it was good to be with them. Just as well your mother refused to come.'

Edgar said nothing more but gave his father an uncharacteristic hug. Morgan was even more quiet than usual on the long journey south. From his occasional sigh Edgar guessed he was reliving the moment had he arrived in his sister's house in Pennsylvania, to be greeted with the sight he had most dreaded. His mother lay, immaculate as ever, in her best black bombazine, tiny and wizened, in the incongruously ornate coffin his sister had chosen.

'No-one at home would be seen dead in a coffin like that!' Morgan had thought to himself while a little grin played over his solemn face at his involuntary choice of words.

'What ever are you grinning at? This is no time for mirth.' Mary Ann was shocked. 'That is the best coffin in the funeral parlour, I'll have you know.' With that, his irritated sister had stomped out.

Alone with his mother, Morgan had recalled all the comforting phrases he had used throughout his ministry, the texts and prayers he knew so well, which he had often used to comfort the bereaved. This time they did not seem so powerful. He took his mother's icy, unresponsive hand.

'Into thy hands, O Lord, I commend her spirit' he had murmured, bent to kiss her head, turned and left the bedroom, as the tears came.

All these images replayed before Morgan's eyes as the train chugged through the little hills of Shropshire and Herefordshire.

'Come on, Dadda,' Edgar attempted to rouse his father from his reverie. 'We'll be in Cardiff soon, and you'll need to be a bit more lively when we get home.'

William was waiting at Cardiff to accompany them up the valley and his father had time to share the sad news with his other son before they reached Min-yr-Afon. As the little train rattled up the valley, Morgan was struck by the smallness of the scene through the window of the train. Little houses clinging to the narrow valley sides, low stone walls marking the boundaries of the few farms left in the valley, but most of all it was the people who caught his attention. Even the people seemed smaller – bent and shrunken, their shoulders hunched against the wind, the women with shawls around their heads and toddlers clinging to their skirts. All seemed in some way diminished, compared with their transatlantic counterparts. Morgan was shaken by the contrast and wondered to himself why it should be so stark.

William bombarded his father with a string of technical questions about the ship, the layout of the colliery in which his cousins worked and the rates of pay received by the American miners – none of which his father could answer.

'Ask him about the chapels, Will, where he preached and what the singing was like, then you'll get some answers,' prompted Edgar in an attempt to lift his father's spirits.

'I'll tell you one amazing thing that happened.' Morgan gave a faint smile. 'A few days after my mother's funeral, the minister of the chapel in Nanticoke asked me if I would like to preach one Sunday before I came back. I was very grateful and I was sure I could prepare a sermon, as long as I could check a few references over first. Of course, my sisters were thrilled. We sang "For Ever with the Lord" which was one of Mamgu's favourite hymns. After the service I was standing on the steps to speak to the congregation as they left, when a fellow came up to me and shook my hand. He'd enjoyed the sermon, he said, it reminded him of one he'd heard many years ago in Treorci, Rhondda! As I spoke to him he suddenly asked, "Reverend Morgan Jones, are you any relation of that wonderful preacher the Reverend Morgan *Humphrey* Jones?"

'He couldn't believe his eyes at first, then he shook my hand over and over! You can imagine how I felt, so the girls had to ask him for tea and we met a few times afterwards to talk over old times. He very kindly accompanied me on the train to the East River Pier in New York to board the ship to come home. It was an amazing coincidence!'

Margaret Ann and the girls were ready at the door, and if they had not exactly killed the fatted calf, they had made sure there were enough Welsh cakes and *bara brith* ready and waiting for Morgan's return. Margaret Ann busied herself with directing proceedings, but even she was unable to avoid stealing surreptitious glances at the wanderer, and William was amused to see how it was apparently necessary for his mother to lean against his father's shoulder as she handed him his tea.

The family received the sad news of Mamgu's death respectfully, but as only Edgar really remembered her, conversation was not subdued for long. Gifts for all the family were produced as was traditional for anyone who journeyed away from home, be it only a day trip to Cardiff. Arthur was overjoyed to receive a real Indian tomahawk and Agnes was given a carved bone-handled button hook, which became her most treasured possession.

Among Margaret Ann's presents was a beautiful American patchwork quilt from her sisters-in-law, which, for reasons known only to herself never graced any bed in her house, not even the one in the guest bedroom. (Many years later, the quilt was found in the attic, still wrapped in newspaper dating from 1909 and tied with string.)

The family quickly settled down to being complete again. Morgan was careful not to talk too much of his experiences in America in his wife's presence but he was happy to recount them to his children when the opportunity presented itself. Arthur was convinced his father would return with exciting tales of cowboys and indians, and was disappointed to learn that the only feathered headdress his father had seen was in the museum in Philadelphia. Arthur's older brothers and sisters were fascinated by Morgan's stories of life on board ship and Gladys wanted to know if everybody was seasick. His descriptions of the skyscrapers going up along the banks of the Hudson River in New York, the noise and bustle of traffic and the grandeur of Philadelphia enlivened many evenings while Margaret Ann was occupied elsewhere.

The traveller's tales sowed the seeds of lifelong enjoyment of travelling in all his children and strengthened their interest in life outside the valley. Morgan himself wanted to hear all about Edgar's political activities in Merthyr while he had been away. The country was going through turbulent political times and he took to reading several daily newspapers avidly to the annoyance of his wife.

One morning towards the end of 1909 he called out to Margaret Ann as she passed from one room to another. 'Quick, Margaret Ann, come and read this! The *Western Mail* is saying the House of Lords has rejected Lloyd George's budget, and parliament is to be dissolved. There's going to be a general election.' He waved the newspaper excitedly.

'The sooner, the better, then. The quicker these Merthyr people decide whether they want Edgar or not, the better pleased I'll be. He spends all his time with politicians and he's never home before eleven o'clock. He's got Morgan James all worked up too, and they are forever in some meeting or other. Mrs Kane told me about a meeting in Newport last week when our Edgar held the floor and everyone cheered and clapped. She asked me to guess who should have been on the platform with him – only Lloyd George himself. The great man was late and missed the start of the meeting but he listened in the lobby, and apparently said our Edgar will go far.'

Morgan could not resist adding, 'I shall just be pleased and proud when all is settled and we can write "MP" after Edgar's name. What an achievement that would be! He's come a long way from catching the mailbag. First teaching in Porth, then a lawyer, and soon we hope a member of parliament.'

'You may well hope that, but once you write MP after Edgar's name on letters to London, that is the last of him we will see in this house.'

'Come now, Margaret Ann, Min-yr-Afon will still be his home, though he will need to find somewhere to live in London while the House is sitting. He'll have to get plenty of legal work too, to pay his way and keep a roof over his head.'

'And how long will it be before his life is all in London and nothing left for Wattstown?'

Morgan rose from his chair and walked over to Margaret Ann. He caught hold of her hand and pulled her towards him. 'Listen to me. if you think that Edgar's success will cause him to forget his family and his home, you are seriously mistaken. If he does abandon us then he can blame it on us, you and me. He knows how important we are to him – you and Will and me, as well as the younger ones, but that doesn't mean he has to stay in Cwtch till his dying day. Go to London he will anyway, and if he's successfully elected, he'll be a diligent MP and will spend plenty of time in his constituency, so he'll be around more than you think. All our children have a right to go their own ways. If their departure is to make you weep, you will have to weep in private and not use your tears to prevent their going.'

'Tears? Weep, you say? There is no time for weeping in this house. When have you ever seen me weep? Go on, out of my way, and let me get on with my jobs. There'll be time enough to think when the election is over.'

It was true. Margaret Ann was not given to tears. Morgan had always known how intensely his wife felt for her children, and yet how difficult she found it to demonstrate physical affection towards them. He had given a lot of thought to the problem over the years but had failed to come up with a solution, other than to offer his children more affection himself, but he was fearful as to the strategies Margaret Ann might employ to keep her family about her. Perhaps it was he who should weep for his children, not because they were leaving, but at the tight hold their mother continued to exercise over them, to confine them in the fortress she had built. At the moment the only absentee was Maggie, now studying at Exeter College, an experience she was greatly enjoying. Away from the restrictions placed on her at home, out of Jane's shadow, she discovered a sense of fun, a love of art and an ability to make friends amongst her fellow students.

As soon as the general election was called, to everyone's surprise, the new Liberal candidate's most enthusiastic family supporter was Morgan James who threw himself into the campaign. He dealt with correspondence, checked the arrangements for meetings, and in effect became his brother's secretary. His sister Jane reserved her support until Edgar publicly declared himself to be in favour of votes for women but once he had done so, she campaigned with as much enthusiasm and energy as Morgan James, much to the amazement of the other young women in Wattstown. The Votes for Women campaign was gathering pace nationally and the dramatic account in The *Western Mail* of the arrest of 120 women for demonstrating had enraged Jane. Soon the young women in the valley were flocking to join Edgar's campaign, causing much anxiety to their parents who feared their daughters were in serious moral danger.

Edgar spent many hours preparing and refining his first speech of the campaign, and was heartened when Margaret Ann announced that she would come to listen to him when he held his first election meeting at the Market Hall in Merthyr. Speaking as a Lloyd George Liberal, he made absolutely clear his position on the burning questions of the day. He supported votes for women, free trade, old age pensions and the reform of the House of Lords. He also declared himself a wholehearted supporter of the disestablishment of the Church of England in Wales. He was skilful in not causing antagonism between himself and the Socialist candidate, Keir Hardie, who had a devoted following in the valleys. Edgar stated frequently that while he did not fully embrace the Socialist creed, he had a true respect for the Labour Party and believed profoundly that the proper study of government should be the social welfare of the people.

The day of the first election meeting, Margaret Ann herself ironed Edgar's shirt and refused to allow 'the girl' anywhere near the starch mixture she had prepared for the stiff wing collar Edgar preferred. Before Edgar left the house he was required to stand in front of his mother while his jacket was brushed so vigorously he was forced to beg her to stop while there was still some cloth to be seen.

The family arrived in good time for the meeting and were ushered into prominent positions towards the front. Margaret Ann disguised her concern for her son by snapping at all and sundry who came near, but she need not have worried. Edgar was in his element. Years of listening to his father's sermons with their measured cadences, and his own sense of the dramatic made him an impressive speaker. When he finished speaking in the Market Hall, with the exception of Margaret Ann, the family joined in the hearty cheering. His mother allowed herself a dignified handclap. Edgar glowed. He had proved himself well able to handle diverse audiences, to answer questions with ease and wit, and to deflect heckling likely to cause problems. His frequent public speaking opportunities had allowed him to develop a concise and succinct delivery, and the techniques he had perfected in his previous speeches came in very useful. His supporters were convinced he could say more in five minutes than many of his political opponents could say in twenty-five!

Morgan attended most of his son's meetings and was an enthusiastic critic of their content and presentation. He himself was an accomplished public performer in the pulpit, experienced in judging the reaction of a congregation, and Edgar was grateful for his father's advice. On the way back from another lively meeting Edgar revealed his disappointment at the reception he had received. Keir Hardie was sure to be one of the two successful candidates elected by Merthyr Boroughs but if Edgar were to defeat the other two contenders, it was vital that he should capture at least some of Hardie's votes.

'Where am I going to find those extra supporters, Dadda?'

'You are missing a golden opportunity, my boy. You forget you're speaking to a Welsh audience. You need to remind them that you are a native of these valleys, born in Cwmamman, and your first language is Welsh. Keir Hardie can't compete with that. Try it and see.'

At his next meeting in Cefn Coed y Cymmer, Edgar took his father's advice and began his speech in Welsh. The cheers which followed were sufficient for the *Merthyr Express* to report on the great popularity of the candidate and the delight felt by the electorate that the candidate was one of their own.

On New Year's Eve 1909 the family assessed Edgar's campaign, each bringing their own hopes and fears to the discussion. It was a Friday, but Margaret Ann and her daughters had prepared a dinner more in keeping with a grand Sunday roast. It was the first time for several weeks the entire family had gathered round the table and Ann had been persuaded to leave little Thomas with her parents so that she could share in the general air of excitement. The women bustled around serving food and clearing plates and joining in the conversation.

'Keep on about votes for women, Edgar.' Jane instructed her brother. 'It's a disgrace we are expected to run homes, bring up children, and teach the next generation of men, without having a say in how the country should be run! Have you heard they are giving Welsh lessons to women in London so they can heckle Lloyd George in his own language!'

Morgan was convinced that Edgar's bid to enter parliament would be successful. He was impressed with his son's power of oratory, and knew how the miners responded to the power of the spoken word. William was of the opinion that Edgar had made some converts from socialism but thought the votes of the small shopkeepers up and down the valley would be split between his brother and the Independent Liberal. He had often heard the views of Ann's parents on the matter, but knew better than to upset the amiable tone of the dinner by mentioning their names in front of his mother!

Amy, as well as Jane, had worked hard to help her brother's campaign and both his sisters were hopeful for his success, and Maggie returned to college convinced that her big brother would soon be a member of parliament. Morgan James had only one wish, to see Edgar returned to Westminster, because his own plans depended on that result. What those plans were, he kept to himself. Agnes was the least interested in Edgar's latest 'venture' as she called it. Her self-imposed detachment from the family resulted in a vicious circle of little or no news of the campaign being shared with her, which left her feeling more left out than ever. Margaret Ann said little and kept herself aloof from the excitement. She was completely torn between pride in her eldest son, a burning wish to see him succeed and fear of the consequences if he did so.

∽ ∽ ∽

As Ann and William walked back down the valley in the twilight they mulled over the mealtime conversation.

'I think Edgar could do it, you know, Will. He's very popular and everyone I talk to has something good to say about him.'

'That's not enough Ann. People have to believe he'll do something to improve their lives. Better homes, more chances for education and more support for people who are unemployed. That's what will get Edgar in, and Lloyd George, too. We'll just have to keep our fingers crossed. That's enough politics for today though. Let's go and see how Thomas has got on being ruined by your mother.'

On the night of the election the returning officer for the constituency settled the matter. Edgar topped the poll in a resounding victory, returning the highest number of votes cast for a Liberal. The other successful candidate was Keir Hardie, for Labour. As he listened to the announcement, Edgar was momentarily overwhelmed with emotion and pride, but as the applause continued to ring out he raised his head to thank his supporters.

'We've done it. Thanks to you, I'm off to Westminster!'

It was a particularly good result for Edgar as the Liberals were returned to power with a greatly reduced majority. He and his father were well known and respected in the community and many people in the Rhondda Fach shared the family's pride and delight. Immediately after the result was declared, late in the evening, Edgar set out on a tour of the constituency. Several of his wealthier supporters were the proud owners of motor cars and willingly lent them to the successful candidate, so that Edgar's new constituents could see their MP in the flesh. By the end of the night seven cars had joined the motorcade and Edgar was frequently forced to stand up in the back of his vehicle and make yet another short and enthusiastic speech. Morgan James, who had been at Edgar's side during the whole campaign, was beside himself with excitement. At last he could see where his future lay and he was invited to join the cavalcade in the second car. Edgar's sisters were furious as the cavalcade set off. Margaret Ann deemed it was unladylike to ride in such a procession in the dead of night and they were reduced to standing on the steps of the Institute to wave as their brothers rode by.

It had been an exhausting campaign, but the Liberal battles with the Tory-dominated House of Lords continued. The death of Edward VII in May 1910 produced a truce but it was only temporary, and before the end of the year a second general election was called. This took place in December and meant the Jones family were called upon to support Edgar again in the second election within twelve months. The family anxiously awaited the result. To their delight Edgar again topped the poll with 12,258 votes, while Keir Hardie came second again with 11,507.

By then Edgar had established himself in a flat in Smith Street, Chelsea, and had found a place in Chambers. He was earning money as a writer as well as practising law. His father's prediction that he would make frequent visits to Min-yr-Afon to attend to his constituents' problems proved correct. It was on his second visit, when Edgar and Morgan James were working in the parlour on constituency business, that Morgan James said, 'I seem to be occupied most of the time with your correspondence here. It's almost a full-time job. I'm wondering if it would be more sensible if I came to London with you?'

There was a pause, before Edgar replied, 'Possibly, but you have a job here in the National and I do not yet make enough to pay you what you are getting there.'

Morgan James appeared to think for a moment. Then he divulged his plan. 'Well, I am working for you and National at the moment so no doubt if I can do two jobs here, then I can do two jobs in London. If I am a good secretary to one MP, I can be a good secretary to two MPs. I thought you might look around and find someone else in need of a secretary. If you start paying me and the other one does as well, I'll manage to keep myself, especially if you'll let me put a camp bed in your box room for now.'

'What on earth will Mam say if I lure you to London?'

'Come on, Edgar, you know as well as I do that this valley's not for me. Will is settled with Ann and the baby and you're in London half the time. I've no interest in staying here. Mam's always done as she sees fit, so I don't see why the rest of us shouldn't.'

Impressed by his brother's determination to take control of his life, Edgar promised he would find another MP in need of a personal secretary. True to his word, he persuaded the MP for the Forest of Dean to offer Morgan James a post and it was not long before Morgan James joined him in London as private secretary to two members of parliament.

Morgan James loved London. No-one knew him; his comings and goings were entirely his own affair and he could indulge his love of art by visiting a different art gallery every week. The bustle and glamour of Edwardian London suited him perfectly and he was able to indulge his taste for colourful ties without fear of his mother's rebukes.

Margaret Ann had feared that it would be Edgar, once established in London who would forsake the land of his fathers. In reality it was Morgan James who did so, but then he had always resisted being brought too close into the family. 'The cat who walked by himself' was a fair description of Morgan James, but to his mother his departure was yet another threat to family unity. Consequently, she pulled the bonds that held her daughters and her youngest son Arthur even closer.

CHAPTER 24
MORE MOVES

The summer of 1911 brought Edgar home for a few days, while young Morgan James remained in London busy with his secretarial duties. He still found time to dine with friends, and enjoy the latest art exhibitions. The discovery of the theatre had given him a new passion and every spare penny was spent on a ticket for one of the latest productions. Edgar seemed quite happy to provide a roof over his brother's head and as long as Morgan was 'on hand' to do his bidding, the arrangement suited them both.

Delighted at the prospect of having Edgar home and helped by the latest girl, Margaret Ann was turning out the parlour for its regular weekly clean with more than her usual gusto. As she finished beating the cushions Edgar came into the room in search of some notes. 'You've not seen my copy of Lloyd George's last speech have you, Mam?'

With an edge to her voice his mother remarked, 'There are books and papers everywhere in this house. Your father brought enough of them here without you adding to it, and since you've got those letters after your name the books alone seem to have doubled.'

'What's wrong with books then, Mam?'

'I'll tell you what's wrong with these books. They take up too much space and too much of my time moving them from one place to another in order to dust them and clean behind. Soon the place will be all books and papers and we will be living in the backyard.' With exaggerated effort she started to move another pile of books on the table.

Never one to engage in a battle of words with his mother, Edgar found the papers he was looking for and disappeared in search of his father.

'Mam is carrying on about the books in the parlour, Dadda. She thinks we will soon be living in the backyard and books will take over in the house.'

'There is some truth in that,' chuckled his father. 'I would have thought that with Will gone and you two away most of the time, the house ought to be big enough, but it seems there is never enough space. Arthur has the little bedroom to himself now when you aren't here, but Gladys is still in with Amy and Agnes, and Jane and Maggie will be back from college soon.'

'I agree with you, but where would you find a bigger house in Wattstown? There's only Glenside and I don't think the National would build another house for the manager. I do need to keep many of my books and other possessions here. I can't get any work done when I'm in the constituency office. I'm too busy meeting people and talking. With Morgan James sharing my rooms in London, I certainly could not move them up there. Besides I need a proper address in the constituency.'

'It needs thinking about but I don't know what the solution might be. I was considering going down to Ynishir this evening to have a word with Will. He's often got a bright idea about this sort of thing.'

'That is a good plan. I'll walk with you. It's time I looked in on young Thomas Humphrey or I won't recognise my own nephew, he's growing so fast.'

The house in which William and Ann lived in Yynshir was located in 'Knobby Row', so called because the gatepost finials were decorated with stone spheres. William was just finishing repairing the latch on the kitchen door when he heard the welcome sound of his father's voice. Hastily, he put down his tools.

'Edgar, you too! How good to see you! How's London looking? How long are you home for? Tell me, how is Mam? Last time I was up there she was laying the law down to Arthur about the time he spent hanging about with his pals. It sounded just like the way she used to lay into me. Come on in, Dadda, and Ann will put the kettle on.'

'How's Ann doing, with a new one on the way?' Edgar enquired.

'She's fine, but it's as well her mother is a midwife I think. I don't think we'll have nine though! We'll see how these two turn out first. P'raps we'll end up with one like you and one like Arthur!'

Their father chuckled. 'Arthur's not at all interested in school, not like Gladys. She is never happier than when she's in the classroom. The holidays just have to be got through so she can get back to her lessons but her brother is a different kettle of fish. He's only happy when he's messing down the brook, or playing football!'

The three men went inside and chatted quietly while Ann duly made a pot of tea. When she came into the room with Thomas, the two-year-old ran to his father clamouring to be perched on his knee, while the grown-ups resumed their conversation.

'Mam is threatening to move us out to the backyard to make room for the books Dadda and I are collecting.'

'It is not only books we need room for,' said Morgan. 'The girls are forever looking for room to prepare their lessons and make all the illustrations they deem necessary to teach the children.'

Edgar looked at his brother. 'I don't suppose you know of a bigger house do you, Will? Dadda is quite right, the girls do need more room, with three of them sharing, and the middle bedroom is very cramped. I could move out altogether, and buy another house for myself in the constituency, but I don't think Mam would find that to her liking.'

'You'll not find anything much larger than Min-yr-Afon about here, and you're right about Mam. She would hate it if you were to set up your own house on her doorstep. No, if it is a bigger house you need, Dadda, you would do better to build your own. I've thought for some time that Min-yr-Afon is too small for you. What on earth you'll do when Maggie gets back from Exeter, I don't know. I could make enquiries in the office about possible plots which you might be able to buy from the Estate.'

'Go about it quietly then, my boy,' his father urged. 'It will do no good to rush things until Mam herself thinks it is necessary.'

'She will think it necessary quickly enough if Edgar mentions moving out on his own. I'll put a word in a few ears and see what I can find. You can trust me to make sure Mam knows nothing for a bit.'

For the next hour or so the men continued to talk. Will told his father and brother the good news he had received that very afternoon. Impressed with his management of the stores at the National, the colliery had offered him a new post as colliery manager at Abergorchy, a larger pit in the other valley, where he would be entitled to a company house that was a good deal larger than their present one. It had five bedrooms, a drawing room as well as a dining room and study, and a large garden with a tennis court. Most importantly, it had electricity. The prospect excited him, not least because it would distance Ann and little Thomas from her family in Ynyshir. Although he defended the *ceiliogs* from his mother's attacks, both of his sisters-in-law had tuberculosis, and Joanna was now seriously ill. William had been long concerned by the amount of time Ann spent with her sick sisters and feared the contagion of tuberculosis would come into his own household.

Edgar and his father were delighted by Will's good fortune. They knew the extent to which he had supported the family in Wattstown for many years, and felt he well deserved his promotion. Just he was being congratulated, Ann appeared with young Thomas.

'Say goodnight, Thomas, to your grandfather and uncle Edgar. Be a good boy for Mam now and start off up the stairs while I say goodbye to our visitors.'

After a few more minutes of peaceful conversation Edgar announced he had work to do and took his father's arm. Will went with them to the door. An idea suddenly struck him.

'Now I think of it, you might be able to get hold of that bit of land at the top of the village. The National have just completed a row of houses for the men further along and I've not heard of any plans for the end plot. It's a good size. Pleasant View, they've called it. Shall I see what the chances are?'

Edgar thought for a moment before saying, 'It is a bit of a climb up there, if you mean that row they have built below T'ir Gwaeth farm. But it'll do no harm to ask as long as it can be done discreetly. D'you remember running up there for the milk when we were little, Will?'

Morgan smiled at their immediate response to the problem, but warned his sons, 'Remember, Mam is to know nothing about it yet.'

On their way up the valley, Edgar suggested to his father that it would be a good idea if he were to approach his mother on the matter of a move to a larger house. The threat that Edgar would have to move out on his own, books and all, might be enough to encourage her to consider the proposal. With his customary decisiveness, before returning to London, Edgar suggested to Margaret Ann that the family had outgrown Min-yr-Afon and a larger and more comfortable house might suit everyone. His mother was just beginning to marshall her arguments against such a plan, when Edgar produced his trump card.

'Have you heard Will and Ann are to have a new house, now Will has been promoted? It's got five bedrooms and a room for a live-in maid! They'll be very pleased to move to Waun Fawr, Crosskeys. If you are opposed to a move I was thinking I might be able to rent a room off them to keep my books and things. I must have an address in the constituency.'

His mother was aghast. 'You will do no such thing. You have always got a room under my roof. Anyway what on earth have they decided they need that much room for! There's no need for it. No matter how many children they might have! Our circumstances here are completely different. There are eight of us in here and I've been thinking we'll need more space when Maggie gets back from Exeter. Why don't you see if there's anything around? But it'll have to be in Wattstown mind.'

Edgar was astounded. Without a battle, he had received his mother's agreement to a move from Min-yr-Afon, as long as it was not away from Cwtch. Edgar made it clear to his parents that he would be responsible for the major capital investment, on the basis that his social standing as an MP required a more prestigious house. Will was instructed to begin negotiations for the piece of land lying vacant at the end of Pleasant View and Margaret Ann raised no objection to the considerable climb up the hill. To her, as long as the new house was in Cwtch, its exact location did not matter.

Once their mother had acknowledged the need for a house in keeping with Edgar's status, her sons did not let the grass grow under their feet. The piece of land chosen by William was purchased by Edgar who immediately engaged an architect to draw up plans. The whole family were excited by the possibility of living in a new house, even if some of the younger generation would have preferred a smarter location. Two years in prosperous and fashionable Swansea and regular visits to Cardiff had widened Jane's horizons and she would have much preferred the move to have been to either city as she now had a considerable circle of friends outside the confines of the Rhondda. Amy, too, favoured a move outside the valley but although Gladys was just about to leave for college in Exeter it was to Wattstown she intended to return in the holidays. Both she and Arthur had no intention of leaving. All their friends lived in Cwtch and as far as they were concerned they were going nowhere else.

Agnes made it known that she considered it madness to move to the top of a hill. The little mound known to generations of children as 'the tump' made the climb even steeper, and although provisions could always be delivered, school books still had to be carried. Maggie was indifferent. She was completely engrossed in her life in Devon and felt that Newton Abbott was currently the centre of her world. She had no plans for returning to the valley, and imagined that her future would be as a farmer's wife, rather than a valley schoolmistress.

Gas had been available in the valley for some years and had long been used to light the rooms in Min-yr-Afon, but electric lighting could only be installed with the goodwill of the colliery, which generated its own supply. Will was called upon to negotiate for the supply of electricity to the new house and with such a modern amenity the girls considered they really would be living in the twentieth century. Electricity would be a source of considerable envy amongst their neighbours but suspicious as ever of 'new fangled fads', Margaret Ann was gravely concerned with the fire risk. She believed disaster was inevitable if electricity were to be installed. No amount of reassurance made any difference. The flames of the gas lights she could keep an eye on, but electricity was invisible and therefore highly dangerous.

The architect's plans were at last submitted to Edgar who brought them on his next visit home, to allow his mother time to examine them and express her views. It had been books and the need to find space for the ever growing collection which had been the seed from which the idea of a larger house had grown. Edgar had therefore asked the architect to allow for a decent study in the plans. He returned from London with a large cardboard tube under his arm, and on his first evening he produced the tube with a flourish, and unrolled the plans on the kitchen table. As they were all studying them Margaret Ann asked, 'What is this space here, next to the bathroom?'

'A water closet, Mam.'

'A water closet! Not inside my house! A water closet upstairs! Never!' she almost shrieked. 'Out the back is the place for a closet. Look! here is one on these plans in the proper place. A *ty bach* should be outside, next to the wash house and the coal house.'

'Mam, it is much better to have one inside the house, and upstairs is the best place. Then no one needs to go outside and there's no need for the emptying of chamber pots.'

Edgar tried reasoning but his mother was adamant. She would have no inside water closet in her house and Edgar must tell the architect to remove it and revise the plan accordingly.

Morgan was only concerned to find that there was indeed the promised study and that the architect had placed it well away from the other downstairs rooms, at the end of a short corridor, with the pantry as its only neighbour. The kitchen, with a scullery leading

212

off it, was at the back of the house, and the dining room and the parlour, now upgraded to a drawing room, were located each side of a large square hall. This had a handsome glass panelled inner door leading to a partly glazed porch and an oak entrance door. Large bay windows adorned the left side of the front of the house and the stairs were lit by a long window at the back of the house, picked out with panes of stained glass. The main landing led to four bedrooms, a box room and the bathroom. More stairs led to two attic rooms, one for a storeroom, the other an extra bedroom. The plot of land allowed for a fair sized garden at the back of the house and a flight of elegant steps rose to the front door. Just as Agnes had feared the house was indeed perched on top of the tump overlooking the village.

Edgar informed the architect that the water closet was to be removed from upstairs, but otherwise the plans were approved. Amy, Agnes and Jane were aghast when told of the embargo their mother had placed on the upstairs water closet. They had all experienced the discomfort of going to the lavatory at the bottom of the garden in the cold and dark of winter nights as well as the misery of emptying chamber pots. During their time in their various colleges they had become accustomed to the convenience of inside water closets and they did not intend to go outside again. Amy and Jane made a desperate effort to make their mother lift the embargo. Agnes thought it wise not to be part of the delegation, convinced that if her mother thought she was in favour of an upstairs water closet, it would make the possibility of acquiring such a luxury even more improbable. In spite of the intense pressure, after several days of negotiation, the delegation was forced to admit defeat. Margaret Ann was triumphant.

With some reluctance Jane decided it was time to bring William into the argument. As he and Ann had just welcomed the arrival of their first daughter, Jane and Amy had the perfect excuse to make the journey down the valley to see the new baby. After the two sisters had duly admired the latest arrival, named Hannah Margaret, they began a recital of their tale of woe. William listened patiently before asking, 'What is Edgar doing about all this? It's supposed to be his house, isn't it?'

'Huh,' Jane snorted, 'he's gone back to London, hasn't he?'

'And we think he has told the architect not to include the upstairs lavatory, just because Mam says.' Amy added.

'I don't know what you expect me to do. If Edgar has been in touch with the architect, it will be too late anyway.'

'Well,' said Jane, 'you'll have to write to Edgar at once and tell him Mam is unreasonable.'

William laughed. 'He ought to know that by now. Anyway, why are you girls making such a fuss? At least there will be one water closet in the new house – better than an earth one, and a lot nearer than the one you've got at the moment in Min-yr-Afon.'

'There's an upstairs one in Glenside and…' began Jane.

'Oh! Now I see, the new house is to compete with Glenside, is that it?'

'Don't be silly, Will. It's all very well for you to laugh. No one in your house has to walk down the garden. Waun Fawr has two inside lavatories!' Amy snapped. Jane joined in.

'Competing with Glenside has got nothing to do with it. Mam must be made to see sense. With water upstairs for the bathroom, it's nonsense not to include the lavatory. If she gets her own way, she'll regret it in the end.'

'Very well, if I have time I'll write to Edgar but I'm not going to talk to Mam about it. It's a waste of time, as you girls should know. Once she gets an idea in her head, talking will not make her shift.'

With that reply, the girls had to be satisfied. Will duly wrote to Edgar in the hope that the letter would reach him before he had contacted the architect, pointing out the folly of allowing their mother's prejudices to prevent the installation of an essential modern amenity.

'My advice would be to leave the lavatory where it is. Even Mam will not insist on its removal when all is complete. Face her with the job done and she will have to accept it.' William's common sense prevailed and Edgar agreed.

For now, William had far more important issues to deal with. He was more than occupied with the demands of his new post at Abergorchy, as well as supporting Ann, who was struggling to cope with the two little ones. The death of her older sister from tuberculosis and the declining health of her younger sister was an additional source of anxiety for them too, and William occasionally found himself looking at Ann with a terrible sense of foreboding. For several months now, he had been aware that his wife was occasionally wracked with bouts of coughing, which she just attributed to 'winter damp.' William was not convinced and insisted that Ann agreed to consult a well known chest physician in Newport. The outcome of the consultation struck fear in his heart. Rest, winters in Torquay and nourishing broths were prescribed and all contact with her surviving sister was to cease. William and Ann returned to Waun Fawr and drew even closer to each other.

By springtime 1912 the new house was completed. Morgan named it 'Gorwel', Welsh for 'horizon.' The completed building did indeed include the controversial upstairs water closet. Surprisingly the architect had somehow forgotten to delete the new-fangled facility from the plans and as William had predicted, Margaret Ann did not demand its removal. However, she decreed that it was to be used only for the convenience of visitors. Chamber pots were to continue to be used in the bedrooms, and the outside lavatory was for everyday use by the family. The house was duly wired for electricity and by the end of the first week no-one heard any more about fire risks from Margaret Ann as she showed curious visitors into the darkened parlour and then switched on the lights with a flourish.

From the elegant bay windows Margaret Ann looked down on the narrow valley, filled it seemed, with the giant mounds of the coal tips that increased yearly, as yet more and more coal was ripped from the earth. The strange shapes of the colliery winding gear, almost disappearing into the lowering dark clouds, the tall chimneys belching steam at the pithead baths and the rattling and clanking of the coal trucks gave the little valley an almost nightmarish quality. Her gaze moved to the busy railway, where the trucks carried the black gold down the valley to Cardiff to be shipped all over the world. She remembered the sparkling streams, which were now black with coal dust. Gone were the bluebells and the birch trees overhanging the river banks, the clumps of primroses on the banks and the ferns unfurling under the hedge rows. She had thought it the most beautiful place she had ever seen but all that was gone. Only the mountain tops were the same, and in the autumn the higher slopes of the steep valley sides still turned purple with the heather.

She shook her head. Margaret Ann was not given to introspection. There was no point thinking about the valley as it used to be. Instead she remembered how proud she had been the day she arrived in Cwtch with her two small boys. She had opened her shop, the pit disgorged its first coal and the population of the village had more than trebled. How much had changed. She was fifty-six and had borne nine children, all fit and well. Edgar was an MP and rapidly making a name for himself in parliament, William was managing the colliery in the lower valley, and four of her daughters were all qualified schoolmistresses. Even Morgan James was doing well, although she was not quite sure at what. She and Morgan had much to celebrate and surely now they could rest on their laurels.

'We've risen to the top like the cream in the milk' she thought to herself. 'The family has certainly gone up in the world and not just up the tump either.' No longer would she be Mrs Jones, the Shop, or even Mrs Jones, the Post. From now to the end of her days she would be Mrs Jones, Gorwel.

CHAPTER 25
LIFE IN GORWEL

Morgan was delighted with the new house. The room at the end of the short passage, known to all as the Little Room, became his sanctum. Regimental rows of leather-bound books clad the walls from floor to ceiling. An elegant rug, which had been given to Edgar by a grateful client, lay on the floor and Morgan's old desk, polished to within an inch of its life, took centre stage. He had salvaged his postmaster's chair and it made a splendid addition to the room. Agnes had stuffed a cushion for the seat and made a cushion cover from crotcheted squares so that her father should be more comfortable – a gesture which prompted Margaret Ann to make one of her habitually astringent remarks about unnecessary pampering. Perhaps though, it was Agnes's concern for her father's well-being, which accounted for an unaccustomed impulse purchase by Margaret Ann. On a furniture-buying spree to Cardiff she bought a smart chaise-longue upholstered in the latest tartan, for the Little Room so that her husband should be able to put his feet up and read in comfort.

The rest of the rooms were furnished in some style as Margaret Ann was unwilling to admit that William's house down the valley was furnished more smartly than hers. Jane and Maggie, who between them had excellent taste and a good eye for colour took the lead in matters of interior design. The dining room furniture in heavy polished mahogany was the last word in elegance, and the carved owl heads with their amber eyes, which formed the handles of the drawers to the sideboard, delighted young visitors.

Margaret Ann allowed no-one to decide on the equipment and furnishings for the kitchen. Her old dresser, which had caused the removal lads such difficulty when they tried to move it into Aberllechau Road, was installed against the long wall and she arranged her jugs as carefully as ever on the top shelf. For forty years her lustre jug had been her prized possession and it still had pride of place in the middle of the row. Cupboards and drawers filled the alcoves either side of the new range, but the old deal table around which so many family meals had been eaten, still dominated the middle of the room.

Much to everyone's surprise Margaret Ann had agreed to the installation of a large new kitchen range with an extra oven. She justified the extravagance on the basis that everyone would now be able to have their dinner served hot, as latecomers would simply take their plates of food from the lower oven and to be late home from school would not now mean cold dinner. The latest girl was less happy, as maintaining the larger range in its pristine state was clearly going to take a lot of cleaning and polishing.

Edgar was so delighted with the success of his scheme that he was happy to provide the necessary funds for the new range, and the transformation of the new house into the family home was soon complete. Letters addressed to him at Gorwel, Wattstown, found their way with no difficulty, and the opening of a constituency office lower down the valley meant that he could fully discharge his MP's responsibilities. The telephone in the hall ensured he could always be in touch with his constituency and his sisters had a means of contacting William in Waun Fawr in an emergency. Margaret Ann decided objections to yet another new-fangled machine were pointless. She never touched the telephone and insisted that, as it was a receiver, her daughters used it only for incoming calls.

Margaret Ann and Morgan were installed in their large, new bedroom overlooking the valley. Their final extravagance was to replace the old mattress on which they had slept for more than thirty years. The girls shared out the remaining bedrooms. Amy, as the eldest, chose the other front bedroom which she would share with Gladys when she was at home. Jane and Maggie claimed the back bedroom and it came as no surprise to anyone that Agnes chose the little attic bedroom. Arthur became the proud possessor of the box room and was the source of enormous envy amongst his friends as he was not required to share it with anybody. The remaining bedroom was solely for Edgar's use when he was at home and busy on constituency business.

New house or not, the family routines changed little from the regular pattern of life in Min-yr-Afon. Margaret Ann's latest maid was called Kate, and in a break with tradition she kept her name – in fact every maid who ever came to work for Mrs Jones, Gorwel afterwards was called Kate, regardless of the name they really owned. An extra girl – Florrie – was found to help with the additional housework and cleaning, which was essential if the house were to be maintained in its shiny newness; between them, they ensured that the floors and windows sparkled, the brass shone and the pristine kitchen range continued to gleam.

For the first time in her life, Margaret Ann felt content. Gladys was about to complete her college career in Exeter with distinction. The four eldest girls were established in their chosen profession, all teaching in primary schools in the Rhondda. Amy and Jane impressed their senior colleagues with their skill and imagination in the classroom, while Maggie found teaching the youngest a satisfactory outlet for her maternal instincts. Working in a different school from Jane, she no longer felt the need to compete with her sister, but enjoyed sharing her ideas and helping her three older sisters with ideas for art and craft at which she excelled.

Agnes was also a teacher, but she liked neither her job nor the children she taught. To her, teaching resembled the cleaning of the Augean stables, with each day bringing more of the same dreary activities, never to be completed and endlessly repeated the next day. Lacking interest in the pupils and bereft of ideas, she depended on her sisters to provide suggestions for her week's lessons. Lesson plans were then carefully written out in the all-important record book

219

that had to be filled in weekly by all of them and submitted to each headmistress for scrutiny.

Gladys became a fully-fledged qualified teacher that summer. Unlike Agnes, she loved both her job and the children she taught. Her classroom was full of interesting and stimulating bits and pieces produced from her school bag each morning, including the now popular picture postcards. Gladys begged and borrowed all the cards she could and attached them to maps pinned to the classroom walls, so the children could learn about life outside the narrow confines of the valley. Her love of reading and storytelling came into their own, too. The children would sit in attentive silence, eagerly awaiting another of Miss Jones's stories. Music, however, was her downfall. She had no ear for music and she could neither remember a tune nor sing one correctly. But, ever resourceful, she appointed one of her more musical pupils as weekly 'music monitor.' The small musician's task was to choose a song for the week and teach it to the rest of the class. In this way Gladys could duly report to the headmistress that her class was regularly taught music.

One Sunday evening when all the sisters were busy in the dining room with their record books, Agnes complained as usual that she couldn't think of anything to do with her class for the following week. Gladys looked up in amazement.

'Well, Ag, you can always read to them. They love stories and they don't get much reading at home. My class made a play last week from a story I'd read them and they loved it.'

'Read to them! I've read enough stories to you and Arthur to last me a lifetime. It's all very well for you, Glad, you never had little brothers and sisters to amuse all day. I've used up every scrap of imagination I was born with, on you lot.'

Her sisters stared at her in amazement. The bitterness in Agnes's voice underlined the deep, unhealed wounds of her unhappy childhood. As well as the usual chores of child-minding for her four younger siblings, she had never forgotten those six weeks when she'd been incarcerated in the sick room, reading to two-year-old, pneumonia stricken Arthur. She had thought those days would never end! Why had she, all alone, borne the burden of those miserable six weeks?

As ever, Amy tried to improve matters. 'Come on, Agnes, that was a long time ago and you've had lots of time since then to find new ideas. I had to look after the little ones too, you know, the same as you.'

Agnes glared at them all, slammed her record book shut, stood up and stormed from the room. Her sisters heard her running up the stairs and then the faint bang of the attic bedroom door. Maggie tutted, and continued cutting out the gold stars which she awarded weekly for her pupils' best work. 'She's better off up there on her own. She really doesn't like the children in her class and she's always moaning about school. I don't know why she keeps doing it.'

In spite of having five independent, professional daughters Margaret Ann still kept them well in hand. Their household tasks were organised with the strictness of the school timetable and took priority over any other activity. Preparation of lessons filled the evenings as well as Sunday afternoons, leaving almost no time at all for any socialising. Their mother expected to be told where her daughters were going and why, and what time they expected to be home. On their return from any outing she questioned them closely about the company they had kept.

Amy and Agnes were naturally more compliant and generally put up with the cross-questioning, but Jane was much less inclined to relinquish her privacy and guarded it fiercely. She had relished her independence in Swansea and had no intention of allowing her mother to retake control of her life. This led to frequent complaints to Morgan in the quiet of their bedroom such as 'that Jane is a close one' or 'she must be up to something'; but Jane continued her visits to Swansea and Cardiff regardless of her mother's disapproval. Only Maggie was aware of Jane's growing fondness for a young artist she had met on a visit to the art gallery in Swansea and for once her sister managed to control her desire to *clec*.

Gladys had followed Maggie to college in Exeter and was free from the constraints of home for the time being, but unlike her sister, she had made her friends among other students with a Welsh background and was content to spend her college holidays with her old school friends. Maggie's friends at college had been the daughters of Devonshire farmers and she had spent holidays and weekends with their families, often staying away from home for several weeks at a time. Her delight in the company of the brother of a college friend who lived on a farm near Newton Abbott was only noticed by Jane, and the sisters colluded in keeping Maggie's regular correspondence with him away from their mother's sharp eyes.

∽ ∽ ∽

Arthur was in his last year at the county intermediate school in Porth but any questions put to him relating to his activities out of school, his friends or his future, were neatly deflected. His relaxed attitude to life worried Morgan greatly. He was pleased to see his son happy and well, but he felt Arthur's lack of direction was alarming. Even Morgan James had been easier to manage and Morgan spent a considerable amount of time worrying about his youngest son, wondering what he intended to do when he left Porth. The parents' quiet evening discussions when they retired for the night, frequently focused on Arthur and his behaviour. Morgan had tried mildly remonstrating with Margaret Ann about the ways in which she favoured the boy, but to no avail. Margaret Ann could not bring herself to confront Arthur about his lackadaisical ways and she became very used to addressing remarks to his disappearing back.

As the youngest son in a large family, he was thoroughly indulged and his mother rarely used her sharp tongue on him. Arthur was also the best-looking and tallest of the nine children, with a sunny personality and sociable nature. As soon as he appeared at the bottom of the tump, a bevy of young girls would appear and dawdle behind him down the road, until he disappeared into the Institute. Then they would sit on the wall and chatter like a row of starlings until the object of their adoration reappeared. Arthur would then stroll back up the hill complete with his entourage and noncha-

lantly ascend the steps to his front door. He rarely addressed a word
to any of his admirers, and frequently paid them no more attention
than an airy wave, which merely enhanced his attractions.

Arthur's ability to attract the girls increased his father's anxiety
about him. His parents had brought up eight children who were
all apparently unaware of the attractions of the opposite sex and
this was a new phenomenon. Margaret Ann's long held theory that
any behaviour of which she disapproved would be eradicated by
hard work and an endless list of household tasks seemed to have no
effect. Arthur was well practised in offloading undesirable activities
on to Gladys or even Maggie, and he combined this skill with an
ability to disappear whenever chores had to be done. Eventually his
mother would give up waiting and instruct the girl to do them.

ော် ော် ော်

But Arthur and his 'goings on' were completely forgotten one
dreary evening in early November. The rain was lashing down the
windows and the lights from the colliery down in the valley were
almost obliterated by the driving rain. Jane and Maggie were busy
preparing for the next day's lessons, when Amy came in.

'Maggie, does Ethel Edwards still go to painting classes?'

Maggie giggled. 'Not any longer. Not since our Morgan James
has gone to London. She gave up when he left, even though she
used to sit by me.'

'Well, I heard something interesting today. To judge by your
giggles, Maggie, it might interest you, too.'

The two sisters gave Amy their full attention. Anything relating to
their mysterious brother was significant.

'Come on then,' said Jane, 'what have you heard?'

'Sarah Williams, who teaches with Ethel Edwards in Ferndale,
says Ethel goes home to Risca at weekends and Morgan meets her
in Newport! He comes down on the train from London and they
go to the station buffet. Then he goes back up to London!'

Her sisters stared at her in disbelief. After an amazed silence
Maggie said, 'Are you sure? Are you going to tell Mam?'

'Not yet. You know what she was like when our Will and Ann started courting. Stuck in the kitchen and scrubbing everything, and on the warpath from morning till night. I'll wait and ask Edgar next time he is home. He might know what is going on.'

It was so unusual for Amy to restrain herself when gossip was in the air, her sisters were sure something was in the wind. On his next visit home, Edgar was subjected to severe interrogation until he was forced to confirm the rumour that Morgan James was indeed visiting Newport at weekends, and moreover Ethel and her mother had actually visited Morgan James when they were in London! He advised Amy most strongly to continue to keep the information from Margaret Ann.

'You know how Mam carried on when Will decided to marry Ann.'

'Everyone knew our Will was courting though,' Amy observed. 'As usual nobody knows what our Morgan is up to.'

'Better to leave it that way then,' said Edgar. 'When you hear that Ethel Edwards has given in her notice from school, will be time enough to tell Mam. And warn Maggie not to drop hints about it. Mam is no fool and she will put two and two together and then you'll all suffer.'

'Just like our Morgan to cause trouble and then disappear back to London,' complained Agnes.

Amy had indeed done her homework and revealed to her sisters that Ethel Edwards had graduated from the university in Aberyst-wyth, and had come back to the valley to teach. She remained aloof from her valley born colleagues and was not popular. She was a thin, plain, red-headed woman, who favoured very fetching hats, and was always elegantly dressed. His sisters thought Morgan James could have found a prettier, nicer girl from the valley, even if she had not been to university.

A few months later, Amy came bursting in to the kitchen one evening after school, with the news that Sarah Williams in Ferndale had heard that Morgan James had been to Ethel's home to meet her parents.

'That,' Amy informed her sisters portentously, 'means only one thing.'

'What means only one thing?' Margaret Ann enquired, hurrying in to the kitchen on the way to the scullery. Her daughters looked at each other in horror. There was no way they could keep the news from their mother now. Amy tried to leave the kitchen, only to be ordered by her mother to stay where she was. Maggie of course could not resist the temptation to tell all, in spite of glares and glances from her sisters.

'Our Morgan has been to Risca to Ethel Edwards's house and he's met her parents.'

'Who on earth is Ethel Edwards?' Margaret Ann sat down on the nearest chair with a thump.

Amy, Jane and Maggie looked at each other, drew breath and told her at considerable length, all the information they had discovered. They also revealed that all of them thought Ethel Edwards was strange and did not like her.

'She's always kept herself to herself,' muttered Jane. 'She reminds me of "the cat who walked by herself" in the *Just so Stories*. I read that story to my class this week and it reminded me of Ethel.'

'Never mind that! How long has this been going on?' Margaret Ann demanded.

'She's been after Morgan James for years,' contributed Amy.

'And she only came to painting classes and sat with me to keep an eye on him,' added Maggie.'

'It means only one thing,' Jane added her pennyworth. 'She clearly intends to marry our Morgan.'

Margaret Ann waited for the chatter to die away before speaking again. 'If that's what she wants and she is the sort of person you say she is, then no doubt marry him she will.'

Morgan's sisters were dumbfounded at their mother's reaction. The girls had expected their mother to announce her intention of ordering Morgan James home from London at once, and of giving him a piece of her mind. They found it difficult to believe she was accepting the possibility of her third son's marriage without putting up a fight.

'Mam,' said Amy, 'surely you do not want our Morgan to marry her?'

'It's not what I want, my girl, it's what this Ethel wants and it looks to me she's made her mind up, so Morgan James has probably got used to the idea.'

With that, Margaret Ann picked up her mending basket and went into the Little Room where her husband was reading. Without preamble she said, 'Morgan, the girls tell me our Morgan James is visiting Risca with that Ethel Edwards who teaches in Ferndale. Have you heard anything about this? Who on earth are the Edwards? We don't know them at all.'

'Sit down, Margaret Ann,' said Morgan, quietly putting down his book. 'What is this all about? Surely the girls are making too much of a very little. Do they know the lady concerned?'

'Maggie seems to have known her in a painting class. That's all they seem to know, but they do not like what little they do know. I wonder what Edgar knows about it. He said nothing about it last time he was home. Mind you, he won't say anything until Morgan James says he can. Ever since those two went off to London they've been in each other's pockets.'

'I suppose Morgan James knows what he is doing. He's hardly a boy! As long as Morgan James likes her, whether the girls like her or not is irrelevant.'

Margaret Ann looked up from her mending, pulling hard on the thread. 'That one has always known what he is doing. The trouble is, nobody else is allowed to know what he is up to.'

Ever sensitive to his wife's feelings, Morgan realised that she was not at all pleased at the prospect of Morgan James taking a wife, especially one unknown to her. Margaret Ann might criticise and denigrate the Thomas family of Ynyshir, but even a Thomas daughter-in-law was preferable to one about whom nothing was known. Morgan opened his book again and resigned himself to several days of scrubbing and polishing.

The valley gossip soon brought the news to Gorwel that Ethel's family had agreed to the marriage of their daughter with Morgan James, and that the wedding would take place shortly. Margaret Ann was furious that half the village appeared to know before she did, but eventually Morgan James deigned to appear and inform her of his forthcoming nuptials.

She received the bride-to-be with glacial politeness. Her daughters were no more welcoming to their future sister-in-law and it was left to Edgar to show family solidarity. Morgan James found a smart apartment in London, through a parliamentary contact of Edgar's and following a quiet ceremony in Cardiff, he and Ethel – known forever to all the family as 'the Ginger Cat' – went up to London to begin their married life.

CHAPTER 26
'THE SOUL OF THE RIGHTEOUS...'

On a bleak Sunday in January 1913, the family were returning from the evening service at Calfaria. Amy and Maggie walked at a brisk pace, discussing who had been in chapel, and commenting on the unfairness of Arthur's being excused from worship yet again. They knew he had only been making excuses, complaining of aches and pains, but ever since his childhood attack of pneumonia he had played the invalid card whenever it suited him. As usual Jane had volunteered to stay with him, less in his interest than her own. She wished to write a letter and had no desire to answer the inevitable questions from her mother as to the recipient. Arthur was a willing accomplice as he was very happy to take the letter to the letterbox before Mam returned from chapel, as long as Jane had the necessary fee in the form of a silver threepenny bit.

Margaret Ann and Morgan moved more slowly up the hill, and Agnes dropped back to walk alongside her father. As the road became steeper, her husband's increasingly slow pace tried Margaret Ann's patience and she hurried to catch up her two daughters. Agnes was happy to adjust her pace to her father's.

'Tired after preaching, are you, Dadda?'

'I am that, and to think I used to preach twice a Sunday and travel twenty miles to do so.'

Realising that her father was struggling to catch his breath on the steep road, Agnes said, 'Shall we go round the farm road, Dadda? I cannot bear scrambling up that old tump.'

'Your mother and the girls will wonder where we are if we go round. It takes a good quarter of an hour more.'

'They will not wonder for long. They will be too busy putting the supper on the table. Take my arm and we can pull each other up.'

At last they reached home but Agnes had been wrong about her mother being unaware of their slow progress because she greeted them sharply. 'You two took your time, didn't you?'

Morgan flashed a warning glance at Agnes and merely said, 'We came round the farm road for a bit of a change.'

His wife gave him a cursory look but said nothing. Chatter enveloped the supper table but Margaret Ann and Morgan were both silent, which was unusual for her, if not him. The brief glance she had given her husband on his return had forced her to admit that it was not only tired he looked, there was a greyness about him. Later, when they were alone together she said, 'Tomorrow it's down the surgery for you to get the doctor to give you something to liven you up.'

'Liven me up, Margaret Ann! No, no, there is no need for another lively one in this house. Walking up here tires me, especially after two climbs into the pulpit, but it's not too bad if I take my time.'

'We will see about it, all the same. If you do not want to go down the surgery, the doctor can come up here. So perk up a bit, or I'll send down a note for him in the morning.'

Monday morning all was hurry and bustle. Snow flurries swirled down the hill towards the house and the feeble daylight gave a monochrome appearance to the rooftops of the terraces below. In the cosy kitchen, the girls tackled the loaf of bread each in turn, to make sandwiches for the mid-day break. While she cooked the customary bacon and fried bread for breakfast, their mother regularly reminded them not to ruin the loaf by cutting uneven slices. Margaret Ann prided herself on her ability to slice a loaf with the precision of a slate cutter and at a similar speed and it irritated her intensely if she found the loaf had been hacked about.

Suitably victualled for the day, Arthur and his sisters left for their various schools and Margaret Ann called the girl in for her breakfast.

The priority on Mondays was the washing. Margaret Ann's rigid routine of washing on Mondays, starching and drying on Tuesdays, and ironing on Wednesdays only varied in the most dire circumstances. The latest girl was already in the wash-house, lighting the fire under the copper she had filled with cold water. Once the water was boiling, the weekly wash was transferred from the big wooden tubs in which it had been soaking since the beds had been stripped. Some Mondays Arthur complained vigorously that Kate the maid was wrenching off his sheets while he was still occupying his bed, so keen was she to get on with the laundry. Today, all was proceeding according to long standing custom in the wash-house, and Margaret Ann was satisfied.

She was surprised when she returned to the kitchen to find her husband's breakfast still keeping warm on the top of the range.

'Mr Jones not down yet?' she asked Kate who was now clearing away the dishes.

'I've heard him moving about upstairs, but I have not seen him this morning.'

'You go and get on out the back to help the girl, or we'll be running late. I'll go and check and then finish in here when he has had his breakfast.'

Margaret Ann mounted the stairs. When she entered the bedroom, she found Morgan dressed and sitting on the edge of the bed. He looked at her and said, 'Sorry, I seem to be a bit slow this morning.'

'Better slow than sorry. Come on now, we'll go down and you can eat your breakfast and let me get on with the beds.'

Morgan took his wife's arm and together they descended the stairs. Then, leaving her husband to his bacon and fried bread, Margaret Ann returned to the task in hand. The fresh sheets were put on, the eiderdowns were tossed, pulled and buffeted as usual, and pillowcases changed, but Margaret Ann's thoughts were still on her husband. He had always moved slowly and taken his time about most things, but lately he had been slower than ever. Unless she chivvied him into doing something, he spent his time in the Little Room with his books, and the chaise-longue, on which he had taken to having an afternoon nap, seemed to be in constant use. She dismissed her idea of sending him to the doctor because it would mean he must walk back up the hill, which, she now realised, he had nearly failed to do last night. The doctor must come to him. She would definitely send a note down with Amy in the morning. No good telling Agnes to do it, for 'that one' would start a rare fuss if she knew her father needed the doctor. Margaret Ann was well aware of the intensity of Agnes's feelings for Morgan, although quite unaware of her own feelings towards 'that one' of her daughters. The decision about her husband's welfare reached, she got on with her work.

The next morning Margaret Ann called Amy as she left for school, and gave her the note asking Dr Davies to call, with the strict admonition not to tell Agnes.

'Is it about Dadda? Agnes was on about him all the time yesterday. She says he struggled up School Street with hardly a breath in him.'

'You can tell Agnes to stop fussing. I'll see to your father. You just make sure that note gets to the doctor.'

Margaret Ann found it difficult to settle into her routine that morning, but Kate was duly set about the Tuesday task of cleaning the dining and drawing rooms. She was warned not to have chairs from the rooms out in the hall, in case the doctor came, and she was instructed to listen for the door. It was noon before Dr Davies arrived. Kate let the doctor into the hall and hurried through to the kitchen for Margaret Ann.

'Doctor's here, Mrs Jones, and I've put him in the hall.'

Dusting her floury hands on her apron, Margaret Ann ushered the doctor into the Little Room where her husband had been reading. Briskly she announced, 'Now Morgan, doctor has come to see you so you had better put that book away and tell him what is the trouble with you.'

Morgan looked up at her and was surprised to note that she had failed to remove her apron before leaving the kitchen. 'I wonder what's bothering her now?' he thought to himself, before turning to the doctor with his customary courteous greeting.

Margaret Ann closed the door quietly and returned to the preparation of the midday dinner, but her ears were cocked for the sound of the doctor's departure. At last she heard him call out.

'Mrs Jones, I'm off now. I'll see myself out. Your husband and I have had a long chat. Let him rest as much as he likes and send Arthur down to the surgery tonight. I'll get some medicine made up and we will see how things go on.'

Before she could speak to him, the doctor had disappeared through the front door. Margaret Ann went straight to the Little Room.

'Well? What did he say was wrong with you?' she demanded to know.

'Not much except that the years are catching up with me and he will get his dispenser to make up a medicine to help me get my breath.'

'That's alright then. Nothing to worry about. Come and get your dinner now and Arthur shall go for the medicine when he comes from school.'

The week went by as all other weeks had done, Morgan duly took the obnoxious brew the doctor had prescribed, and by Thursday evening said he was feeling better. Agnes and her mother had exchanged a few bitter words about Morgan because Margaret Ann, firm in her belief that to sit about was unlikely to cure anything, had asked her husband to fetch the bucket of coal needed to replenish the kitchen range. Agnes was furious.

'My father is supposed to rest and not undertake strenuous household tasks. Why on earth can't you get Arthur to do something useful for a change?'

'You leave your father to me, my girl. Arthur has plenty of school-work to do if he's to get his certificate and leave school this summer.'

Agnes gave her mother a withering glare and disappeared to her attic.

On Friday morning, after everyone had gone, Margaret Ann put the coarse sacking apron over her usual morning one and went out to the coal house. She had ordered the regular load from the coal merchant further down the valley and was expecting its delivery.

The previous week the snow had prevented the cart from getting up from the village and the prospect of a chilly house was too awful to contemplate. The essential ritual of preparing the coalhouse for a fresh consignment had been completed by Arthur. Any remains of small coal from the last load were swept into a corner in order not to be buried by the new coal. The coal house reflected the orderly way in which everything was stored in Gorwel. Each lump of coal was piled against the walls with a skill a stonemason would be forced to admire. The smaller lumps, known as curlings, had an appointed place on the floor, together with the small coal used to damp down the fires. A short while later Morgan came through the kitchen door to tell his wife the cart could be heard coming up the farm road.

'I'll give you a hand with the buckets later,' he said. 'I'll fill them and you can carry.'

Morgan went back indoors, while Margaret Ann went into the wash-house where she took down the old zinc bath with handles and collected the buckets that would be needed. The coal cart had negotiated the sharp turn from the farm road with much shouting and 'Whoa, there!' from the carter to the horse, and was now stationary outside the gate to Gorwel. The haulier tipped the half-load of coal, which Margaret Ann had ordered, on to the side of the road and checked that the thick board which divided up the various loads had not slipped as the cart tilted. He righted the cart, ready to continue up Pleasant View to deliver his second load when he saw Margaret Ann coming round the side path armed with her buckets. As he moved round to the horse's head he called out.

'I heard the Reverend Jones isn't too well. Can I get someone to give you a hand with the load, Mrs Jones?'

'See if Jim Lie is about would you? If he is working afternoons perhaps he could come up. The quicker the better by the look of the weather. I don't want a load of snow in the coalhouse.'

With a long-handled shovel she began the task of filling a couple of buckets with the shiny black coal lumps. As she turned with the two buckets she saw her husband walking slowly down the path.

'Jim Lie is coming in a minute,' she told him, 'so there is no need for you to do anything. Go back in and sit by the range or I'll have Agnes after me.'

'I can do a bit, if I go gently.'

Morgan went on down to the gate where he could see Jim Lie already hurrying down the hill towards the house.

'Leave that to me now, Mr Jones. It's not a job for you or your wife. I'll not be long getting this in, it's only half a load!'

'I'll just do the bath, then I'll stop, Jim. It's a cold job for everyone this morning.'

Margaret Ann had stationed herself in the coalhouse to supervise its proper organisation. She knew Jim Lie was a good collier and kept his own coalhouse in good order but even he marvelled at the meticulous way this one in Gorwel was kept. Jim carefully emptied his buckets exactly where the mistress of the coalhouse directed and set off on another trip back to the gate with the empty buckets. As he turned the corner of the house he suddenly realised he could not hear any coal going into the old zinc bath Morgan was filling. Years underground had taught him to listen, to appreciate that a sudden lack of sound in the pit was often a forerunner of danger and he broke into a trot. At the gate he saw Morgan lying face downwards on what remained of the heap of coal and shouted, 'Quickly, Mrs Jones, your husband has fallen.'

Dropping the buckets, Jim Lie hurried to Morgan and carefully turned him over. Margaret Ann ran down the steps to the gate and clambered over the coal to reach her husband. Jim Lie was endeavouring to clean Morgan's nose and mouth of coal dust and Margaret Ann knelt amongst the coal to cradle her husband's head. The families up the hill who were similarly engaged in getting their coal in before the snow arrived, heard the commotion, and several of them hurried down to help.

Jim directed his troops with quiet urgency. 'Down the hill with you to the surgery as quick as you can for the doctor, Evan, and let your dad and Dai Cwtch give me a hand to get him in. Mrs Evans, see to Mrs Jones will you?'

'Come now, Mrs Jones,' said Mrs Evans, 'let us carry him inside for you and we will get the doctor.'

Strong arms helped lift Margaret Ann from the mound of coal, but once on her feet she needed no more support. She watched her neighbours lift her inert husband off the coal, and hurrying into the kitchen full of dread, she called to the girl to fetch a bowl of warm water and a towel. Kate was called to fetch blankets and to clear the books off the chaise. Regardless of the coal dust on their boots, the colliers walked straight in through the front door and laid Morgan in his beloved Little Room. They hastily removed their caps and stood motionless for a moment before turning away.

His wife walked slowly in behind them and knelt beside him. Automatically, as though he were a child she began to wash the coal dust from his face and hands, and gently closed his eyes. In a daze she lifted the now lifeless hands and gently wiped each one before resting them back on her husband's chest. Margaret Ann knew the doctor would need do nothing other than make the final dread pronouncement and write the death certificate. Gazing into her husband's face, begrimed as it still was with coal dust, she suddenly remembered the story Morgan had told her many years ago of how his mother had brought the children over the mountains from Penrhyncoch and how it had been four-year-old Morgan who had recognised the coal-streaked face of his father.

Once she had finished the cleansing, for some time Margaret Ann remained utterly still, silently kneeling beside her husband's body. She was numb. Then she stood up as she became aware that other women had entered the little room.

'We did knock, but there was no answer. We've brought you a cup of tea, Mrs Jones. Will you come and sit down and drink it?' Margaret Ann slowly untied the coarse apron with which she had covered herself before starting on the coal.

'The coal, the coal, we had not finished. It's still all over the road.' She sat down on the old post office chair as her legs went from under her.

'No need for you to worry, Mrs Jones, the men have almost

finished clearing it. It's all away in the coalhouse and they are just sweeping up.'

Briefly Margaret Ann hoped Jim Lie would see the coal stacked tidily, but now there were other things for her to think about. The doctor's arrival in the Little Room saw the discreet withdrawal of the women back to the kitchen.

'I'm so sorry, Mrs Jones.' Dr Davies reached for her hand. 'There's nothing I could have done for him. He's with his Maker now, and at least he did not suffer. It would have been all over in a few minutes. Perhaps there is something I can do for you?

'It's Will I need. He'll have to come up. Would you get a message to Will in Abergorchy for me and he can take care of things.'

'And what about your daughters? I could get a message perhaps to one of them.'

'Time enough for them to know when they get back this afternoon. They are better off in their classrooms for now, but would you see Mrs Evans about the laying out?'

'I will telephone Abergorchy as soon as I'm back in the surgery, and one of the women in the kitchen will go down to Mrs Evans for you. Now you get that cup of tea and rest for a while, and Arthur can come down for the certificate in the morning.'

The doctor left the Little Room and Kate paused in the ritual of lowering the blinds, to show him out. Margaret Ann turned once more to her husband. She picked up the blanket Kate had left neatly folded on the postmaster's chair and tucked it tidily round him. Then the tears came. A lifetime of love washed down her face and splashed on the still warm body of the man who had tolerated her foibles and loved her spirit, and who had let her spread her wings as far as they could go in the narrow valley in which they had lived. A sense of desolation overwhelmed her as she began to realise what she had lost, but a sound in the hall reminded her she was not alone and with an enormous effort she wiped her face with the corner of her apron, picked up the now cold tea and went back to the kitchen.

236

CHAPTER 27
BRYN CALFARIA

The newly installed telephone at the colliery brought the news to William and in that brief moment his world changed. At first he sat, stunned with shock, and stared at telephone receiver he had just replaced on its stand. Then he stood up, hastily tidied the papers on his desk and called his clerk in.

'Bad news, I'm afraid. My father died suddenly this morning and I'm having to go up to Wattstown. Send a wire to Mr Edgar at his chambers, and ask him to telephone to let me know when he's coming down. You'll have to get hold of Jimmy Kane if there are any problems here, and I'll try to come in tomorrow afternoon. I'm off now to Waun Fawr to tell Ann, and then I'll go to my mother.'

His clerk silently held out his overcoat for him and William picked up his hat. He closed his office door and as he heard the latch click he thought of his father's life brought to a close in a second.

'The family is broken,' he told himself as he walked to Waun Fawr, 'broken for ever. Mam might have been the public face of this family, but it was Dadda was its heart.' His eyes filled as he remembered the journeys back and forth to Ystrad in the trap, when he and his father had set the world to rights. How peaceful they had been! It was an image of his father to which he returned over and over again in the following weeks and years.

Peaceful was never a description of his mother, but of Dadda it was perfect. He smiled grimly as he recalled the various tirades on which his mother had embarked. Who on earth would calm her

237

down now? She always seemed so strong, but he had more than a suspicion her strength came from his father. The thought of his mother brought him back to the present and he increased his pace.

Ann was in the kitchen supervising lunch for Thomas Humphrey and spooning rice pudding into his little sister. She looked up with surprise.

'You're early, not off to Cardiff this afternoon are you?'

'Dadda's gone. This morning. Heart attack, Dr Davies says.' William sat down with a thump on the nearest chair and put his face in his hands. Both the children stared at their usually cheerful father, and Thomas began to cry.

'Quickly Maggie, take over here,' Ann instructed her nursery maid, and she hustled Will into the drawing room. Alone together William allowed his tears to flow. 'I loved him, Ann. I loved him. He was the rock this family was built on. What ever will we do without him? I'm not ready for him to go. I've got the others to tell too. They don't know yet.' Ann put her arms round William and held him close.

'Grieve for yourself, Will, and never mind the others. He was the only one in your family who welcomed me and I'll grieve with you, but he's reunited with his mother and sisters now, and that must comfort you. Come and have a cup of tea and I'll get you some cold ham and then you can set off up the valley.'

William gave her a hug and took out his perfectly laundered white handkerchief. He blew his nose and took a deep breath. 'Ann my girl, I can even face disaster with you to hang on to!' and he took her hand as they left the drawing room.

Later that afternoon, William walked along School Street through the sleet and looked sadly up at Gorwel. In accordance with custom all the blinds had now been drawn and the house's prominent position made it seem that the whole village was being told of the departure of the Reverend M H Jones, though doubtless most of the inhabitants would have heard the news already by word of mouth. As he walked towards Gorwel, William allowed himself time to reminisce about his father. Years ago, Morgan had written a verse in Welsh on the flyleaf of a volume of *Pilgrim's Progress* he had given Will on his marriage. As he began the steep ascent of the tump, Will recalled that verse in which his father had looked forward to the end of his life's journey, in the sure and certain hope of reunion with those who had gone before. His faith had been a rock for him, just as he had been for many other folk in the valley. 'A Good Man' would be a sufficient epitaph for his father. But William had no doubt that the preachers would say rather more than that, if they got a chance at the funeral.'

He reached the steps of the house and stopped for a moment marshalling the strength he knew he would need. He opened the back door, passed the girl who was replacing the passage mats on the newly washed floor, and went into the kitchen to find his mother at the range, busy with cooking the evening meal for Arthur and the girls. He put his hand on her shoulder and turned her towards him. 'Well, it had to come, sooner or later, but I don't think any of us are ready for this. How are you, Mam?'

'Your father went as quietly as he lived, with no fuss and no trouble, but that's not to say I'll not miss him,' his mother said, turning away to stir the sauce.

'You will not be the only one to do that, Mam. Can't you get Kate to do the dinner, then you could have a rest?'

'There'll be plenty of time for resting when I'm gone, too.'

William knew better than to interfere with the principles which had governed his mother's life. Work was solace, never more than now. Instead he said, 'I've wired Edgar already, and he will tell Morgan James. I've sent a wire to Exeter asking that Gladys be allowed home. I'll send a telegram to America this afternoon. Do the girls know yet?'

'No.' His mother poured the sauce on to the meat and put the casserole in the oven. 'That can wait until they are home. A fine scene we will have from Agnes. You know what she is like about her father.'

'Leave her to me, I'll tell her,' said William. 'But now I'll go and see my father. Where have they put him?'

239

'Mrs Evans has already done the laying out. Dr Davies sent her up. But we left him on the couch in the Little Room. There was no point in taking him upstairs.'

In the Little Room, which had brought his father so much pleasure in the short time he had been allowed to enjoy it, his father lay on the chaise-longue, immaculate as ever in his preaching suit. Will was surprised at the shortness of the body. He had never thought of his father as a man of small stature. 'You're no bigger than Hwmffra Bach, you really aren't, Dadda.' He recalled the name given to his great-grandfather in those far off Cardiganshire days; the grandfather who been the postillion on the coach between Aberystwyth and Machynlleth almost one hundred years ago. William pulled up the old post office chair on which his father liked to sit to write his sermons, and studied the still form lying there. Memories came flooding back. The sound of his father's voice, rarely raised in anger, had set such a powerful example to William himself; his patience and tolerance, and his strong sense of duty... The click of the back door opening roused him from his reverie. He moved quickly into the passage to see Jane and Maggie hanging up their coats.

'What are you doing here? Why are the blinds down, Will?' they chorused.

'Is someone dead in Cwmamman?' Maggie asked.

'Not in Cwmamman, no. It's Dadda...' as the old childish word left his lips, William was unable to continue and turned away. The girls looked in astonishment at their brother.

'Dadda?' they repeated, followed by the cry, 'Oh no! Mam! What's happened? Where are you?'

Margaret Ann was standing at the kitchen door and William was glad to leave the girls with her. He stepped out into the damp and drizzle and looked up at the lowering sky. The swirling fingers of mist seemed to be clutching at the mountain top, closing everything in. As he passed the coalhouse, he remembered he would need to thank Jim Lie and the other men who had finished the coal carrying. He opened the door and was relieved to see that the men had stacked the coal, if not to his mother's standard, at least well enough not to offend her. He closed the door and stood waiting. He hoped fervently that Amy and Agnes would have travelled together up the valley without hearing the news on the way. That way Amy could be with her mother, when the storm broke around Agnes. He was about to walk down the path when he heard the gate click and saw that his other sisters were indeed together. They ran up the steps towards him.

'What is up, Will?' Amy asked. 'The blinds are drawn.'

'It's Dadda.' This time he did not choke. He stood firmly on the path as Agnes gasped and reached out her hand to her sister.

'Stop her, Amy, don't let her go in yet,' ordered Will. Amy turned in time to grab her sister's coat and pulled her sister down on the steps.

Oblivious of the miserable sleet and the chilly step, Amy held on to her sister firmly, while the sad tale of the morning was recounted.

'I knew Dadda was ill, I told Mam on Sunday.' Agnes's voice rose almost to a shriek. 'Why did she make him fill the coal? Why was he having to carry those heavy buckets? What was he doing when he…?' The anger in Agnes's voice was palpable.

'Nobody made him. You know how he always helped Mam when he could,' Amy said, her face crumpling with tears at the thought of her father. Amy reached out for her sister who was wrenching at her coat in an effort to free herself.

'Stop it, Agnes. Sit still.' William's authoritative tone rang out. 'Amy, you go into Mam and leave Agnes to me.'

As Amy moved towards the back door, William held Agnes firmly by the arm. 'Now, listen to me, my girl, you are not going in there to make a scene. Your tantrums won't bring Dadda back and there's Mam and the rest of us, all feeling the same as you. You know he would want us to set a good example to the younger ones and look after Mam. He's been spared much suffering which is more than some poor folk in this village can say, and we've got each other to hold on to. So mind what I say.'

Agnes turned her tear-stained face towards him. 'Mam and the rest of you always have each other, but I have never belonged in this family. You don't know what it's like always to be in the middle, not belonging to the big ones or the little ones. Dadda was the only one who knew how I felt and I've got nothing now he is gone, and it's not just to America this time. There's no waiting for him to come home, now. He's gone for ever.'

She folded her arms, buried her head in her chest and sobbed. William looked at her in bewilderment. Could it be true that the family had caused Agnes to believe that only her father had cared about her? He searched for words with which to comfort her.

'Do you know, Ag, maybe you will find out when this day is behind us, there is more room for you amongst us than ever you thought. We have different ways of showing it, maybe, but we're all Dadda's children, don't you forget. Let's stop thinking of you for a bit, I need your help. You can help me to tell Arthur. He'll be up from school soon. He and Gladys are still young to lose their father and it will hit them hard. You and I have had him around till we're adults, but Arthur will never have that. When you've pulled yourself together you and I will go and meet Gladys from the train. She should be up on the nine o'clock. Now go in to Mam and remember what I've said.'

The sad duty of relaying the news to everyone fell to William. Over and over that day he repeated the events of the morning, and when he met the train bringing Edgar and Morgan James down from London late that evening he was exhausted. With an enormous sense of relief he returned to Abergorchy that evening, to recharge his batteries in his own home, with his wife, their little son and baby daughter.

'There's one thing to come out of this awful day, Ann,' he said when both the children were fast asleep. 'I've decided it's time to get a car. I've been up and down this valley all day and I must have walked at least twelve miles. In a car I could have been up and down in no time. Mam is distracted at the moment so she'll have nothing to say about it.'

Ann stared at him in delight. 'Oh, Will! A motorcar? Are you sure? How will you drive it? There are only a few in the valley! Will you need a driver? Won't it cost an awful lot of money?'

'I'll get someone from the pit to show me the ropes. It's not difficult and our Edgar can share the cost. He's always complaining how much time it takes walking to the Institute, then the Liberal Club, then his constituents, to say nothing of the journey to and from Cardiff for the London train. There is a new garage opened in Newport now. One of the shipping men was telling me about it. They've got a couple of cars in the showroom. I'll go down tomorrow and see what they've got. Edgar and Morgan James are here now and I've done more than my share of sorting things out today. They can do their turn tomorrow with Mam and Edgar can get on with the funeral arrangements. It's a pity Dadda won't be able to see it. He'd be tickled!'

Once William had a plan, it was as good as done. By six o'clock the next day a shiny black Morris Oxford car was sitting on the drive outside the front door of Waun Fawr. To their mutual delight, and Ann's consternation, William had time to give his little son a rather jerky ride along the drive before bedtime.

Even had she wished to, Margaret Ann had little time in the next few days to sit and mourn, or to bemoan her lot. Saturday saw all Morgan's children at home, and a constant stream of callers arriving to express condolences. The girls were all kept busy making Welsh cakes and serving *bara brith*, as everyone had to be offered the comfort of a cup of tea and cake. Even Arthur was pressed into service keeping the kettle on the boil and the coal scuttles filled.

Edgar sat in the dining room, dealing with the numerous ministers who called. He listened patiently as each and all staked their claim to take part in the funeral and expressed their opinions as to the form the service should take. Edgar was an experienced chairman of many committees but he found this a much more difficult task. By late afternoon he had had enough. This was not just another committee, and it was time to call a halt to the discussions. It was time to remind the gentlemen that the Reverend M H Jones had been first and foremost a husband and father, and that important as his role in the community might have been, the family's wishes should be paramount. He excused himself and sought his mother.

243

'Mam, what do you want this funeral to be? Those ministers in there are so busy arranging things, I think they have forgotten you.'

'Don't worry yourself, son. Your father often reminded me that I was the grocer, and he was the minister of religion. Let him be buried as a Baptist minister. He worked hard against all the odds to be ordained and he served the ministry well. I'll not rob him of the ceremonies to which he is entitled.'

Edgar returned to the dining room where he offered no objections to the arrangements being made. The Reverend Christmas Jones should preach the sermon, and out of respect for the English Baptists whom his father had served for many years, two English hymns should be included as well as the traditional Welsh ones.

Tuesday, 28th January, 1913, was a bleak day for the family, with more driving sleet and grey skies adding to the gloom. As the coffin was taken out from Gorwel on its journey to Calfaria, neighbours gathered around the gate to pay their respects to a courteous and caring man who had set everyone an example of loyal service and Christian charity. Edgar and William led the procession with Morgan James and Arthur behind them. All the male mourners walked in solemn lines behind the hearse and the female members of the family rode in state in the two limousines provided by the undertakers. Ann and Ethel were driven in a smart Morris Oxford which had mysteriously appeared, and were driven directly back to Waun Fawr after the service without raising any questions from their mother-in-law.

Calfaria was the chapel in which Margaret Ann had finally been able to forget the animosity she felt to all chapels, which had been such a problem in the early years of her marriage. It was the place where seven of their children had been baptised and it was full to bursting. Not a seat was empty and many latecomers were forced to gather round the door at the back. The Reverend Christmas Jones paid tribute to a faithful servant of Christ, and the hymns, two in Welsh, two in English, were sung with great fervour by the chapel choir, augmented for the occasion by singers from up and down the valley. Heartfelt prayers were offered by the many

244

ministers who had revered the deceased. At the end of the service Margaret Ann and her daughters were driven back to Gorwel while the cortege, escorted now only by the male mourners, made its slow journey down the valley to Trealaw cemetery, where the body of the Reverend Morgan Humphrey Jones was laid to rest.

Margaret Ann and her children returned to Gorwel where the customary funeral tea awaited the more favoured among the mourners. Mrs Basso had organised a team of ladies in the kitchen to keep the kettle boiling and the cups and saucers washed. As all his siblings were in attendance, William was glad to be able to escape back to Ann and his children after the interment. His driving skills were still limited and one of his drivers from the colliery had volunteered to be his chauffeur for the day. He leant back against the leather seats of his new car and drew a deep breath. 'Thank goodness that's over and without Mam spotting the car too. Now I can get back to Ann and stop her overdoing it.'

Up at the house, Edgar and Morgan James read out the telegrams of condolence from the family in America, much to Margaret Ann's annoyance, and the girls were kept busy offering tea and sandwiches until the last guest had left. They had all obeyed their mother's order that the social demands of the occasion be honoured, and no outward signs of grief were to be shown. Agnes found this extremely difficult and would have sought refuge in her attic, had she not feared her mother's anger if she were to disappear. As it was she moved amongst the guests in silence, while her sisters scolded her for sulking and not taking her full share of making the mourners welcome.

Edgar found time for a talk with his mother in the Little Room that evening, before leaving for London the following day. He and William were of the opinion that with the four girls earning good salaries, soon to be joined by Gladys, their mother would have no financial difficulties. Rent was still coming in from the houses she had bought years ago and although Morgan's small pension would cease, the family exchequer had long ago become accustomed to their father's negligible financial contribution. It was therefore with some surprise that his mother started the conversation by saying, 'I do not know what I am going to do.'

'Now come Mam. It's early days and Will and I are sure you'll have enough,' said Edgar reassuringly.

'It's not the money.' She paused before adding, 'it's about Arthur.'

'What about Arthur? He is no trouble to you, is he?'

'Not yet, but it's time he gave some thought to his future. Your father and I...' her voice wobbled, 'he says he wants nothing to do with teaching or college and will leave school this summer.'

'I'll have a word with him when I come home at the Easter recess. In the meantime, you ask Will what he thinks.'

'I've done that already. All I get from Will is that the girls spoil him and as long as he has a few bob in his pocket from them he is not likely to think of the future. Mind you, Will's not beyond giving Arthur a few bob out of his pocket either. I don't know what we're going to do with him.'

'Leave it for the moment, Mam. Today is not a day to be fretting about Arthur. I cannot see him living off us for the rest of his life. He'll want his own money one day. Try to think of yourself for a bit and don't run yourself ragged. When I come back at Easter I don't want to see you worn to nothing. I've got a lift down the valley, so I'll be going back on the early train tomorrow, but I've told Morgan James he can have a few days here to sort Dadda's papers, as Will has got more than enough to do at the moment. I thought Ann looked very poorly at the funeral and it isn't helping that her children are such a handful. I wish she and the children had stayed in Torquay for the winter, but I know she and Will hate being apart.'

'Anyway, Mam, I'm off to bed and it's time you went up. I'll get Maggie to bring you up a cup of tea. It has been a long day for us all, but I'm sure Dadda would have been pleased with the service. He loved to see the chapel full. He would have said he didn't recognise himself in all those tributes. I only hope he knows how proud of him we all were.' He rose quietly from his chair.

Edgar dropped an unaccustomed kiss on the top of his mother's head and went up to bed.

CHAPTER 28
WAR

Margaret Ann found the double bed cold and lonely. Morgan's warmth on which she had relied all her married life, was gone. It was at night when the busy day was over and she could no longer vent her grief through energetic domesticity, that she felt her widowhood. Stretching her hand out across the bed in the small hours, automatically seeking comfort, she found nothing. Outward displays of emotion had always been abhorrent to her but in the privacy of her bedroom she ceased to exercise the iron self-control that was so characteristic of her. Only Amy, who had the bedroom next to her mother, realised her mother's anguish, and she would not have dreamt of intruding or of revealing her mother's misery to anyone.

Margaret Ann had never been a dependent wife in the accepted way of her generation, but she had depended utterly on Morgan's love. The affection he had always shown in the privacy of their married life was vital to her. Her public face had always been one of strength and control and no one had ever seen her demonstrate weakness of any sort. Her pride would not allow it. Therefore bereavement, she decided, would not be allowed to alter anything, and life in Gorwel would change outwardly as little as possible. This was to be her defiant response to her fate. Throughout that year she wore her widow's weeds with dignity but those offering sympathy were met with a sharp retort. She would not be a focus for pity as Reverend M H Jones's widow. She was Mrs Jones, Gorwel, and she was now the undisputed head of the family. She was not to know that cataclysmic change was on the horizon, over which even she would have no control.

In July 1914 Gladys returned with a distinction award from college and was appointed to the staff in Aberllechau School and the fifth daughter began to contribute her full financial share to Gorwel. Margaret Ann had been a widow now for eighteen months and the pain of Morgan's death was easing for all except Agnes. Mrs Jones, Gorwel, continued to rule her daughters and regulate their lives by the various duties she allocated within the house, but to the girls' surprise she no longer questioned what they did with their money as long as the monthly house keeping contributions were made. This came as relief to Maggie and Jane in particular, as their expenditure on stamps and writing paper, and day returns by train to Cardiff or Newport had raised their mother's eyebrows on more than one occasion.

The long summer holiday stretched before teachers and pupils alike. The girls began to make their holiday plans. As they sat down for supper one evening shortly after Gladys' return, Maggie pulled a letter from her pocket and airily announced, 'Edith Amery has written to ask me to come and stay on the farm with her in Devon.'

'Is that the friend of yours from college who got married this Easter?' her mother enquired.

'Yes. She's living on the farm now, and she and her husband have just moved into the farmhouse. Her mother-in-law is going to live in the farm cottage with Edith's brother, Cyril, now their father has died. I would like to spend time with her to help her with cushion covers and curtains and things.' Maggie carefully adjusted her napkin on her lap and hoped the rest of them would not notice the brother's proximity. Only Jane gave her sister a quizzical look.

Margaret Ann grunted. 'And what about the rest of you?'

'Jane and I are thinking to go down to Swansea,' said Amy. 'There's a ladies' boarding house in Mumbles near the park where we can stay, and it's close enough to the promenade and the pier. Jane's friends from college live near and we will be able to visit those cousins of Dadda's.'

'How you can all talk of enjoying yourselves, with Dadda not dead two years I don't know,' snapped Agnes, picking her plate up off the table and slamming the door as she rushed into the kitchen.

'It's time that one pulled herself together,' her mother said mildly. 'Don't tell me you're disappearing as well, Gladys? Surely Cwtch is good enough for you?'

'I've had enough of being away and there'll be lots to do to get ready for September as well as catching up with all my friends. Are the girls using Dadda's room for preparing lessons now? Can I have a corner in the Little Room too?'

'As long as you watch what you are doing with that paint and glue you are always fiddling with, and clear up after yourself. Kate's not here to be a school caretaker, remember.'

'What's Arthur planning?' asked Amy as she began clearing the table. 'He's got his certificate, but he told me it was only any use for lighting fires!'

'Spending all his time at Waun Fawr, cleaning that car Will's so proud of, I shouldn't wonder.' Agnes had reappeared from the kitchen and rather shamefacedly joined in the conversation. 'Arthur told me Gwyn Basso is teaching him to drive it.'

Arthur had failed to turn up for his dinner as happened quite often on a weekday, and his mother continued to be concerned. Every time she cornered her youngest son and challenged him to make a decision about his future, his response was a combination of charm, wit and teasing, in the face of which she was helpless. Yet again she turned to Edgar and William to pull their brother into line. Edgar suggested the law as a career, but Arthur made it very plain he was finished with books. William thought office work would be suitable and pointed out his own success with the National. Firmly Arthur replied that office life would certainly not suit him, and he would be perfectly happy being Will's chauffeur, and driving Edgar around the constituency, as long as they paid him.

❧ ❧ ❧

His future was resolved in a way unseen by any of them when, a few weeks later, on 4th August, 1914, war was declared against Germany. Jane had heard the momentous news in Cardiff that morning, as she was refurbishing her summer wardrobe ready for the trip to Swansea and she hurried back up the valley with the news.

'I hope that doesn't mean I can't go to Devon.' Maggie looked downcast.

'It'll be over by Christmas, and you can go in the spring.' As ever, Agnes was happy to see her sisters' plans disrupted, especially as she had none of her own.

'Of course it doesn't mean you can't go. now It won't affect us here, and Amy and I are definitely going to Swansea.' Jane was adamant. 'Anyway Edgar is home next week and he'll know all about it.'

Two days later Maggie set off for her longed-for visit to Devon. William had promised to send up the car for her so that she could set out for Devon in style, and her excitement knew no bounds. Her mother was mystified as to why a visit to some remote Devonshire farm should produce such a fuss. The necessity for new dresses and a sunshade complete with frill, was discussed several times over breakfast and, for once in her life, Agnes agreed with her mother. The expenditure was ridiculous.

Jane kept quiet on the matter. She was well aware of the real reason for Maggie's excitement. She had seen the photograph of Edith's brother, Cyril, being packed carefully into the suitcase and was sworn to secrecy. Maggie had shown Jane the latest letter from Devon, which ended: 'I am counting the days until we are together…', and Jane was pleased at the prospect of Maggie's happy future. Her own visit to Swansea was not without subterfuge and she was busy planning how she could persuade Amy to take some time off from her chaperoning duties. She constantly reassured her sister that there really was no need for her to spend hours dragging in to Swansea – she was quite capable of going there alone. Amy could enjoy the music at the bandstand on the seafront in Mumbles, or take in the views of the bay from the Mumbles train.

Agnes and her mother managed to keep out of each other's hair for the few weeks they were on their own. Various distant family members appeared and disappeared, to spend a day in Wattstown, which broke the monotony, and discussion of the war ensured no one had time for petty family squabbles. The travelling sisters eventually returned in high spirits. Jane and Maggie retreated to their bedroom 'to catch up' and later Agnes was treated to a detailed account of the glorious weather Amy and Jane had enjoyed in Swansea. Amy was enthusiastic about the beauty of Langland Bay, but couldn't resist a comment about the surprising amount of time Jane had spent in the Glyn Vyvyan Art Gallery in Swansea. That summer holiday was to remain a golden memory for the rest of their lives.

∾ ∾ ∾

In September the new school year began, and a few days later, just as the family were sitting down to dinner Arthur came in through the back door, took his seat and looked across at his mother. 'Well, Mam, I have found something to do so you can stop nagging.'

'And what might that be, Arthur? You have shown little interest in all the suggestions your brothers have been making.'

'I'm going to join up, Mam.'

'Join up what?' his mother asked, genuinely perplexed.

'Sign on for the army. I'm going to be a soldier and fight for my country. They will be raising a battalion for the Welsh Regiment in Porth soon. We were all down on the bridge this morning and quite a few of the boys in my class are going. We reckon we haven't got much else to do and I'm not going down the pit like some of them. Far too dangerous! So as soon as they get things sorted I'll go along and sign up. They are opening up that old shoe shop on the corner as a recruiting office, and there were a couple of sergeants in there already, so it won't be long. Apparently they will call me for training as soon as the paperwork is done. It'll be a lark. I've never really been out of Wales, except a couple of times to London to see Edgar.'

His mother looked at him long and hard, while the girls held their breath wondering if the storm of her anger was about to break.

To their surprise, she said, 'No doubt it will do you some good, Arthur. For once in your life you will have to learn to do as you are told, the minute you are told to do it. If you can stick at it, I've no doubt you will do well. You've always got on well with people and they seem to like you, so I suspect they will follow you, too. Now get on with your dinner, I don't cook good food for it to go cold.'

Greatly relieved that Mam had approved, and that Arthur had managed to find a way to get out from under his mother's feet, the girls resumed eating and the noise from their chattering increased. Agnes envied her brother's freedom to leave the family hearth, while Gladys tried to hide her fears for him. Exactly as Arthur had predicted, six weeks later he turned up in his uniform and his sisters thought he was the smartest, best looking soldier in all the valleys.

In spite of everyone's predictions, the war was not over by Christmas. As news from the front grew more and more grim, families in the valley felt the direct impact of the war. Every week anxious faces scanned the lists of casualties pinned up on the notice board of the local newspaper. 'It reminds me of the National disasters,' Mrs Basso remarked to Lisa Jenkins as they stood peering over the shoulders of the women in front of them. 'I'll never forget waiting for news about the men after that explosion. but I think this might be worse in the end.' She was to be proved right.

But for those not at the front, the war brought some benefits. Lloyd George appointed Edgar to work with him at the Ministry of Munitions. Young Morgan was immediately promoted to the rank of Lieutenant Colonel for his work in recruiting soldiers to the battalion which had been raised by the MP for whom he worked. However, there was an endless drive to keep up with the demand for new recruits on the Western Front. Margaret Ann's amazement at her third son's exalted status did not diminish, but even she was forced to admit he looked the part in his impeccable uniform with his swagger stick tucked under his arm. There was more promotion for William, who was now responsible for ensuring supplies of best 'Welsh steam coal' to the Royal and merchant navies as well as maintaining supplies to homes and industry. He was torn as ever between his duties and his need to be with Ann who was becoming more frail and whose third baby was due in January 1915.

With their brothers all occupied in war work, Gladys, Maggie and Jane volunteered as nursing auxiliaries with the Voluntary Aid Detachment, reporting for work when their school day was finished as well during the holidays and weekends. Apart from endless sessions rolling bandages and preparing dressing packs to be sent to the front, most of their duties consisted of escorting injured soldiers returning from the battle lines back up the valley from Newport or Cardiff, and settling them back at home. This gave both the girls the opportunity they craved. For Jane and Maggie their roles as VADs allowed them precious time well away from Gorwel, and both the girls were free to meet with friends with no fear of detection.

By patronising the new cafes opening in the centre of Cardiff, Jane was able to meet her artist friend unchaperoned, and she and George Downing took every opportunity to spend time together. It was more difficult for Maggie. In spite of a dramatic increase in the number of trains running between London and the west country, travel for civilians between Cardiff and Exeter was not easy. Farmers all over the country were working round the clock to feed the nation and Cyril often struggled to find time just to answer Maggie's daily missives.

One Friday morning Maggie blandly announced she would have to go down to Cardiff straight after school to meet the 4.30 train. 'More injured for some poor family to cope with. I only hope all this suffering is worth it in the end,' said Margaret Ann as she cleared the remains of the breakfast from the table. Maggie looked quickly at Jane and left the room relieved that no further explanation was required. All day Maggie watched the clock while her pupils enjoyed a degree of freedom they rarely experienced.

By 4.20 p.m. she was on the platform waiting for the train from Penzance. As it drew in she hurried along the carriages until she saw him. Cyril jumped from the train and the two of them disappeared into the crowd of passengers. For almost two hours they sat in the crowded buffet car and planned their future. The prospect of being a farmer's wife entranced Maggie. She was already known and accepted by Cyril's family and as soon as the war was over... They were oblivious of everyone, until the train announcer's voice cut in. Maggie found herself standing on the opposite platform waving to the Exeter train as it drew out of the station with tears trickling down her cheeks. As she sat in the train back up the valley she clenched her hands in her lap. She had never thought he'd have to go to fight. She thought he would have to stay on the farm. If anything happened to him.

Her thoughts were interrupted as the train stopped at Porth and the new minister from Calfaria got into the carriage. In order to keep the trip hidden from her mother she was forced to chat pleasantly to him until they got out at Ynyshir.

Jane was in the Institute rolling bandages when Maggie arrived. One look told Jane what the situation was, but it was not until they were back in their room that Maggie could share her news.

Work was her salvation. Just like her mother, Maggie threw herself into school and housework. Each of Margaret Ann's daughters had a very specific set of duties in Gorwel. Maggie was the run-around who settled the milk account in Ty'r Gwaith farm, paid the butcher and the grocer's bills and called on Calfaria members who were sick. Ever since her husband's death Margaret Ann had distanced herself from chapel duties and delegated them to her daughters. The visiting tasks were not Maggie's choice, but her mother considered it to be necessary even though it resulted in the derogatory comment from Agnes that Maggie was always 'running about the roads'.

Amy's duty was baking the cakes and pastries but she was not trusted to bake the bread. Her mother reigned supreme when it came to turning out a decent loaf. Outside the family circle as usual, Agnes kept her own attic bedroom clean and took her turn with the cooking rota. Her most important duty was caring for her father's grave in Trealaw cemetery, and she trusted no-one else with the task.

Each week Gladys faced a mountain of ironing produced by the bed and personal linen of six women. Regardless of the weather, wet or dry, it was expected to be completed by Wednesday evening. The flat irons were heated on the range and the ironing blankets which covered the kitchen table, became heavier and hotter as the neat piles of ironed linen grew. It was exhausting work.

Jane believed she was more delicate and refined than her sisters and persuaded the others to believe it too, so her duty was dusting the drawing and dining rooms and maintaining the growing collection of cacti which graced the front porch. All the other chores were done by Kate the maid, and her small assistant.

∽ ∽ ∽

Ann and William's new baby – a girl, named Hilda Elizabeth Gwent – was born at the start of the new year on January 6th, much to her parents' delight and William was relieved that Ann's health seemed to improve a little. A few months later, Arthur finally left for France in 1915 with his regiment, already holding the rank of second lieutenant. Margaret Ann's observations on his leadership skills were echoed by his training officers who were impressed with his enthusiasm and attention to detail. She wrote to him every week as she did to all her children when they were away from home. Arthur occasionally replied.

On a summer day in 1916 a telegram was delivered to Gorwel and taken to Margaret Ann by Edith, the current girl, with some trepidation. Margaret Ann wrenched it from the girl's hand and walked with unsteady steps into the Little Room. 'Oh Morgan, please no, please no.' As ever in moments of danger it was to Morgan she turned. She sat on her husband's chaise longue and slit open the envelope. It read: *Lost finger. Convalescent leave granted. Home on Wednesday. Arthur.*

'Just like him,' snapped his mother. 'It's Wednesday today.' She opened the door and shouted to the girl. 'Edith, air the sheets and get them on Arthur's bed. Make sure the room is clean and tidy, put fresh soap in, and if you can find any of those daughters of mine send them to me at once.'

Hurrying off to do as she was told, Edith managed to find Amy and Maggie. 'Mrs Jones wants you in the Little Room.'

Amy blanched. 'What is it, Mam? What's happened?'

'It's Arthur. He's coming home on leave today for some reason, apparently without his finger.'

The wry smile hid his mother's relief that a digit was all he had lost. 'Maggie, get down to the butchers and get any bit of best end he's got, and some liver and kidneys for tomorrow. Find Amy and tell her we'll need cake for tea and pikelets. They're his favourites. She'll need to get extra flour. Agnes and Gladys are still down at Waun Fawr playing tennis and keeping away from that Ann and her chest, I hope. As soon as they are back they can find Jane, when she's in from her gallivanting, and send her to me. I don't know why she had to go to Cardiff again today.' Amy and her sister reeled from the list of instructions and set off to implement them.

∞ ∞ ∞

Having thus marshalled her forces, Margaret Ann went into the kitchen to prepare a dinner fit for a man to eat. She had hardly started when there was a great clatter and din round the side path leading to the back door. Then Gladys burst in to the kitchen, followed by her sisters dragging a kit bag.

'Mam, guess who we found on the train coming back from Will's? First Jane and then Arthur of all people and he's home for a month!'

Through the door came her youngest son. A sharp look told Margaret Ann that all was not well. Apart from his right arm in a sling, he looked pale and exhausted.

'Well, that's quicker than I thought. We only got your telegram this morning!' She held out her arms and gave her youngest child an unaccustomed hug.

'Now stop your clacking, Gladys, and take that bag upstairs. Agnes, put the kettle on and make a pot of tea. Jane, when you have put off your finery, you can help Edith finish these vegetables. You will be wanting to rest, Arthur.' To everyone's amazement, Arthur was led by his mother into the Little Room, and installed on the chaise-longue.

256

It was only at dinner they learned how Arthur lost his finger. In a few terse sentences he described the battle and then casually mentioned he had won the Military Cross during the battle for Mametz Wood. The citation in the *London Gazette* gave the family an opportunity to share their delight and pride with their neighbours, but Arthur resolutely refused to talk any more about his experiences on the Somme even to Gladys. Many nights during Arthur's leave, Gladys was disturbed by the cries from his little bedroom, but even when she rushed in to comfort him he could only cling to her, while great shuddering sobs wracked his frame. Speechless, he would remain clutching at his sister until, in the early dawn light, the terrible dreams faded.

Edgar managed to appear in Gorwel to congratulate his youngest brother, and promised to see what he could do to expedite the presentation of the medal. Sure enough, a few days later Will arrived in Gorwelwith the news that the medal was to be presented to Arthur at Buckingham Palace before he returned to the front.

'I thought I would ask Edgar and Will to come with me.' Arthur said to his mother. 'They will enjoy it and I would like them to be there.'

'For Edgar that will be easy enough,' she replied, 'but if you can prize Will away from Ann's side at the moment, you will have more luck than I have.'

'Is Ann still not well then?' asked Arthur.

'That family is riddled with TB. I told Will that when he first took it into his head to marry her, but no notice did he take of me as usual. One sister's gone already and I fear for those children if their mother goes as well.'

But Arthur proved to have more influence over his brother than his mother did. Both brothers went with him to the palace to receive his medal. Back home after the ceremony Arthur had to recount moment by moment everything that had happened, from the second he woke and dressed in his best uniform, until he ascended the great golden staircase which led to the palace ballroom. There, he received his medal from King George V. As far as his sisters were concerned he was Rhondda's greatest hero and they spent several days cutting and pasting all the newspaper accounts of the investiture (and the bravery of their brother) into a large scrapbook, which was prominently displayed in the drawing room.

⋙ ⋙ ⋙

The week Arthur's leave came to an end, Gladys went to the station at Porth to see him off. Her brother was quiet and unsmiling, not a bit his usual, sunny self. Her observations and light-hearted gossip seemed to fall on deaf years. and she began to feel uncomfortable. As the train pulled in Arthur turned to her and in a quiet but determined voice said, 'I can't go, Glad. I can't go back there. I can't get on that train.'

'But you have to go back, they will be expecting you.'

'I can't go, Glad,' he repeated. 'I can't go back there.'

The guard's call of 'All aboard' was ignored and the train pulled out of the station, leaving the two of them still standing on the platform. Gladys thought quickly.

'Come into the waiting room, Arthur, and we can go down on the next one. I'll send a telegram to Will to meet us at Cardiff. He'll know best what to do and then…' In a flash of genius she added, 'Mam won't have to know until it's all sorted out.'

Arthur allowed himself to be led into the waiting room, while Gladys pulled her hat more firmly onto her head and left the station. She picked her way across the tram lines to the post office where the old postmaster was on duty. Gaily she said, 'Good day, Mr Evans. Arthur and I have missed his train! All my fault as we were busy talking, but I will have to let Will know as he was to meet us at Cardiff.' She dictated a bland message:

'Missed train. Important you meet A at Cardiff for connection to Paddington. Due in at 11.17.'

She then bought herself a return ticket to Cardiff, hurried back to Arthur and with some difficulty persuaded him to board the next Cardiff train with her.

The telegram baffled William, but he realised something was amiss. Leaving instructions with his young secretary he hurried out of the office and made his way to the station. He arrived in Cardiff just as the Porth train was pulling in. The three of them adjourned to the station buffet. Over a cup of tea Gladys explained to William why she was there and asked what was to be done. Pale and determined, Arthur kept repeating, 'I can't go back. You don't understand. I can't, I just can't.'

William's brain was racing. The consequences of a young officer failing to report for duty were too terrible to contemplate. Only that morning he had heard of the fate of a young soldier who had been sentenced to death for desertion. Quietly he said to Gladys, 'Get Arthur more tea or something. I am going to try and get hold of Edgar. He's bound to be in the War Office this morning. Between the two of us we may be able to bring him up to scratch.'

Gladys duly entertained Arthur with the antics of some of her pupils until William returned, all hustle and bustle, just as the Paddington train drew in.

'Thanks, Glad. You get off home now. Not a word to the others until we know how this works out. Just tell Mam we met on the platform as I had to go up to London urgently on business. Get Agnes to call in on Ann for me and tell her to collect Hannah Margaret at the same time, she's proving a bit much for Ann at the moment and she could do with a visit to Mam. The baby takes a lot of Ann's time. Right! Come on Arthur, it's on to the train for you.' Giving Arthur no time to think or react, he flung his arm round his brother's shoulders and bundled him and his kitbag on to the London-bound train.

By the time the train pulled in to Paddington, Arthur had accepted the inevitability of his return to the front. Edgar was waiting for them anxiously with his official car and driver, and two young officers from the South Wales Borderers. The nod from Will and the way Arthur responded to the sight of the reception party reassured Edgar a little, and with a smart salute from his fellow officers, Arthur and his kitbag were escorted to the waiting staff car.

'Best get him across to Victoria as quick as you can, Edgar. He's running a bit late and it might be as well to keep those officers with him for the time being. He's in a bit of a state. Come to Waun Fawr when you are down this Saturday and we will have a good talk then.'

To Arthur he said, 'Well done, lad. Good luck! You will be home again before you know it and when you are, we will go walking in the Beacons and talk about what you're going to do when this is all over.' Giving him a quick pat on the back, William turned on his heel and set off to find his homebound train.

He and Arthur never got to go walking in the Brecon Beacons. The following January Arthur was seriously wounded in a night sortie near Ypres. The telegram from the field hospital sent to Edgar made it clear that Arthur might not live. Edgar, who was now a senior War Office minister, crossed to France at once to ensure everything possible was being done for his brother. For several weeks Arthur hovered between life and death, but on 5th February, loss of blood, infection and finally gangrene meant his left leg had to be amputated well above the knee in order to save his life. It was his twentieth birthday.

Throughout the spring he hovered between life and death, as he was moved from hospital to hospital, but gradually he recovered sufficiently to be transferred to a convalescent hospital on the south coast. By the summer of 1917 he was back in Gorwel, to be once more cosseted by his sisters and ruled over by his mother. She had never doubted that he would survive and she counted the loss of a leg as a mere nothing when measured against the numbers of blinded and gassed and injured soldiers returning to the Rhondda, or as Mrs Basso had predicted, those not returning at all.

CHAPTER 29
GRIEF AND JOY

Month after month the list of casualties reported in the local press continued to grow. The Welsh regiments serving in the Somme suffered appalling losses and hardly a family in the villages of the Rhondda was spared. Arthur gradually began to contemplate life without his leg and slowly his health improved and his natural optimism returned. One afternoon Margaret Ann was preparing to entertain the knitting circle of the Calfaria Ladies' Guild in Gorwel. A large plate of Welsh cakes sat under a spotless tea towel on the kitchen table and the teapots were warming when there was a sharp knock at the front door. Surprised, Margaret Ann herself went to the door. The lad from the post office stood on the step and held out a telegram. She gave it a cursory glance, realised it was not addressed to her and was about to send the boy away with a piece of her mind for mis-delivering an important War Office telegram. As the boy went on standing there she took the missive from him and read the name more closely. It was addressed to Miss J M Jones, Gorwel, Wattstown. Margaret Ann was nonplussed. She put her hand in her apron pocket and handed the boy a penny. As she closed the door, her mind was racing.

'What on earth is this all about? It can't be for our Jane, surely?' Margaret Ann was on the point of opening the envelope when the first of the Calfaria ladies turned into the gate and so the telegram was hastily stuck behind the lustre jug on the dresser. At half past three, the knitting circle finished. Margaret Ann tidied up the cups and saucers and went into the kitchen to wash them up. As she did so, she remembered the telegram, but at that moment Jane came in through the door on her way back from school. Margaret Ann looked at Jane as she dropped her bag on the kitchen table. She reached behind the jug and handed her the telegram. Slowly Jane took it and without a word left the kitchen. An hour later, Maggie arrived from school.

'You'd better go up to our Jane. She's had a telegram. There's been no sign of her since.'

Maggie turned and hurried up the stairs to the bedroom she shared with Jane. She pushed open the door and saw her sister lying face down on her bed. Maggie sat down on the bed and reached for her sister's hand.

'He's missing, Maggie,' Jane sobbed. 'Why didn't they look after him better? He should never have gone – he wasn't a fighter, he was a painter.' She re-read the telegram:

'On July 1st, whilst leading his platoon with great bravery. Missing, presumed dead. Letter follows.'

'I don't want a letter. I want him. I promised I'd wait for him, and now I'll have to… wait for ever.' Her voice rose in a pitiful wail and she drummed her feet against the bed cover. Jane had shared so many visits to art galleries with him. They had spent so many happy hours painting together, but the young man, with no family of his own, was never found. Jane later learned that 19,000 men died that day on the Western Front. It was the greatest loss of life ever sustained in a single day by the British army.

Jane never married, and never spoke of her loss, but she sealed his memory up in her heart and in that way kept him close. A few months later, she went to Cardiff to an art shop with a pair of watercolours to be framed. The paintings were found rolled up carefully in a cardboard tube in his kit bag, along with his paintbox, and were returned to her as his next of kin. They had been painted by the young officer when he was on leave in France, and she hung them opposite her bed, so that she saw them as soon as she woke in the morning, every day of her life.

At Waun Fawr, William was seriously concerned about Ann's health. His mother's constant warnings about keeping her away from the *ceiliogs* had not prevented Ann from doing her full share of nursing her two sisters, both of whom had now died from tuberculosis. Only one of Ann's sisters, Edith Mary survived the scourge of the terrible disease.

By late summer 1916 William had become desperately worried. His elder son Thomas was seven and Hannah Margaret was a lively five-year-old. Hilda was eighteen months old and although both the older children were in school, Ann's daily duties were becoming too onerous for her. William was distraught. Every time he looked at Ann he felt sick with dread. He had watched his sisters-in-law succumb to tuberculosis and he feared for the future.

Ann had all the domestic help she needed and more family holidays were taken in Torquay in the hope that the mild dry climate would delay the onset of her winter cough. Every new treatment that became available was tried and throughout that winter Ann spent many hours on the train to London as Will insisted that she visited a London chest consultant regularly. In spite of everything, Ann was now finding everyday life very tiring, so Will asked his mother's youngest sister to take over the care of little Hilda in her home in Cwmamman.

Ann was pregnant again for the fourth time, and so Will's older daughter Hannah Margaret was sent up the valley to spend prolonged periods in Gorwel with her grandmother and aunts, to allow her mother extra rest. William was the only one who could cope with his eldest child, Tom. but he had no time to concentrate on the boy's needs, and so Tom was sent to boarding school in Worcestershire.

Throughout the year Ann's condition deteriorated and by Christmas William was given the news he most dreaded. There was no more to be done for Ann and there were now fears for the life of the unborn baby. A few days after Christmas, Ann gave birth to a tiny baby daughter, but there were no celebrations for the family that year in Gorwel as every day brought worse news from Waun Fawr.

William's promise that he would give Ann jam on her bread if need be, had been honoured. He could not have known it would have to include a doctor and all possible medical and nursing help. But in spite of all the extra care, the further pregnancy proved too great a strain for Ann's frail health and in January 1918, tuberculosis claimed another victim. Will was beside himself with grief.

Ever since Christmas he had been aware that Ann's death was inevitable and he had barely left her side. Her constant fretting about her children had distressed him beyond words and he had tried desperately to reassure her. His anguish was increased when the new baby daughter died a few days after her mother. Will laid them both to rest in Trealaw cemetery where he had buried his father only a few years before. After the funeral he went back to Gorwel hoping for some of his mother's strength to face a future, which at the moment seemed utterly bleak.

He entered the kitchen where his mother was laying the tea tray.

'Come in, boy, you look frozen. Have a cup of tea and get yourself warm.' she said. William took off his overcoat and gloves and sat down heavily on a kitchen chair.

It's all over now, Will, you've been sorely tested these last few years and you did your best for Ann. Now she and the baby are laid to rest, and there's nothing more you can do for them. Your job is to look to the future.'

'You're right, Mam, I am thirty-eight years old and the children and I might have a future, but it's my dearest Ann who has been deprived of hers. That is my sorrow, not yours, and it will be so all my life.' He stared unseeing at the drizzle obscuring the hillside.

'You will need to get a housekeeper, Will.' Margaret Ann persisted. 'Waun Fawr has been left too long without a firm hand in control. And the sooner the better, because if you don't, you will have Edith Mary and her mother moving in. They will tell you it is best for the children and they will be in there before you know it.'

'There's no fear of that, Mam. Ann made it clear she didn't want her mother and sister taking over. I've dealt with Edith Mary already, and told her I'll not have her or her mother interfering with the children. I'll bring them up my way, not theirs. It's a bad start they have had and the first thing is for me to get the little one back from Cwmamman. She's been away from us too long and she's three now.'

'Never mind about Hilda, it's that other one you had better see to. Hannah Margaret could do with a firm hand. Young she may be, but she's determined to have her own way and ready to defy anyone who tries to prevent her. We've had a few ructions in here, I can tell you.'

William looked at his mother. 'She's not the first I've met in this family like that. I've never known a firm hand have much effect on you.'

'Let me tell you, my boy. There is a firm hand lays hold on all of us, sooner or later. It's called Life, and obey it we must. But there's no need for me to tell you that. Go along with you now, get back in that fancy car of yours and try to get a good night's sleep. Tomorrow you can start to find your housekeeper. There'll be plenty of people who'd fancy having Waun Fawr as a place to live. Meanwhile, keep those children away from Ynyshir.'

Once Will had gone, Margaret Ann and her daughters sat down for their supper. Ann's death had not been unexpected, but the funeral had been a very sad occasion. The girls had all enjoyed the hospitality at Waun Fawr, which was a gracious house with attractive gardens, a tennis court and a meadow. They saw it as a place of respite from the rigid routine of school and home. They knew how much their brother had adored his young wife and were distressed for him, and the three motherless children who now depended on him. The death of the baby was an added sorrow.

'What will happen in Waun Fawr now, Mam? Do you think the *ceiliogs* will go there?' Maggie risked her mother's anger, as any mention of the Ynyshir family usually produced rage, but Margaret Ann answered calmly, 'No fear of that. Will has told them straight to keep away. But he will need to put someone else in pretty quick or they'll be straight in the door.'

'He must find a housekeeper,' said Jane. 'Other men in a similar situation do that. He needs to get someone soon because those maids are getting lazy, and when Tom is home they all spoil him.'

All the girls joined in and gave full rein to their concerns – the laziness of the maids, the children's behaviour and most worrying of all, William's grief.

Agnes had remained silent throughout, and her sudden intervention brought immediate silence.

'I'll go there.'

'You!' exclaimed Amy. 'How can you go? You've got a job in Blaenrhondda.'

'How do you know Will would have you there?' Maggie wanted to know.

'Fine housekeeper you'd make.' retorted Jane. 'You do the minimum about this house. You spend most of your time in your attic. You know nothing about running a house'

Practical as ever, Gladys asked, 'If you don't teach, what will you do for money?'

For several minutes Agnes said nothing, but then she muttered, 'I'd sooner be there than here.'

Her sisters stared at her aghast. Margaret Ann silenced them by saying, 'We all know you'd sooner be anywhere but here. You remember, my girl, wherever you are, you are not likely to be satisfied with it for long. You've got to learn to live with yourself first, but if Will agrees I'll not stop you going. But if you go, you stay. Those children can't put up with any more upheaval.'

At that moment the conversation was interrupted by the sharp ring of the telephone in the hall and Gladys got up. From the hall came a gasp of surprise and a small squeal of excitement.

'Edgar, no! On today of all days. When? How amazing. What do we call you?' There was silence for a few minutes followed by a quick 'goodbye' and a few seconds later Gladys reappeared at the dining room door.

'It's Edgar. He's got a knighthood! A knighthood from the King, in the New Year Honours list! It was announced in *The London Gazette* on January 7th.' Her sisters stared at her.

'He didn't want to tell us before, because of Ann and Will, but he's got to come down on Saturday to see the constituency and the reporters from the papers will be here. He will telephone Will himself tomorrow.'

Their sadness briefly forgotten, the sisters were beside themselves and took to referring to their brother as 'Sir Edgar' at every opportunity. His mother merely remarked that it had taken longer than she had expected.

The next evening, on her way back from school, Agnes called on William in Waun Fawr. The older children were squabbling in the hallway over a scooter and three-year-old Hilda was sitting in the kitchen staring miserably at the supper prepared for her by the maids. William was sitting alone in the unlit drawing room; looked up with some surprise as his sister was shown in. Without any preamble she announced, 'I've come to help, Will. I'll come and look after you and the children. I'll give up school, and start as soon as they can find someone to take my class.'

William stood up and held out his hands to his sister. Exhausted with grief and worry, he was struggling to cope with his demanding job and the management of the household, to say nothing of his anxiety about his children. Long aware that his mother and Agnes were a constant irritation to each other, and that she had no close ally among her sisters, William was quite content to accept Agnes's offer and felt she might well be happier in his home than in Gorwel, but he insisted she continue in her profession, and that her role in Waun Fawr should be supervisory. Agnes disliked her job as a teacher so much she would willingly have abandoned it, but William's insistence won the day. He was determined that she should not relinquish her independence so easily, and certainly not before he could assess the success of the new arrangement. A compromise was reached and Agnes agreed to apply for a post in a Newport school to which she could travel much more quickly than to the one in Blaenrhondda.

It was agreed that Agnes should move in as quickly as possible to undertake the organisation of the household and the housemaids. Both the older children were in school, so only Hilda was at home during the day, and she was less of a handful than her older sister. William and Agnes decided that a new nursery maid should have responsibility for the children, which allowed one maid to take over shopping and cooking, and the other one to look after cleaning and washing.

Freed from the tension and competition of life with her sisters Agnes relaxed a little and gradually bonds began to form with her nieces and nephew. The day-to-day running of the household presented her with no difficulty. She applied the model Margaret Ann had used so successfully all her life, to the grander establishment in Waun Fawr and by the late spring William and his children were settling into a new way of life. Regular visits from Margaret Ann ensured that standards were being maintained and Agnes's sisters were forced to admit that their sister seemed to know quite a bit about running a household. Arthur became a regular visitor and the company of his small niece coupled with gentle exercise in the beauty of the gardens formed an important part of his rehabilitation.

In spite of his heavy ministerial responsibilities in Whitehall, Edgar maintained his regular visits to his constituency. Out of deference to William's grief, little had been said within the family about Edgar's amazing news and Edgar had seen William only once since Ann's death. The daffodils were flowering profusely around the lawn at Waun Fawr when Edgar arrived to see Will and the children one Saturday and he was shocked at the change in his brother. All William's natural ebullience had gone and his long silences were in stark contrast to his usual cheerful conversation. Edgar gave his brother a hug and announced, 'I've come to cheer you up a bit, Will. How would like to prop me up at Buckingham Palace? The investiture will be on 7th March and Morgan James is coming. I've asked Mam, but she's busy pouring cold water on the whole thing.'

'Now come on, Edgar,' said William, 'you know what she's like. She's proud as punch really although she can't bring herself to say so. Dadda would have been be thrilled to bits too.'

'Maybe, but what about you, Will?'

Will thought for a minute. 'Of course Edgar, I'd be honoured to come. Thank you. It would be a chance to draw a fresh breath, and Agnes and the children are doing better than I'd dared hope.'

A second visit to Buckingham Palace was now planned. Edgar took William, Morgan James, and, to everyone's surprise, his mother. No one had expected her to accept the invitation. On a sunny day in early March, she ascended the golden staircase in Buckingham Palace on Morgan James' arm. The band played, the brass buttons shone and the feathers in the stylish hats fluttered in excitement.

Margaret Ann reflected that Edgar had come a long way from catching the mail bags. His father would be so proud. She took her place on the front row of golden chairs, with two of her sons. As Edgar was ushered in to kneel before the King, his mother gripped her parasol handle and drew a deep, calming breath. Now was no time to make an exhibition of herself. She saw her husband's face and heard his voice as clearly as though he were present. In a moment the ceremonial sword briefly touched Edgar's shoulders, and with a few words from the King it was over, and Sir Edgar Jones KBE strode confidently out of the palace ballroom, to be joined later by his proud family.

As soon as she was back in Gorwel, Margaret Ann retold all the experiences of the day to the family with uncharacteristic detail. For Arthur, it was a chance to remember his own visit, but for Hilda it was a fairy story, with kings and queens and knights and swords. Only the Round Table and Sir Galahad were missing.

∽ ∽ ∽

William was busier than ever as the war effort demanded more and more coal. and he threw himself into work. It prevented thoughts of Ann from creeping into his mind, but he still found time to get home in time to write to Tom and see his daughters at the end of the day. He filled his spare time with producing the wooden toys which Arthur and Gladys had so loved, and Hilda's doll's house was the envy of the neighbourhood, complete as it was with furniture and little people. Sitting quietly in the summer house where he kept his tools, William drew strength from his quiet whittling as he stored away memories of Ann. Slowly the raw anguish of his grief began to subside.

By summer, the death toll of village men at the front, had risen further. It left a trail of misery around the village and Margaret Ann spent many hours offering support and comfort to the bereaved families.

Maggie and Jane were returning one evening from visiting yet another bereaved church member when Jane suddenly said, 'You know, Mag, it would be easier for me to do this visiting if I could say to those women that I know how they feel. Mrs Hopkins nearly said just now that we had no idea what she was going through. I wanted to shout at her. I do. Every day, every night I think of him and what might have been but I have to keep it all bottled up inside, just in case Mam ever gets to hear about it. Not even you really know how I feel. Will is the only one who would understand.'

Maggie grasped her sister's hand sympathetically. 'I know, but I can't help being glad it's nearly over. Last time Edgar was home from Westminster he said Lloyd George has said it will be all over before Christmas. I'm going down to see Edith in Devon at half term to help her get ready. There's a chance Cyril's battalion will be coming home on leave. They've been in France since last May and perhaps they won't have to go back, if what Edgar says is true. I think I'll start counting the days. We've always done that!'

But Maggie didn't have to count very many days. In early September 1918 a letter from the Amery family told her that their son Cyril had died of wounds at the end of August, following an assault on a German position during the battle of Arras. Now two of the sisters had joined the ranks of thousands of women whose lives were shattered by loss. In stark contrast to her last excited visit to the farm just as war broke out, Maggie returned to Devon at half term, but not for the joyful reunion she had hoped for. The time was spent instead in comforting and being comforted, and she came back to school after the half-term holiday knowing that the children in her class would be the only children she would ever have.

At eleven o'clock on the eleventh day of the eleventh month of

1918, the war was over. Margaret Ann received the telephone call from a jubilant Edgar, and walked slowly into the Little Room. She slumped into her husband's old post office chair. 'We've come through Morgan, all of us. Not unscathed, but we've survived. And Arthur will learn to cope. Whether any of it's been worth it, I'm not sure. Most of the families in this valley are worse off than they were, but no doubt you would tell me to "Trust in the Lord" so we'll see.'

She lifted herself from the chair, and walked along the passage to share the news in the kitchen.

CHAPTER 30
PEACE AND LOVE

In November 1918 the armistice was signed. The 'war to end all wars' had been fought and the country prayed fervently that peace would now reign and that life would soon return to normal. The last four years had brought misery and sadness to the family in Gorwel, but in Margaret Ann's hearing at least, resolute stoicism was the order of the day. Outward displays of emotion were never tolerated and met with a sharp rejoinder to 'control yourself'. William and his young family knew that they 'had to get on with it' and now that Agnes was well established at Waun Fawr with an efficient team of housemaids, Margaret Ann was confident that the children's physical needs at least were met.

Eventually, spring came to Wattstown and with it came a welcome diversion for the children in Waun Fawr. Lieutenant Colonel Morgan James Jones arrived with his wife on one of their occasional visits to his mother and sisters and divulged the news that Edgar had twice been seen escorting a young lady to the theatre and that Morgan and Ethel had entertained them both to dinner at the Savoy Hotel. His sisters were agog for more information, but Morgan had no more to give.

'I've told you all I know, and I'm only letting on, to give Mam time to come to terms with it. You'll just have to be patient until you hear from Edgar himself.'

Ethel, on the other hand, was very happy to share the gossip and for once the 'Ginger Cat' was the centre of attention. She informed her sisters-in-law that the young lady was very beautiful, came from an excellent family and the engagement was soon to be announced. As soon as Morgan and his wife had left, the four sisters disappeared to discuss the matter. Amy was delegated to call in at Waun Fawr after school on Monday to give Will and Agnes the news and to extract from Will any further information he might have about Edgar's intentions. Jane and Maggie tried hard to mask their own feelings and decided to act as fashion advisers if a London wedding were planned. Gladys announced she and Arthur would go up to London during the Easter holidays and 'find out what was going on.'

Margaret Ann kept her counsel. She missed Morgan Humphrey's calming influence more than ever in times of family upheavals. The quiet conversations at bedtime and the oft repeated phrase 'Now, Margaret Ann...' had prevented many a situation from escalating. Without him she had to resort to iron self-control. Inwardly she was raging. 'William went and married into that *ceiliog* family and look how that ended,' she muttered to herself as she gave the kitchen table another vigorous, but unnecessary scrub. 'We knew precious little about Ethel and that Risca lot, with their airs and graces, but we know nothing at all about this one Edgar's found. Excellent family indeed! It's more likely she thinks Edgar is a catch now he's got his knighthood. It's time he came down here for a dose of common sense. That's what he needs! He's spending too much of his time in London being pandered to.' Margaret Ann smacked the scrubbing brush down and resolved to put pen to paper to let her eldest son know her views on the matter.

By return of post, Sir Edgar duly informed his mother that he had indeed asked Sir George Brackley for permission to marry his daughter and Miss Lillian May Brackley had consented. The marriage was to take place in London at the beginning of September in the following year, and he hoped very much that all the family would be present. Margaret Ann folded the letter into her writing case and longed for Morgan so that she could air her feelings. Instead she stared out at the valley below her.

The engagement was reported in the *Aberdare Leader* not long afterwards, and wedding preparations grew to fever pitch when Gladys and Arthur returned from London with the news that the ceremony was to take place in one of London's most fashionable churches, where Lloyd George himself worshipped.

'Guess what! The Prime Minister is on the guest list together with anybody who is anybody,' reported Gladys, 'and the wedding breakfast is to be at the Savoy.' Her voice rose excitedly, 'There are to be six bridesmaids, and Edgar wants two of them to be from the family. Margaret and Hilda are to be the two.'

Sir Edgar took a house for the month near Hyde Park so that the family could come and go through the summer holidays, and Hilda and Margaret grew more and more excited. Shopping trips and fittings continued until Jane was satisfied that the family was attired sufficiently stylishly to compete with the other guests.

This confirmed her mother's worst fears that her newest daughter-in-law was determined to 'put on a show.' Margaret Ann was persuaded to wear lavender crepe as befitted a sixty-four-year-old widow, which was in stark contrast to her usual tidy black. Hilda and Margaret were delighted with the frills and furbelows in which they were decked out and almost fainted with joy when they were handed bouquets of flowers to carry. As the limousines arrived for the journey to the church, the girls became convinced they were living in a dream. They were given a sharp lecture by Aunty Agnes on the need to behave impeccably all day and managed to survive without getting a pinch from Aunty Amy for 'letting the family down' – one of the worst crimes in the book.

The day was a triumph in spite of some disappointment among the guests that the prime minister was unavoidably absent. The banks of flowers, the elegant surroundings, the opulent dining room at the Savoy and the uniformed flunkeys everywhere, silenced even Margaret Ann. Edgar's sisters were transported from their usual humdrum environment into a world of glamour and style, the like

274

of which they had never seen before. As they collapsed on their beds in the hotel that night and kicked off their shoes, images of the day twirled before the eyes.

'I don't think I'll ever be the same again,' sighed Gladys. 'What a day!'

ℝ ℝ ℝ

The trip to London had shaken William out of his gloom a little and the change encouraged him to give serious thought to his own future. A few weeks after Edgar's wedding, an unexpected solution presented itself. William decided that the memories in Waun Fawr were still too painful to bear and that a change of scene and the company of Edgar and young Morgan James would help. He decided to accept a post with one of the shipping companies with whom he had built strong connections during the war. He bought a spacious house – Glenthorpe – in the elegant suburb of Beckenham and moved the entire family, including Nellie the nursery maid, to London. Agnes was only too happy to resign her teaching post and take over a full-time role as housekeeper. Will was soon as much at home in his City office as he had been in the stores at the National in Wattstown, but for Nellie it was all too much. The traffic terrified her and she found it impossible to understand the south London accent. After many tears she returned to the Rhondda and a new nursery maid was found.

The children soon became used to commuting between Gorwel (which they called home) and their London address. School holidays were spent in the Rhondda except for Christmas when the attractions of London proved irresistible. Jane, Maggie and Gladys were determined to escape the humdrum valley for a fortnight. The sophistication of a London Christmas entranced them, and so first class rail tickets were dispatched by Will to his sisters and his mother. Compared with the shop windows of Porth and Pontypridd, the effects of the Christmas lights and decorations of the West End stores coupled with severl theatre visits left everyone astounded.

Although Arthur was still spending long periods in hospital as various surgeons attempted to repair what was left of his leg, he never failed to accompany his mother and sisters on the Christmas visit. William's children adored him, especially Hilda, whom he nicknamed 'Barrel.' He was forced to spend most of the day in a chair as his wounds could still not support his artificial leg and thus he took charge of decorating the Glenthorpe Christmas tree. As soon as it was installed in the drawing room he took over, using Hilda as his assistant. She did double duty as a crutch and a runner, fetching pieces of wire, plugs and other bits of gadgetry and then standing motionless for minutes on end while Arthur fussed about the position of every bulb. When everything was to his liking he summoned his mother and sisters for the 'switching on.' Margaret Ann thought it was a fire hazard, but her view on this occasion was entirely ignored, and pride of place in Glenthorpe was given every year to that illuminated tree.

If only Ann could see it, William thought. She would have loved it, and she would have been so comfortable in this house. She would be amazed where we've all ended up.' But honesty compelled him to reflect that perhaps the noise and bright lights of London would not have been entirely to her taste.

The family had not long returned to Wattstown leaving Arthur behind in Glenthorne, when the next shock came from a quite unexpected quarter. Amy, who was rapidly approaching forty, revealed that she had formed a strong attachment to a fellow teacher from the Rhondda who had for some time been persuading her to consider him as a future husband. She broke the news to Gladys one dreary Sunday in early spring, when they were both on 'dinner duty' and her mother and sisters were in chapel.

'Glad, do you know David Morris?'

'That Latin teacher from the county school?' Gladys lifted her head from the oven where she was carefully basting the roast.

'He wants me to marry him.'

There was a crash and the meat tin fell to the floor, distributing joint, juices, and a large portion of roasting potatoes across the kitchen floor.

'Gladys!' Amy shrieked and ran for the mop bucket while her sister hastily bundled the contents of the meat tin back onto the roasting rack and quickly shoved it into the oven. Flushed and panting, Gladys leaned against the oven door sucking her burnt thumb while Amy desperately tried to remove the traces of fat from the floor before their mother returned.

'You can't get married at your age!' Gladys was horrified. 'Why on earth do you want to get married now?'

'I think I'm getting arthritis,' came the calm reply. 'David keeps on telling me how he wants to care for me for the rest of my life, so I thought he should be given the chance.'

Gladys was speechless, and Amy disappeared in to the dining room to lay the table. Shortly afterwards the chapel party returned.

Margaret Ann and her daughters took up their customary places and Amy and Gladys brought in the Sunday lunch. In the absence of a male member of the family, Gladys was the carver. She turned the joint towards her to hide the crushed end, and lifted the knife.

'Don't carve that end first, Gladys,' admonished her mother, 'it will come for cold meat tomorrow. And why are those roast potatoes smashed up?' She stared suspiciously at her daughters.

'We had an accident,' muttered Amy sheepishly.

'An accident? With the Sunday dinner? At your age?' Margaret Ann's scorn was withering.

'She made me jump, Mam, when I was turning the meat, and I dropped it,' Gladys confessed.

Margaret Ann was about to embark on a full-scale investigation when Amy cut in.

'I told her I might marry David Morris from Porth, that's all.'

There was silence in the dining room. All eyes were on Amy, and Gladys continued carving the wrong end of the joint.

'Well you'd better not waste any time deciding. You've not got time on your side and he could well give up waiting, my girl.' As ever Margaret Ann did not mince her words. Maggie and Jane exchanged a meaningful glance and Gladys continued carving, under Margaret Anns watchful eye. 'Mind what you are doing with that meat, Gladys. It's meant to last until Tuesday. You, Amy, can tell me what's what, as we go back to Calfaria this evening.'

By the end of the day, it was all decided. Margaret Ann had decided on another London wedding and Amy was to call on the future bridegroom after school on Monday, to tell him she had finally made up her mind. An exception to Margaret Ann's strict rules about telephone use allowed two outgoing calls. William was telephoned and told to host the reception, and Morgan was instructed to speak to the minister of the Baptist Church near Glenthorpe.

When Amy returned from her meeting with David Morris the following evening, her mother's instructions were clear. 'You can go up to London at Easter, Amy, and take David Morris with you. Jane can go, too, to help with arrangements. And remember that we are not putting on another show, so there'll be no need for new clothes. We had enough of that last year.'

As ever, Margaret Ann had taken a decision and acted upon it. Why she had decided that a second London wedding was appropriate no one knew. All objections were brushed aside, except for one. William insisted that if his daughters were to be bridesmaids again, then different dresses were essential. Amy's dress of dark blue lace was quietly elegant and was a present from her brother. To Hilda's disappointment, gone were the frills and flounces, and instead she and Margaret wore plain white silk dresses threaded with pink ribbon and carried small posies of flowers. After the chapel ceremony the wedding breakfast was held at Glenthorpe, with Mrs Jones, Gorwel presiding. She relished her role of matriarch and her nine adult offspring had long ago decided that life was a good deal easier for them if she were allowed to reign supreme; they had become expert in avoiding confrontation.

Chapter 31
Endings

Whether it was the extra energy demanded by the occasion of the wedding, or whether Margaret Ann had been unwell for some days no-one knew, but at three o'clock the following morning Agnes awoke to hear a voice calling her on the landing outside her room. She shot out of bed and opened the door to see her mother standing there in some disarray, with her hair down. 'What on earth is the matter Mam?'

'I can't get my breath, Ag, and I've got a terrible pain.'

'Well it won't help standing here. Let's get you back to bed before we wake the whole house, and I'll get Will's peppermint water for you.'

Agnes ushered her mother back to her bedroom and set off to find Will's cure for everything. She quite relished the novel experience of being in control of her mother and soon had the patient sitting up in bed, sipping the hot peppermint water. With a few brisk words of reassurance, Agnes returned to her bed.

'Goodness,' she said to herself, 'I've never in my life known Mam to be ill. It can only be something she's eaten so I'll wait till the morning to tell Will.' She was soon fast asleep.

The next morning the whole household was in a ferment. William was woken up by the familiar sounds of Agnes shouting at Hilda, and chivvying the maids. Then he heard his mother.

'I am adamant,' she called down the stairs to Agnes's departing back, 'I am not being seen by any London doctors. They do not know me. How can they possibly tell me what is wrong. I must return to Gorwel *at once!*' She slammed her bedroom door and climbed back into bed exhausted. Jane and Maggie were telephoned and agreed with Mam that no London doctor could be entrusted with the health of one so important as Mam, and home she would have to go. William entered the fray.

'Mam, you are being stubborn and difficult as usual. You will see my doctor today. If he says you are fit to travel you may go home. If he does not say you are well enough, you will stay here. Imagine the scenes if you were to collapse at the station.'

As ever, William had found his mother's Achilles heel. The prospect of being in a 'scene' was enough. His doctor was called, examined the reluctant patient and suggested some tests should be carried out. Mam was horrified.

'Tests! Tests! Nobody is testing me. Go home to Gorwel I will, and Dr Davies can test me if he likes. Get hold of the train timetable William, and get me on the Cardiff train first thing.'

The doctor withdrew from Mam's room, adjusting his winged collar with relief.

'I think you have your hands full with that patient, Miss Jones,' he remarked wryly to Agnes. 'I shall leave her to your tender mercies. I would warn her personal physician that she is on her way, and I'll drop a line to him with my findings. Good day to you.'

Agnes showed the doctor out and returned to the drawing room, where William was busy explaining his non-appearance to his secretary.

'She'll have to go, Will. She'll make life impossible for us here. I'll get hold of Gladys and she'll have to come up and escort Mam home. You sort the transport and I'll see to the rest. We'll have to send a nurse with her just in case and you'll have to arrange a car at Cardiff for them. '

By nine o'clock that evening Gladys had arrived in Glenthorpe. She was not in the best of moods, having been forced to come straight from school. She was mortified at being seen in London in her school clothes and was even crosser when William revealed that she would be going back first class. 'I can't go first class in my school clothes! My clothes will be shown up as drab!'

Her brother raised an eyebrow at her. 'You are being ridiculous. No-one will be looking at you and I can hardly put my mother and the nurse in first, and you down the back of the train in third. Eat your supper and get an early night. You are going to need a lot of patience tomorrow.'

On Saturday morning the cavalcade set off along the tree lined avenue. Agnes breathed a huge sigh of relief and took herself to her room with a large cup of tea. William's car led the procession with William and his driver, Kate the maid with Mam's luggage, and Hilda who couldn't resist a trip to the station with her father. In the second car, which William had hired for the day, came Mam, Gladys, and the nurse who was to provide any medical support which might be necessary on the journey. At Paddington station a team of porters appeared and the drama was heightened by the arrival of Sir Edgar, in his ministerial car and Lieutenant Colonel Morgan James, in full uniform. Both Margaret Ann's sons had felt obliged to ascertain the seriousness of the situation and to witness the amazing sight of their mother in ill health. A small crowd began to gather, clearly under the impression that someone very important was travelling. Margaret Ann was ushered into a first class compartment with Gladys, the nurse and Kate the maid. The rugs were carefully tucked round the patient's knees, and with many instructions from both sides, the journey home into the safe hands and expertise of Dr Davies began.

Margaret Ann's spirits rose as the train brought her closer to the familiar narrow valleys and the rows of terraced houses. The grand houses of south London, with their beautifully manicured lawns held no charms for her. As the train emerged from the Severn Tunnel she began to direct her entourage.

'There's not much time between Newport and Cardiff. I'm not to be rushed, so you'd better start getting organised, otherwise we'll be in Bridgend before you know it. Get those bags down Gladys and make sure the ticket collector knows where I am.'

With some difficulty Gladys and Kate persuaded her to remain in her seat until the train stopped at Cardiff Central station. With William's influence again apparent, the welcoming party on the platform included the stationmaster, the senior ticket inspector, the senior porter and the lad who was to push the wheelchair which William had requested. Another small crowd pushed forward, convinced they were about to witness the arrival of a VIP.

Margaret Ann, attended by Gladys, Kate and the nurse, was helped down from the carriage. The boy with the wheelchair rushed up and Margaret Ann was carefully seated in the chair and the travelling rug tucked round her knees.

'Good to see you, Mrs Jones, how was the journey? said the stationmaster. Your car is waiting at the front of the station.' Margaret Ann gave a dignified nod in his direction, and Gladys was gracious in her thanks for the official welcome. Her mother's status was further enhanced by a sudden shout.

'It's Mrs Jones, Gorwel! Welcome home! Look who it is! Are you better? We knew you'd been taken ill when Miss Gladys left school early yesterday!' It was Mrs Basso. Several other passengers took up the cry, as the ladies of the Women's Fellowship in Calfaria realised who was in the wheelchair. The annual outing to Porthcawl had brought the group to Cardiff, en route to the seaside, and they all pressed forward to reassure themselves that Margaret Ann was not at death's door.

'Move back, ladies, please, let the chair through now,' requested the porter, and Gladys hurried ahead to instruct the driver. The nurse and Kate supervised the transfer of Margaret Ann and her belongings into the Bentley provided by William and the excitement subsided.

❦ ❦ ❦

The weather for once was kind, and the journey up the narrow valley, past the colliery winding gear and the clattering trams, convinced Margaret Ann that she had made the right decision. This was where she belonged and this was where she would recuperate.

Once she was safely back in her own bed in Gorwel, Dr Davies was sent for. He pronounced that too much excitement was the cause of her mysterious collapse, and prescribed heart pills and strict bed rest for several weeks. Maggie, Jane and Gladys looked at each other, and all simultaneously announced that 'leave of absence' from school was impossible.

'It's not as if she's exactly ill.'

'We'll be up and down those stairs all day.'

'It'll ruin our rota.'

Margaret Ann's daughters were united. Kate, the maid, would have her hands full taking on the kitchen duties normally the responsibility of Mam, and the latest girl – Cissie – was too daft to undertake any extra duties. Matters were made more difficult when Arthur telephoned with the news that he had been discharged from his London hospital for the time being and was also coming home.

Gladys as usual had the solution. 'Right,' she said, 'Arthur can bring Hilda down with him. That school of hers is doing no good. She can do the running about for Mam, and in between we might be able to teach her long division – her posh school has failed to do it.'

Arthur was delighted at the prospect of more youthful company, and the following week he and his niece returned to Gorwel. Uncle and niece had built strong bonds in the months after Ann's death, when Arthur was first invalided out of the army. They got on famously, and the little girl made an excellent walking aid for the wounded soldier as she was still just the right height. More importantly she could be relied upon to provide relief from his sisters' constant fussing and his mother's constant demands.

Hilda's duties were explained in words of one syllable, and she was made very aware of the importance of her role. Jane wrote out her duties in case Hilda forgot and put the paper in the lustre jug on the dresser in the kitchen.

Hilda was busy all day, but was allowed 'off duty' as soon as the first aunty arrived home from school. In the evening she was taught by whichever aunt had a spare moment, and schoolwork was set for her to do the next day, in between her errands. Arithmetic, mostly long division, loomed large. Soon every visitor to the house was aware that Hilda couldn't do maths, and offered advice. The sums were to be finished by teatime, when they were marked by an aunt. The answers were mostly wrong. Finally the aunts themselves were forced to admit defeat. Hilda was incapable of coping with the intricacies of long division. This inability was considered to be so extraordinary that it was commented on by all in turn. Even Dr Davies was consulted as though it were some strange physical abnormality.

The struggles with maths had now persisted for nearly a month, when Arthur hobbled into the dining room one morning to see his usually cheerful companion sitting at the table with large tears dripping off her nose.

'What's up, Barrel?'

'Long division, Uncle Arthur.'

'Well, I'm going to need your help tomorrow, so if I help you now that will be a deal won't it? Anyway, long division is easy – give me a pencil.'

With much good humour, and lots of crossing out, Arthur demonstrated his method of long division.

'Line the numbers up one under the other, in columns, Barrel, like soldiers. Keep them straight and don't forget your tables. Now you try. And after Mam has had her lunch tomorrow remember, you have to help me.'

Much encouraged, Hilda redoubled her efforts. By lunch time the next day a page of neat sums was full. Hilda had finally grasped the essence of long division. Unable to believe the miracle, Mam demanded to be shown the proof. Six more sums were set by Uncle Arthur, and Hilda got them all right. By the time the qualified teachers returned from school, several pages of sums were ready for approval. 'All correct!' Disbelief registered on his sisters' faces, and Arthur was awarded another medal. He had taught Hilda long division. 'I wish I could sort my own problems as easily,' he reflected ruefully as he hung his artificial leg on the hook behind the door that night.

The next day was Hilda's turn to help her uncle. During his lengthy rehabilitation Arthur had been prescribed treatment by the newly invented heat lamp. He decided that his mother might also benefit from similar therapy, but in spite of numerous enquiries he had failed to acquire one. He explained the problem to Hilda.

'We could make one, perhaps,' Hilda was confident.

'Exactly. We will use the Little Room as a workshop. Now you will have run to Evans the grocer and fetch me a tin biscuit box. It must have a shiny inside, the shinier the better. Then we will start.'

Hilda reappeared a little while later with two biscuit tins for Arthur to select the shinier of the two. The two of them foraged about the wash-house for the necessary tools.

'Right, Hilda, now we need flex and a bulb. We can use that old lamp from Agnes's attic. She doesn't need it.'

Eventually all the items were assembled in the Little Room and they set to work. A small hole was punched in the bottom of the shinier tin and Hilda carefully fed the flex through. It did not take long to connect up the light fittings.

'Now, Barrel, plug it in.' Instantly the bulb lit up and a warm glow began to emanate from the tin.

'Perfect!' Arthur was jubilant. 'Now for the hard part. You have to carry me and the contraption up to Mam's room!' Slowly the two electricians mounted the stairs, Arthur kneeling from step to step and his assistant carrying the 'sun lamp'.

'Look Mam! See what Uncle Arthur's made for you. It will get rid of your aches and pains and make you better.' Arthur assured his mother that the treatment was just what he had recently received and she would be better in no time. He positioned the lamp and told Hilda to switch on. There was a flash, a bang, a smell of burning rubber, and an awful smell of fish. Mam let out a shriek and the explosion sent Hilda under the dressing table. As the smoke faded, Hilda crawled out and sheepishly gathered up the remains of the sun lamp.

'Something faulty in that socket I think, Mam. It worked perfectly in the Little Room.'

'Get along the pair of you and find something more useful to do,' was Mam's terse rejoinder.

Hilda had now been at Gorwel for more than six weeks and the summer holidays were rapidly approaching. She hoped fervently that the school holidays could be spent in Wattstown. There was no brook to play in at Glenthorpe, and Aunty Ag was so strict. After some discussion it was decided that as Dr Davies had pronounced Margaret Ann to be on the mend, once the Aunts broke up for the summer holidays, Hilda should go back to London.

'She can't possibly go back to London looking so wild. William won't recognise her. We'll have to get something done about her hair. I'll take her to Cardiff as soon as we break up.'

'Take her to a hairdresser? It will cost a fortune, Jane. Don't be ridiculous, I'll cut it myself. There's decent scissors in the drawer.' As ever there was nothing that Gladys couldn't do.

Hilda's hair was cut regularly in the hairdressing salon of a large London department store. It was bobbed, with a fringe, in a style of which Agnes approved. All the aunts had long hair which was worn 'up' so they never needed a hairdresser. When Mam found out about the plan, she insisted that the procedure took place in her bedroom as supervision would be necessary. The floor was covered with newspaper and a chair was placed in the bay window to catch the light. As Arthur was the only member of the family who had experienced having his hair cut he propped himself on the window-sill to give advice.

'She needs a towel round her shoulders to catch the trimmings, and a mirror to look in, Gladys.'

'Rubbish. She's got no need to see herself. It'll only make her vain.' Gladys began to snip. She snipped carefully round Hilda's head, not realising that Hilda was not sitting straight on the chair.

'One side is shorter than the other' laughed Arthur. You'd better go round again.' Gladys did, and the bottom of one of Hilda's ears appeared.

'You've missed a bit at the back,' Margaret Ann called from the bed. Gladys trimmed some more, and more of the ears appeared.

'Even it up, she looks lopsided!.' Arthur by now was convulsed with laughter.

'Please can I look,' begged Hilda.

'Not yet. You've got to have your fringe cut. Sit still Hilda, or Aunty will make a mistake,' instructed Mam. With a final flourish Gladys attempted to cut the fringe in one go. Clumps of brown hair fell to the floor, and Arthur howled with laughter.

'Turn her round so I can see what you've done, Glad,' Mam's voice came from the bed. Gladys turned her unfortunate niece round with some reluctance. Mam gasped. 'Now you've done it. We can't send her back to her father looking like that. That fringe looks like a pig's bristles. She'll have to stay here till it grows.'

Hilda ran from the room to the bathroom to see herself in the mirror. A gasp of horror shook her. Then she laughed. 'It'll be ages before it grows. I'll have to stay all the summer.' And she did.

Margaret Ann made slow progress. She had considered herself to be invincible. Illness was something which happened to other people, mostly as a result of negligence or weakness, but now she had been struck down. She was haunted by the thought that she had reached her biblical milestone of three score years and ten, and from now on she would be living on borrowed time.

All her life she had been in control of herself, her husband, her shop and her nine children. Now she was forced to submit to other people's orders and to relinquish control of her household. Eight of her children had no need of her, and even Arthur would not be dependent for much longer. Will and Edgar were determined he should not hang around in Wattstown for ever. They had several ideas about his future as soon as he was fully fit, and had approached the director of a shipping company in Swansea who had agreed to take Arthur into his export department. Even more humiliating for Margaret Ann was the realisation that she had been added to the 'sick list' in chapel and was to be visited by the minister once a month, and by a member of the Ladies Circle on Thursdays!

By the beginning of September Margaret Ann had become thoroughly tired of staring at the narrow valley from her bedroom window. The large bay gave her a bird's eye view and enabled her to monitor the comings and goings of the families as they toiled up and down the steep hill to the village. But it was a life lived second-hand and Margaret Ann had no time for such a life. She missed her granddaughter's cheerful chatter and Arthur was spending much of his day leaning on a billiard cue in the Workmen's Institute.

'The trouble with you, my girl, is you're lonely and bored.' Margaret Ann adopted the same tone with herself she had used with Maggie. 'You need to get out of this room or you'll wither away in it! It's downstairs you need to be, getting this place sorted out.'

When Dr Davies arrived for his now weekly visit, his patient was already dressed and sitting in her customary chair in the window. As Kate showed him in, Margaret Ann leant forward and announced, 'I've had enough of this. All summer I've been stuck in a chair, forced to put up with being pandered to and it's time it stopped. You can take me off your list and then I can get back to normal.'

Dr Davies hid his smile behind a cough and merely took his patient's pulse. 'Let me see you take a few steps round the bedroom, Mrs Jones, and then we might try the stairs.'

He offered his arm, but Margaret Ann would have none of it and set off along the landing. She was glad of the bannisters as she made her way down, stopping several times apparently to remark on the dust which had been allowed to gather on the newel posts.

Kate heard the descent of the stairs and emerged from the kitchen to open the drawing room door for the invalid.

'You can shut that. The room will be full of dust no doubt if the state of the stairs is anything to go by,' remarked her employer. 'You can put a chair for me by the range, and then I can see what's going on. And then you can show Dr Davies out. He won't need to come in again.' She turned to her long-suffering doctor. 'Let Gladys have the account, and Arthur can call in to the surgery to settle it. You'll know soon enough if I have a relapse,' and she waved a dismissive arm. 'Oh, and by the way, thank you. You've done a better job of getting me up and about than those so called specialists William wanted to get in.'

Dr Davies raised his eyebrows and smiled at his patient.

'Just don't overdo it. Take one step at a time,' he advised, as he followed Kate out of the kitchen.

Within a month Margaret Ann had resumed the reins and for the next quarter of a century, Mrs Jones, Gorwel ran her household and monitored Wattstown life as she had always done. Her family continued to grow and prosper, sharing their lives with her through their weekly letters. They continued to surprise her, but that's another story.

She had walked over the mountain in search of a better living for herself and her children and she was fortunate that in her quest, she had at her side a man who truly loved her. Her ambitions for her nine children had been realised, and they had succeeded beyond her wildest dreams. Their success was a source of intense pride to Margaret Ann, although she rarely let her children know how she felt.

For over seventy years she had lived in the village with three names – Cwtch, Aberllechau and Wattstown – and had known its many changes. She remained an admired and respected figure in the community for the rest of her life. Margaret Ann lived to her ninety sixth year. As was right and proper, all nine of her children were present at her funeral and her four sons escorted her to her grave, where she was buried beside the man who had been her faithful, loving support.

Epilogue

In 1994, more than forty years after her death, I was admiring an exhibition of Welsh quilts in the Victoria and Albert Museum in London. A curator detected a familiar Welsh accent, and came over to see whether any more information about the displays was required. It took only a few moments to establish that his family came from Wattstown in the Rhondda.

'Do you remember Gorwel?' I enquired.

'I certainly do,' came the surprising reply.

'Gorwel was my great grandmother's house. All the family called her Mam Wattstown. My mother spent many summer holidays in Gorwel, with her grandmother and aunts and I often visited my great-grandmother there.'

'Not Mrs Jones, Gorwel? Goodness, she was an amazing character. If my brothers and I stepped out of line my mother would say she'd have to have a word with Mrs Jones, Gorwel! But she was so kind. No-one went hungry in the village as long as Mrs Jones had food in her pantry.

'I remember her funeral. I watched from the pavement. All the men in the village came out on the road to follow the procession and Calfaria was packed.

'My father used to say her husband was a great preacher – he packed out the chapel, and wonderful sermons they were. Her daughters were all headmistresses, you know. Miss Gladys Jones was my first teacher and she taught me to read.

'Fancy you belonging to such a special family. You must be very proud.'

And, as I recounted news of the family, I was.

Glossary of Welsh Words

Bore da	Good day
Nos da	Good night
clecwr, (pl) clecau	tale teller
fach (bach)	small
fawr (mawr)	large/big
coch	red
mamgu	grandmother
ty bach	lavatory (lit. little house)
hiraeth	longing, homesickness
bara brith	fruit loaf (lit. speckled bread)
y clonc	a gossip
y cwn a chati	dog and cat (a game)
ceiliog	cockerel
da iawn	Well done!